handy man's
ELECTRICAL REPAIRS
handbook

New and revised edition

handy man's
ELECTRICAL REPAIRS
handbook

By Robert Hertzberg

A FAWCETT BOOK • NUMBER 431

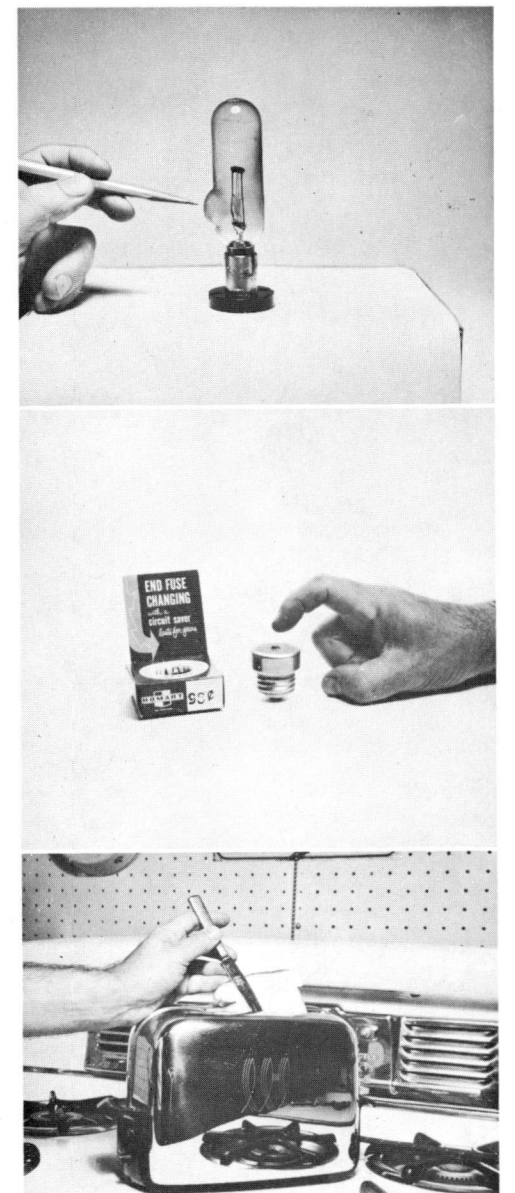

THE DO-IT-YOURSELF SERIES
arco publishing co., inc.
NEW YORK CITY 17, NEW YORK

Published 1962 by Arco Publishing Company, Inc.
480 Lexington Avenue, New York 17, New York

Library of Congress Catalog Card Number: 61-17823

All rights reserved. Copyright 1959 by Fawcett Publications, Inc. Printed in the United States of America.

CONTENTS

Power Where You Want It 8
Two-Way Light Control 9
The Power System in Your Home 10
Power Is What You Buy 18
Is Your Wiring Adequate? 22
Testers and Tools 32
Wire Joints 42
Cable and Conduit 46
Play It Safe 52
The Third Wire Is a Lifesaver 60
When the Lights Go Out 64
When the Bell Doesn't Ring 70
Coffee Maker 73
Don't Let a Cord Tie You Into Knots 74
Re-cording a Lamp 80
Bowl Heaters 83
Let There Be Light! 84
Silent Switch Lets Baby Sleep 90
Extending an Outlet 94
Motors Are Made to Move 96
A Plan for a Fan 108
Projectors 111
Iron Quit Cold? 112
Toasters Should Pop 116
What's Cooking 120
Some Like It Hot 128
Some Like It Cool 136
Batteries and Chargers 140
Electricity Outdoors 142
Clocks and Transformers 143

MASTER?
OR
SERVANT

Electrical appliances are so much a part of the American household scene today that most people take them for granted. Refrigerators, freezers, mixers, irons, air conditioners, clothes and dish washers, ventilating fans, broilers, vacuum cleaners, heaters, etc., all contribute to our comfort, convenience and health. It's only when something goes wrong that we begin to wonder if electricity is our servant or our master. A five-cent fuse in a dark corner of the basement fails for no apparent reason, and life upstairs stops. Food spoils in the freezer, the heating system grinds to a halt, dirty clothes pile up, or a half-cooked dinner sits in a cold rotisserie.

Don't take electricity and electrical servants for granted. Learn something about them and their habits, and how to keep them working for you all the time. This book is a sort of primer on the subject, written for non-technical people who want to know at least a little about a very technical topic. It is a completely revised edition of an earlier book of the same title that appeared in 1955, and incorporates solutions to numerous problems posed by readers in all parts of the country.

— Robert Hertzberg

Power Where You Want It

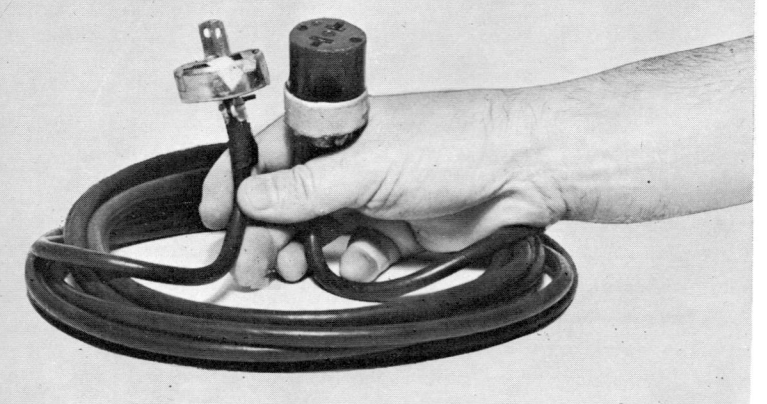

Flexible extension cords with rugged plugs and receptacles of armored type will last for years. Two most useful lengths are 10 feet and 25 feet. To keep fiber center piece of plug (left) from falling out, apply narrow strips of adhesive tape between and around prongs.

AN extension cord is such a useful accessory around the house, shop, garage and garden that after you make and use one you'll probably make another. To take care of heavy current loads, use at least No. 16 and preferably No. 14 flexible wire, with heavy outer covering; thinner No. 18 wire is poor economy. And avoid 10-cent "molded mud" plugs and receptacles. Spend a little more on armored fittings of the type illustrated, and you'll be glad you did the first time you step on them, drop them to a cement floor, or drive the car over them. These fittings and the heavy wire are widely available from electrical, hardware, radio and mail-order firms. •

Above, right: Before trimming insulation off ends of wire, slip cord through cap of receptacle. To prevent strands of wire from unraveling under terminal screws, solder them very lightly, then form into loops with long-nose pliers. Put two or three layers of tape over wire, far enough back so that they come under the clamp of the end cap.

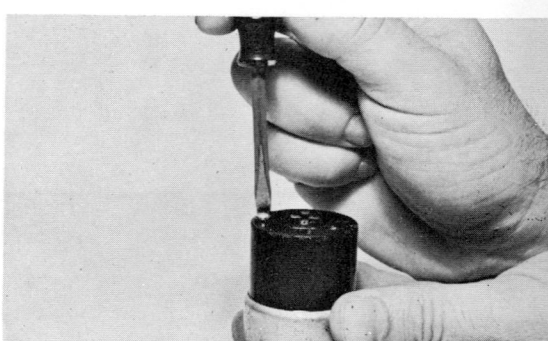

Right: The molded body of the extension receptacle fastens to the armored end cap with two screws. When these are tightened in properly, they are below surface. Use narrow blade screwdriver for job.

Right: Cable clamp on end cap has two screws. Turn them in a little at a time each, so that pressure is distributed evenly around layers of tape on the wire. A pull on the cable will not then loosen the connections to the terminal screws inside. (Attachment plug is assembled in similar manner.)

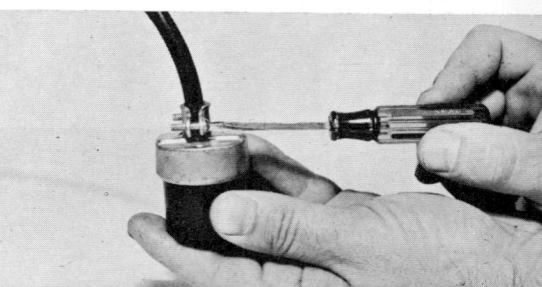

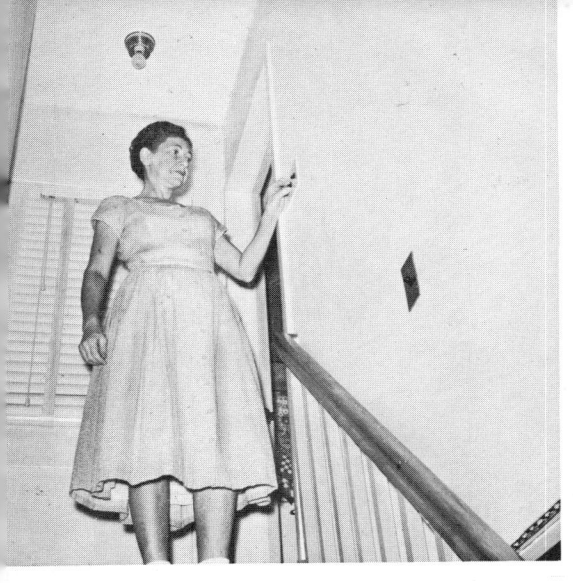

Two-way Light Control

End mishaps in the dark; with switches at both ends of a hall, lights are controlled as desired.

The secret of two-way control lies in the three-wire connecting cable and three-terminal switches, as shown.

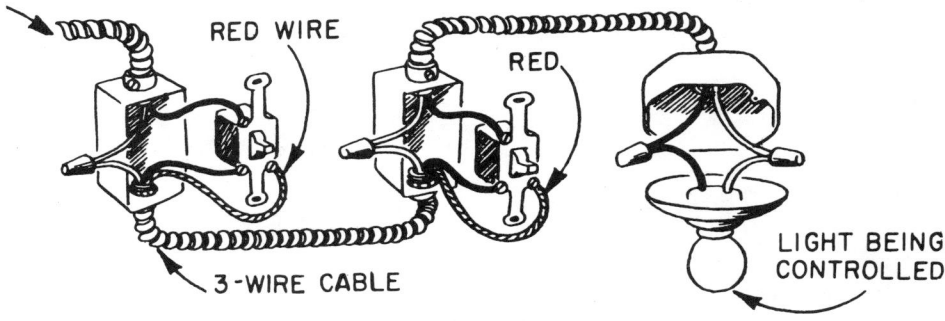

IN MANY houses, the switch controlling an important light in a long hallway or over the cellar stairs is in the right location only if approached from one direction. If you approach from the other direction when the house is dark, you have to fumble around and perhaps light a match to find it.

If you are afflicted with such an arrangement, you can improve it if you can conveniently snake an additional piece of *three*-wire cable through the walls from the present switch box to a new box at the other end of the passageway. You must discard the existing single-pole (two-terminal) switch, and install two new switches known as "three-way" switches. (This is a puzzling misnomer, as they provide only two-way control.) They are of the single-pole, double-throw type, have three terminal screws (which is probably how they got their name), and fit standard wall boxes.

For purposes of identification, the wires in the three-wire cable are colored white, black and red. The switches are mounted in the boxes with the single terminal screws toward the top.

Caution: Before opening the present switch box, kill the circuit by removing the appropriate fuse or tripping the circuit breaker. Have a flashlight handy for illumination.

The accompanying picture diagram shows the hook-up. Note that the white wire (the grounded side of the power line) is carried through without break to the lamp socket. The black wire is cut at both boxes for connection to the side terminals of the switches. The red wire connects only to the single side terminals of the switches. Either switch turns the light on or off. "On" can be either the up or the down movement of the switch arm, depending on the position of the other switch arm. The arrangement is very convenient, and saves many an accidental tumble over a roller skate or a baseball. •

Consolidated Edison Company of New York

The tall chimneys of power generating stations are a prominent sight in many cities. They carry off the waste gases resulting from the burning of coal, used to heat water to make steam to turn turbines.

The Power System in Your Home

You can identify its type by the number of wires entering the main switch box

MOST people take the power system of their homes for granted. They know that all they have to do is flip a switch, and a mysterious, magical force provides light when it's dark, heat when it's cold, and cold when it's hot. This speaks well for the reliability of modern electrical appliances and of the "juice" that makes them work. Inevitably, however, there comes a time when flipping a switch produces only a small noise and nothing else, and that's when you wish you knew something about the wiring and everything connected to it.

That knowledge is fairly easy to acquire. Although there's a lot of wire snaking all through a house, the basic systems are simple and understandable. Let's start where the electricity starts . . . at the generating station or "power house" . . . and follow through to the attic light.

Practically all commercially produced electricity in the United States is now "alternating current." This is usually abbreviated to AC as a matter of convenience in both oral and written references. The early electric generating stations made direct current, or DC, but this suffered from the disadvantage that it could not be transmitted satisfactorily more than several miles from the point of origin. Lamps located near the power house would burn brightly, but those near the end of the line would be much dimmer because of loss of pressure or "voltage" in the wires. The great feature of AC is that it can be converted with high efficiency from any voltage to any other voltage, either up or down, over an enormous range of ratios. This is done by devices called "transformers," which have no moving parts, require only very minor maintenance, and last virtually forever in normal service.

Direct current is so called because it flows smoothly, evenly and without interruption, like water from a faucet. DC is what you get out of all batteries, regardless of size or type. The original Edison "dynamos," rotating machines driven by steam

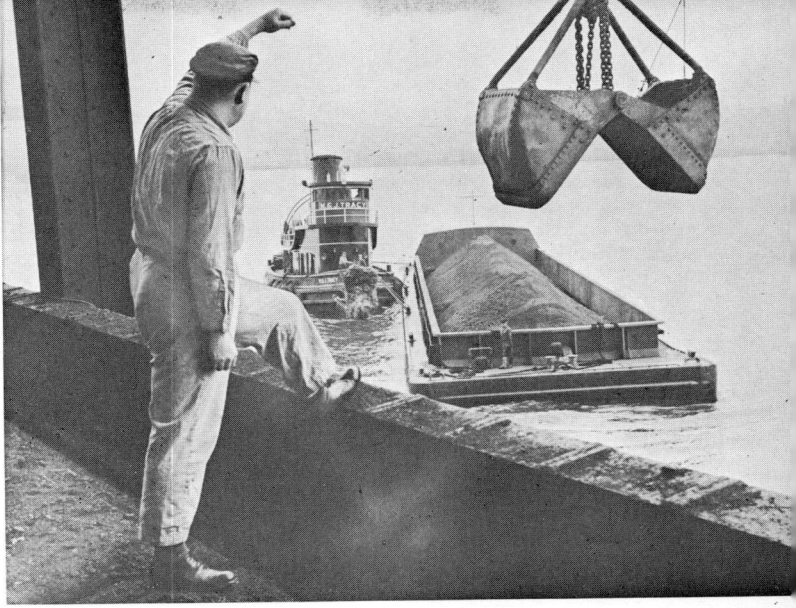

A never-ending job at a power generating station— the taking on of coal. Here a tug nudges a loaded barge toward a waiting scoop at one of the Brooklyn (New York) stations of the Consolidated Edison Company. Many large power stations are located on waterways because coal can be transported more cheaply on the latter.

engines, delivered DC. Their modern counterparts, identical in electrical design but smaller in construction, are the charging generators in automobiles.

AC power is produced by rotating machines called "alternators," to distinguish them from DC "generators." In most large generating stations the actual turning power is provided by high-pressure, high-speed steam turbines. Steam is the vapor of boiling water, and requires a lot of heat. The usual fuels such as coal, oil and gas are used to keep huge boilers cooking round the clock.

The water wheel, a power device dating back to Biblical times, turns the alternators of the biggest generating stations in the world. The water comes from natural configurations in Nature, like Niagara Falls in New York, or from man-made dams which control vast rivers in various parts of the country.

In relatively smaller power houses alternators are driven directly by Diesel engines. In still smaller installations, found on isolated farms or in military service, they are driven by conventional gasoline engines.

The AC "Wave Form"

Figure 1 is the nearest possible graphic representation of the AC "wave form," or the way the current flows in a circuit. Let's follow the action of an alternator in terms

Below, one of the largest power generating plants in the world—the Astoria (Queens) plant of the Consolidated Edison Company of New York. The two large machines are steam-turbine driven alternators.

of time and generated voltage. For measuring time we'll use an imaginary stop watch that reads 1/60 of a second from start to stop; for showing voltage, a zero center meter whose needle moves to the right when current flows in one direction and to the left when it flows in the opposite direction.

With the alternator at rest, nothing, of course, happens. Let's click the stop watch the instant the machine starts to turn, and watch the voltmeter. With the first slight movement of the alternator, electrons in its wires are agitated and the meter needle starts to move, let us say to the right. As the rotation continues, the voltage builds up proportionately. At 1/240 of a second after the starting time the voltage reaches its peak value, and then starts to drop. It falls back to zero after another 1/240 of a second, or a total elapsed time of 1/120 second.

As the machine turns, another section of wires comes into play, and a new voltage is created just as the first one dies to nothing. It builds up in value exactly as its predecessor did, but it flows in the *opposite* direction, as a left-hand deflection of the voltmeter indicates. At 1/80 second after the starting time this second voltage reaches its peak value, which is identical with that of the first voltage, and then it, too, starts to decay. It drops to its zero 1/60 second after the starting time.

If we let the alternator run, the process keeps repeating itself. One complete variation of current from zero through peak to zero, and again from zero to peak to zero the other way, is called a "cycle;" each half is called an "alternation." The number of cycles per second (c.p.s.) is called the "frequency;" in this case 60, which is universally supplied to homes in the United States.

There is nothing magical about 60 c.p.s. It was probably adopted because there are 60 seconds to a minute and 60 minutes to an hour and the number suggested itself to the early American electrical engineers. For certain industrial and railroad purposes 25 cycles is used (why 25 and not 30, no one knows!) and in some factories 400 cycles is found. This is called "high-cycle" current and is advantageous for special applications calling for small but high-speed motors. In most of the rest of the world the standard is 50 cycles.

Because of an ability of the human eye known as "retention of vision," electric lights operated on 60-cycle AC appear to burn steadily. Although the voltage drops to zero three times in every cycle, it does this too quickly for the lamp filaments to cool off.

One alternation of the AC cycle is sometimes referred to as "positive" and the other as "negative." These are purely mathematical terms and are somewhat

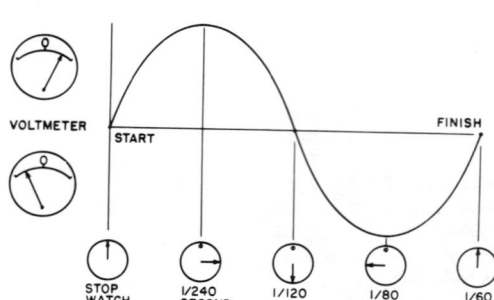

Figure 1: AC in action is shown in diagram form; fluctuations produce magnetic effects by means of which voltages can be stepped up or down.

Power companies are kept busy installing new distribution cables, with the increased demand for electric power; photo shows Con-Edison workmen greasing the path of four-inch electric cable.

misleading because "negative" conveys the meaning of uselessness or nonexistence. The two alternations are absolutely identical in their ability to do work.

The Distribution Network

Power is generated in modern stations at voltages between 11,000 and 14,000. By means of transformers, this is boosted to values ranging from 23,000 to as high as 275,000 volts, the higher voltages being used for the longest lines. The higher the voltage, the lower the current in amperes for any particular power load, and the smaller the wire required to handle the latter. This is an important consideration, as large diameter wire is heavy, is difficult to handle, accumulates dangerous quantities of ice and is buffeted around by strong winds; all these effects are reduced with thin wire.

As power is needed in various areas, the high voltages are brought to much lower levels by step-down transformers. A primary distribution point or "substation" changes them to between 2500 and 15,000 volts. A secondary distribution point, which may be merely a transformer on a pole or concealed in a vault below street level, brings the power down to the eventual consumer level. In residential areas this is usually either 115 or 230 volts, or both on the same circuit. See Figure 2.

The figure "115" is a flexible one. De-

This pole represents the last step in the power distribution network; high-voltage wires on the top of the pole are connected to a step-down transformer (in the large cylindrical case). From this the lower wires run through to home outlets.

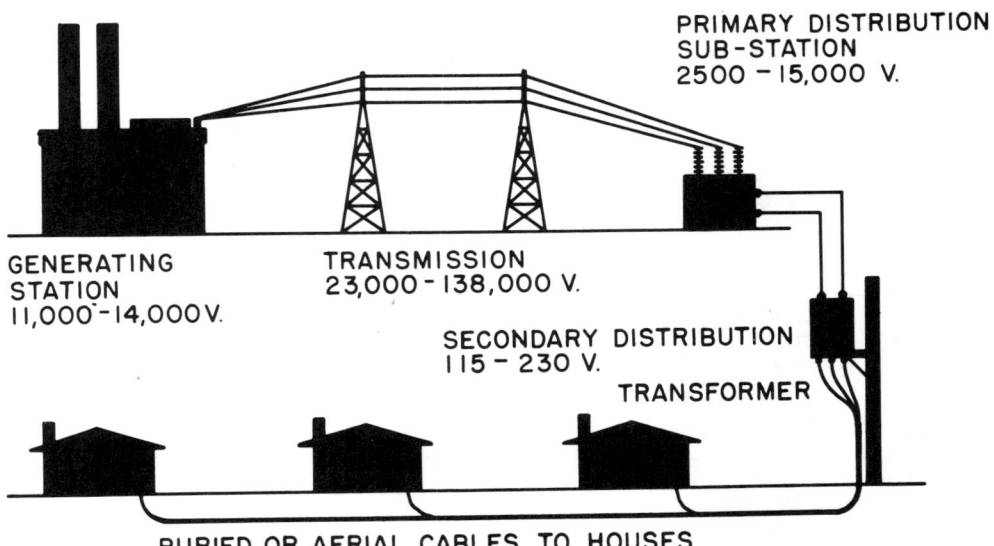

Figure 2:
Simplified diagram of power distribution system. Voltages are stepped up and down by transformers.

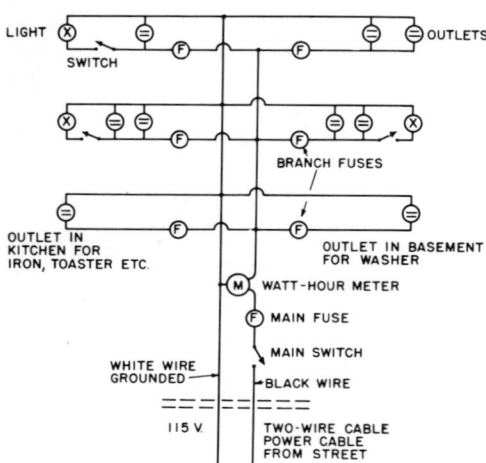
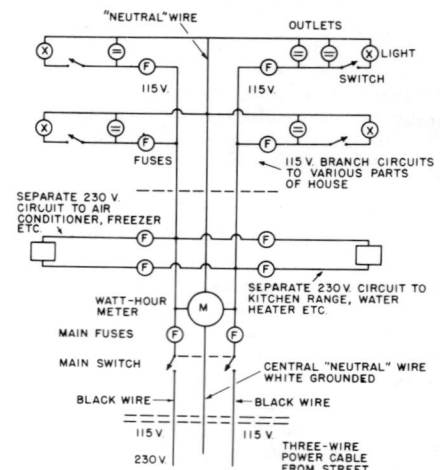

Figure 3 shows basic hook-up of two-wire power distribution generally found in older residences.

Figure 4 shows basic three-wire system, which makes both 115 and 230 volts available in house.

pending on the age of the power system, the number of houses fed by one transformer, the time of the day, the size of the actual wiring in the individual home, and the number and type of appliances in use at one time, the voltage may vary from 110 to 125. In older residential districts it will run to the low side; in newer ones steady readings of 120, 121 and 122 volts are normal. For purposes of discussion let's use 115 volts to represent all values between 110 and 125, and 230 volts for voltages from about 220 to 240. The figure of 208 volts appears in some cases, but this is a special value, not evenly related to either 115 or 230. It is taken up later in this section in the discussion of four-wire systems of distribution.

The Two-Wire House System

The majority of small houses built prior to the television and electric appliance boom of the post-World War II period are fed with a simple, basic two-wire power system. Two wires, running from the nearest secondary distribution transformer, enter the house. They might be suspended aerially from a pole on the curb line, or they might be completely out of sight in buried pipe. With such a two-wire service, the voltage is always "115." See Figure 3. One wire has white or gray colored insulation. It is connected to the nearest water pipe and is called the "ground" wire. The second wire has black insulation and is called the "hot" side of the line only to distinguish it from the other. The grounded wire is by no means "cold" by implication; the two wires can function only together, not separately. Standard practice is to keep the grounded wire a continuous circuit throughout the house, and to insert fuses and switches only in the hot wire.

The main switch and the main fuse are usually in a single steel box. The cover of the latter is linked to the switch handle in such a manner that the fuse is accessible inside only when the switch is thrown to "off." With the switch open or the fuse burned out, the entire electrical system of the house is dead.

The watt-hour meter registers the power consumed in the house. Following it, there are usually several individual "branch" circuits, each with a fuse. These feed power to various parts of the house. If the builder was conscientious, he arranged the branch circuits so that the ceiling lights and the wall outlets in the rooms are on different branches. Thus, if an appliance plugged into a wall outlet blows a fuse, the room lights still work. It is also sensible to provide individual lines for outlets that require a lot of current: one in the kitchen, for instance, for an iron or toaster, and another in the basement for a washing machine.

The Three-Wire System

In many areas power is brought into a building by a three-wire, dual-voltage system, as shown in Figure 4. The center wire is called the "neutral," has white or gray insulation, and is grounded. Between this neutral and either outside black wire is the normal 115 volts. The various 115-volt branch circuits are distributed so that each half of the system carries about the same power load.

In most cases the three-wire system is

14

wired only to feed standard 115-volt lamps and appliances. It is a simple matter, however, to obtain a circuit from the two outside black wires alone to give 230 volts, for the operation of an air conditioner, a large freezer, etc. The advantage of using the higher voltage is that the current in amperes is reduced, and this minimizes heat losses in the line wires and the possibility of overloading the main fuses. A specific example is a standard ⅓ horsepower motor that works equally well on either 115 or 230 volts through a slight shifting of its internal connections. It develops the same ⅓ h.p. in either case and registers the same power on the watt-hour meter. However, while it draws 6 amperes on 115 volts, it takes only 3 on 230 volts.

The importance of minimizing line current is taken up in detail in the chapter entitled "Is Your Wiring Adequate?"

The presence of both 115 and 230 volts in the same house means that special precautions must be taken to prevent 115-volt appliances from being plugged into 230-volt outlets. There is no harm in making the opposite mistake; for instance, a 230-volt air conditioner just wouldn't start on the lower voltage.

The usual safety measure takes the form of power receptacles and matching plugs having oddly spaced connectors, quite different from the ones used with ordinary 115-volt lamps, irons, vacuum cleaners, etc. These fittings are generally of the "crow-foot" or "tandem-blade" type, and are treated in detail in the section of this book entitled "The Third Wire Is a Lifesaver."

To distinguish further between 115- and 230-volt outlets, it is the practice in some areas to paint the latter bright red.

Three-wire installations are standard in homes having all-electric kitchens. There is usually a separate heavy-duty 230-volt line from the meter directly to the range, which can easily take as much as 50 or 60 amperes even at this higher voltage. The range alone thus represents three or four times as much power as required for the entire rest of the house.

The Four-Wire System

The wave form shown in Figure 1 is a picture of AC as it would be generated in a simple, basic alternator. This is called "single phase" power because only one build up of voltage in each direction takes place during the 1/60 second of a complete cycle. In actual practice the large stations do not generate single phase power, but what is called "polyphase" or "three-phase" power. From it single phase circuits are derived as needed.

Until recently polyphase power was used exclusively for industrial purposes where motors of one horsepower or more constituted the major part of the load. With the increasing use of central air conditioning in the home, the power companies are putting

The voltage step-down transformers required in new residential areas are too heavy to be hung on poles. Instead, it is generally found necessary to place these bulky elements in nearby underground vaults.

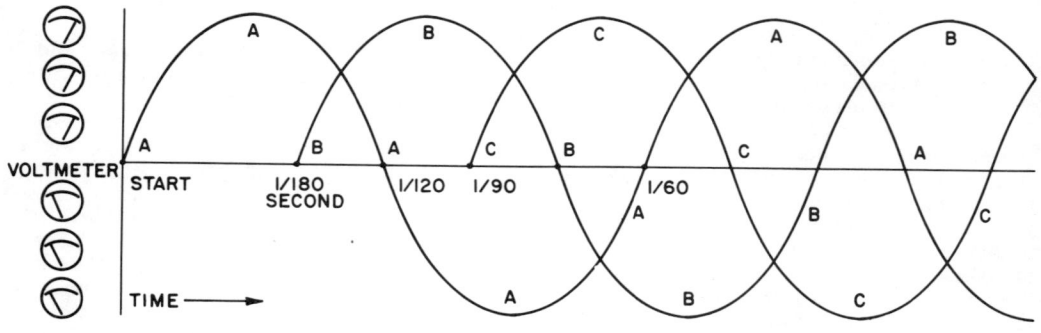

Figure 5: Three-phase power generated by most large generating stations. Curves A, B, C are of three separate voltages which flow in same circuit 1/180-second apart. This type is for large motor operation.

polyphase circuits into many new residential districts. These conditioners run to 2, 3, 5 and even more horsepower, and represent little "industrial" installations all by themselves.

If you have a somewhat older house and are considering the idea of modernizing its wiring, installing a big air conditioner to work through existing heat ducts, etc., by all means consult your local utility. The company's engineers know exactly what kind and size of power lines are available in the neighborhood, and will tell you whether a three-wire or a four-wire system will best serve your needs. This advice is free, as the company is glad to have you increase your use of electricity!

Look at Figure 5. The wave form or curve marked A is the same as that of Figure 1. It represents the voltage developed by one set of windings on the rotating alternator. As before, the first alternation is completed in 1/120 second, the complete cycle in 1/60 second. In an actual machine, there is not one but three sets of identical windings, separated 120 degrees or ⅓ of a revolution. As the alternator starts to turn from its theoretical dead starting point, the first winding starts to generate the voltage A and continues to do so as the motion continues. A scant 1/180 second after the starting time, the second winding comes into play and generates the voltage B, which is exactly like A. While voltage A is building up the second alternation of its first cycle, the third winding comes into play at the 1/90 second point, and generates the voltage C. This is a replica of its predecessors A and B. With the alternator turning over steadily, power is delivered THREE times during each cycle of 1/60 second duration, instead of only once. For motor operation, three-phase supply has the same advantage over single-phase supply that multiple-cylinder gasoline engines have over single-cylinder jobs. The torque is smoother, and the motors themselves are simpler in construction and more efficient in operation.

The three windings on the alternator are in effect three separate generators, and can be connected in a number of very complex ways. Of course, the voltages can be stepped up or down in any desired fashion.

As it reaches the home, three-phase power takes the form of a *four*-wire cable from the street. People with some practical knowledge of electricity and radio are invariably confused by this wiring the first time they see it. They usually know about three-wire, 230-volt service, but they can't figure the four. The arrangement is really quite simple. See Figure 6. One of the wires

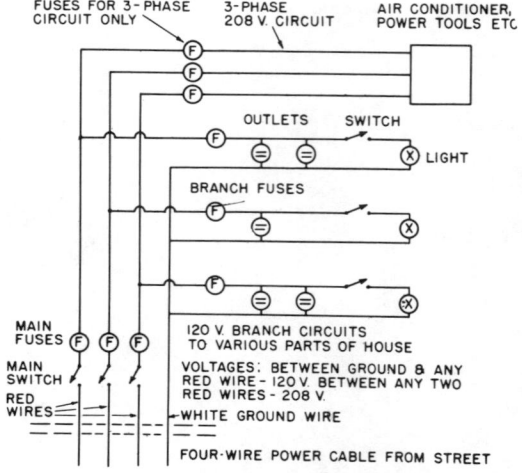

Figure 6: Basic four-wire, three-phase power system, with the watt-hour meter omitted for the sake of simplicity. The 115-volt circuits displayed here are distributed between ground and red wires.

16

again has white insulation, and as you might expect by now, is the grounded neutral. All the other three wires have red covering. Between the ground wire and *each* of the red wires you pick off 120-volt *single*-phase power for the usual 115-volt household machines and appliances. Each branch circuit has its own fuse. The big air-conditioner motor, a three-phase unit, is connected by three leads to the three *red* wires only, through its own set of three fuses. Because of the tricky interweaving of the three phase voltages, a separate return or neutral wire is not needed with a motor load. The voltage between any two red wires of the three-phase circuit is 208 volts when the voltage between ground and any one red wire is adjusted to 120 volts; repeat: 208 volts, NOT 230 or 240.

Both the starting and running current of a three-phase motor are relatively low. In an actual installation represented by Figure 6, the air conditioner goes on and off without having the slightest effect on the house lights or anything else connected to the single-phase branch circuits.

Three-Wire, 208-Volt System

In some residential districts of some of the major cities of the United States, the *only* power distribution system is of the four-wire, three-phase type previously described. The conventional 115/230-volt, three-wire system might not be available at all. A builder of medium-priced homes, which do not have central air-conditioning as original equipment, might not elect to bring the full four-wire service into them. Instead, he will ask for basic "115-volt" service, and let the buyers of the houses worry about the operation of air conditioners, driers, etc., that they might buy later.

Actually, what the power companies then install is *three*-wire service from the *four*-wire facilities on their street poles. One wire is the usual common ground; the other two are random pairs of the outside "phase legs." Neighboring houses are on staggered legs, so that the load is distributed over the wires and not concentrated on any one pair. See Figure 7.

Between the ground and *either* phase leg the voltage is a full 120, and this is led through the house to operate the usual "115-volt" lamps and appliances. Again, the lines are staggered between the common ground and the two phase wires, to distribute the load.

Now comes the joker: *The voltage across the two outside wires is not 240 volts, as it would be in an ordinary three-wire system if each half measured 120 volts;* IT IS 208 VOLTS, just as it was in the full four-wire system as detailed on the opposite page. Even some professional electricians are fooled; they see three wires and immediately say, "That's 115/230." It takes a voltmeter test and a call to the utility company to convince them that the voltages are 120 and 208.

Are there 208-volt appliances? Certainly. All you have to do is go and ask for them. •

Triple fuse block feeds three-phase power to large air conditioner in house having full four-wire service. Three wires on left go only to conditioner. White wire and dark wires on right go to house circuits, as shown in Figure 6 on opposite page.

Figure 7:
In this three-wire system, derived from four-wire, three-phase supply, single-phase power at 120 and 208 volts is available in an average house.

Power Is What You Buy

Volts, watts, amps and ohms are Man's method of measuring quantities of electrical power; to work with wiring, you should have a good understanding of these terms. In this chapter we've printed all you'll need to know—

VOLTS, amperes, ohms and watts are technical terms that add up to one important thing: your monthly electric bill from the local utility company. This is reason enough why you should know what they mean! Their relationship is very simple, and if you know any two of the values in a circuit you can easily figure the others.

Volts, or "voltage," is a measure ot the push or pressure of electrical energy. Ohms, or "ohmage," is a measure of the resistance of the wires, wiring and other electrical conductors through which electricity flows. Amperes, or "amperage," is a measure of the electricity that flows as a result of the push of the voltage against the resistance of the conductors. As appears logical, the higher the voltage and the lower the resistance, the higher the current. These three factors are expressed in "Ohm's Law," the simplest and most useful formula in all of the complicated science of electronics. *amperes equal volts divided by ohms.*

Suppose an electric iron designed for service on 120 volts has a resistance of 10 ohms. How many amperes will it draw? That's easy: 120 divided by 10, or 12 amperes.

By simple transposition:
Volts equal amperes times ohms.
Ohms equal volts divided by amperes.

Like all standards, these electrical units are purely arbitrary. By international agreement, a conductor has a resistance of one ohm if it lets one volt push a current of one ampere through it in one second.

"Power" is the *rate* of doing work. The electrical unit is the "watt," and is merely volts times amperes. Strictly speaking, this should be expressed as the "watt-second," because by its own definition an ampere doesn't become an ampere until the current

The amount of electrical energy used in your home registers on a watt-hour-meter, which is usually located at the power-wire entrance to the building. The difference in readings from month to month, recorded by the utility company's meter reader, is multiplied by the rate per kilowatt-hour to give your bill in dollars and cents.

Consolidated Edison
        Company of New York

has circulated for a short period of time.

(All four basic terms are named for pioneer physicists of the previous century. Ohm was a German, Volta an Italian, Ampere a Frenchman, and Watt a Scot.)

Since *watts equal volts times amperes* a simple transposition gives us *amperes equal watts divided by volts*. This is a very useful formula in practical work, because with it you can calculate the line currents of many appliances from the wattage figures on the name plates. Another useful one is obtained with a little mathematical juggling. You remember that *volts equal amperes times ohms*. Substituting *amperes times ohms for volts* in the power formula, we get *watts equal amperes times ohms times amperes* or *watts equal amperes squared times ohms*.

Impedance Versus Resistance

The foregoing formulas apply to all DC appliances and circuits, and to "heat" appliances used on AC circuits. In the latter category are ordinary screw-in and tubular incandescent lamps (but not fluorescents), laundry irons, toasters, broilers, room heaters, curling irons, immersion and bottle warmers, electric blankets, etc.

In all motor-operated appliances, television and radio sets and other devices using transformers or coils of wire on iron cores of one shape or another, the opposition to the flow of current through the wire is increased and complicated by certain magnetic effects. In addition to the straight resistance of the wire, the latter effects introduce a second factor called "reactance," and the total effect of the two is called "impedance." This is also expressed in ohms. "Resist" and "impede" have the same general meaning, but "impedance" signifies AC operation. Ohm's Law works just as well with impedance figures substituted for resistance. However, impedance values are of limited significance to practical workers; watts and amperes are more important and are readily calculated from simple formulas.

Although the impedance of a "reactive" AC appliance determines the current in amperes pushed through it by the line voltage, amperes times volts does NOT give its true power rating; the product is called the "apparent power." This is where people with a rudimentary knowledge of electricity often go haywire on their calculations. In many AC devices, the current and the voltage do not always act together, odd as this may sound. Sometimes the current doesn't flow until *after* the voltage has passed; sometimes it flows *before*. The true power is indicated by a wattmeter, which is constructed to take these complex actions into account. The wattage figures on appliance nameplates are the true power.

The ratio of the true power to the apparent power is called the "power factor" of the device, and is expressed as a percentage. In pure heating appliances it is 100%, but in some broilers, hair dryers, etc., it may be less because of the motors in them. Motors for household machines and power tools run to as low as 40% and up to 75%; television and radio sets are somewhat higher.

Incandescent lights have 100% power factor so a little straight arithmetic gives their current load. Add up the wattages of the individual bulbs on a circuit, divide by the assumed line voltage of 115 or 117, and the result in amperes is accurate enough for all practical purposes.

Many fluorescent lamps, on the other hand, particularly in older models and in sizes under double-48 inches, have very poor power factor, between about 45% and 60%. This is due to the presence in the circuit of lamp "ballasts," which consist of multiple turns of wire on iron cores. If only one or two such lamps are used in a house or apartment (usually in the kitchen), the extra line current is negligible.

In most newer types of fluorescents, the power factor is brought up to 90% and even 95% by the use of small capacitors (or "condensers"), whose purpose is to cancel or counterbalance the effect of the ballast winding. The extra cost is slight, and the reduction in line current becomes appreciable if, for example, several large lights are used in a workshop.

Regardless of the power factor, you pay only for the true watts. Your bills depend on the power of your appliances, the time they are kept on, and the utility's charge per kilowatt-hour of service. A kilowatt-hour means 1000 watts for a whole hour. Thus, a 500-watt laundry iron used for half an hour registers one-quarter kilowatt-hour on your electric meter. Read that again, and don't be confused by the fractions. If your power rate is say 3 cents per kilowatt-hour, the half hour's ironing cost only ¾ of a cent.

Figuring a Bill

Many people hesitate about buying air conditioners because they think they are "expensive" to run. The starting current of many conditioners is high for about three seconds, but after that they take less energy than many table-top broilers. For example, a typical room conditioner of standard make is rated at 1005 watts. Suppose you leave it running steadily during a very hot spell. For one full day the consumption is then 1005 times 24 hours, or 24,120 watt-hours or 24.12 kilowatt-hours. If the rate is 4 cents per K.W.H., the cost of running the machine is 96.48 cents, less than one dollar!

The wattage ratings found on appliances are figured on a basis of an "average" line voltage of 115 or 117.

Motor name plates bear the nominal horsepower rating and the line voltage and line current. The conversion factor is 746; that is, *horsepower equals watts divided by 746* or *watts equals horsepower times 746*.

On a typical ⅓ hp motor in my shop, the name plate reads "115 volts, 6 amperes." Volts times amperes gives the apparent power of 690 watts, but ⅓ of 746 makes the true power closer to 250 watts. Dividing 250 by 690 gives a power factor of about 40%.

Since the customer pays only for the true power he uses, why should he concern himself about power factor at all? If the wiring in his house is new and very heavy, he needn't. If it isn't, he finds that power factor rises to haunt him as he adds new machines such as clothes washers and dishwashers, garbage disposals, freezers, air conditioners, attic fans, etc., all of which have relatively low power factor. Low P.F. means high line current for the work done. The heating effect on the power wires of let us say 10 amperes is the same whether this current goes to a 1150-watt bowl heater of 100% P.F. or a 575-watt ventilator of 50% P.F.

I used the setup shown in the photo and diagram on page 21 to obtain a quick idea of the current drains of typical appliances:

Coffeepot, rated at 400 watts: 3½ amperes, 100% power factor.

Hot plate, rated at 700 watts: 6 amperes, 100% power factor.

Vacuum cleaner, rated at 550 watts: 6 amperes, 76% power factor.

High-fidelity amplifier, rated at 140 watts: 1.4 amperes, 83% power factor.

The higher the line current under any circumstances, the greater the power loss in the wires. The latter have appreciable resistance, and some work is done in overcoming it. The big joker here is that the heat loss does not go up gently with increased line current, but with the *square* of the current, as given in the formula *watts equals amperes squared times ohms*.

With current values on the order of 10, 15 and 20 amperes *squared*, or 100, 225 and 400, you can see that it doesn't take much resistance in the lines or in connecting devices to cause trouble. A slightly dirty contact in a plug, having a resistance let us say of one tenth of an ohm, wastes 22.5 watts when the current is 15 amperes. This is juice you pay for but does nothing for you. Poor quality attachment plugs found with some table-top broilers and room heaters, which usually draw the 15-ampere legal maximum from one branch circuit, often becomes so hot that you can blister your fingers if you touch them.

High line current, regardless of whether the amperes are honest ones from high P.F. appliances or sneaky ones from low P.F.-ers, introduces a second joker: reduced line voltage at the appliances themselves. This angle is discussed in detail in the section entitled "Is Your Wiring Adequate?" which follows this chapter on pages 22-31.

Knowing the power rating of an appliance and the approximate line voltage, you can work backward and make a pretty fair guess at the line current. It is important to know this so that you can add up the total current in any branch circuit and determine if the wire itself and the fuse or circuit breaker are of suitable size.

The formula was given previously as *amperes equals watts divided by volts* but this does not, of course, take power factor into consideration. Add about 50% more in the case of "reactive" AC appliances and you have a workable result. For example, take an air conditioner marked 900 watts, 115 volts. Dividing the first figure by the second, we get 7.8; call it 8, add 50% for power factor and the result is 12 amperes.

With a device like a coffee pot or an iron, having virtually 100% P.F., the simple division gives an accurate figure. For example, an iron marked 660 watts takes 5.7 amperes at 115 volts.

Low Versus High Voltage

From the formula *watts equals volts times amperes* you might get the glittering of an idea. Ignoring power factor for the moment, consider an appliance that takes 10 amperes at 120 volts, or 1200 watts. Would it do exactly the same job if it were designed to work on 60 volts and 20 amperes, again 1200 watts, or on 240 volts and 5 amperes, still 1200 watts? The answer is a strong, "Yes!" And since the power is the same in all three cases, so is your electric bill.

There is no advantage in going to lower voltage, but there is a tremendous advantage in going to the *higher* voltage: the line current is reduced by half, and with this lowered current heat losses and voltage drops in connecting wires come down, too. Remember that square-law business. With a plug resistance of .1 ohm, just for an example, the heat loss at 10 amperes is 10 times 10 times .1, or 10 watts, but at 5 amperes it is 5 times 5 times .1, or only 2½ watts! Some difference!

The starting current as well as the running current of motors is naturally lower on the higher voltage.

Cutting the current in half by going to 240 volts is the big reason why appliance dealers and utility companies urge customers to buy 240-volt air conditioners and to have an electrician run a separate line from the meter *if the house already has three-wire, 120/240 volt service.* A 240-volt motor doesn't cost any more than a 120-volt one; in fact, many of fractional horsepower motors used in home machines are readily convertible to either voltage through a quick switching of leads.

Practically all electric ranges are 240-volt operated. The wire required for 120-volt operation is prohibitively heavy and expensive to install.

Insulation No Problem

"What about the problem of insulation at the higher voltage?" No problem at all. If you'll examine sockets, outlets and other connectors closely, you'll see that they bear two current ratings, one in the 110-120 volt range and the other for 220-240. In other words, they're specifically designed for both voltages. Any standard power wires are more than adequately protected for 240 as well as 120 volts. Copper wire is expensive, but insulation is cheap.

In England, which must import every inch of copper it uses, the standard power line voltage for *all* house purposes has been 240 volts for as long as anyone can remember. Power cords there really look and feel like "cords," they are that thin.

So greatly does higher voltage alleviate the line overloading problem, and also make initial installation costs lower, that the power companies are going up the scale further than the 220-230-240 volt limit that has been standard in the United States for many years. In New York, for example, where huge new buildings with central air conditioning and whole ceilings of fluorescent lights are going up by the score, the Consolidated Edison Company is making 265/460 volt service available. This is a combination of single-phase power at 265 volts and three-phase power at 460 volts, exactly like the 120/208 volt service described in the section entitled "The Power System in Your Home."

Automobile manufacturers have shifted from six volts to twelve volts for precisely the same reasons of copper saving. The current needed at six volts to operate ignition, lights, radio, heater, cigarette lighter, convertible top, power doors and seats, etc., requires wire so heavy that installation is almost a plumbing job. With the current cut exactly in half at twelve volts, the wiring harness lends itself better to mass production methods.

Ignore any claims that the higher battery voltage is needed to give "increased power" for starting and other purposes in big present-day cars. This is pure advertising hog wash. Power in DC circuits, and there is no purer DC than comes from a storage battery, is just volts times amperes. •

Left, apparatus setup used to measure line current of appliances; AC ammeter is on left, plug-in box is at center and iron under test is at right. Below, right, here is the setup in diagram form. See text.

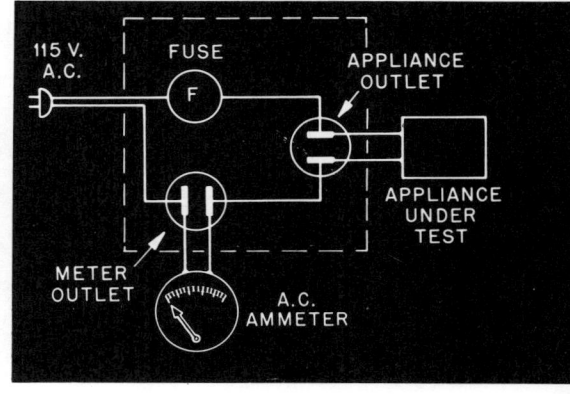

Is Your Wiring Adequate?

Fig. 1. Label on obsolete main fuse box.

Ask your utility company to inspect it. Insufficient wiring causes faulty operation of appliances, reduced voltage and wasted power

THOUSANDS of new homes and apartments built each year are found to be electrically obsolete after only a couple of years of occupancy. When new appliances are acquired, the owners must spend large sums on additional wiring, and in some cases they are forced virtually to rip the old wiring out and to replace it with adequate lines.

"Inadequate" wiring creates a double problem: 1) It reduces the normal line voltage, often to the point where appliances cease to work satisfactorily; 2) It becomes overheated, and can readily start a fire in the home. Lights go dim, TV pictures shrink, a broiler doesn't cook the food in it, an air conditioner can't be used at all . . . all because of inadequate wiring. According to the Joint Industry Board of the Electrical Industry, four out of five homes and apartments in the great City of New York are insufficiently wired for appliances now found in them. The situation in other places is so bad that municipal ordinances are being drawn up which force the users of heavy-current machines to protect themselves. For instance, in Memphis, Tenn., appliance dealers are required to report to the city the sale of any device rated at 1,000 watts or more. The city then inspects the home of the purchaser to see that it is wired properly. Louisville, Ky., under an existing electrical code, can require property owners to install proper wiring or lose electrical service. In addition, the city is considering a new law patterned after the one in effect in Memphis, which would require buyers of appliances to prove they have the necessary circuits to carry the additional load. Affected would be air conditioners, room heaters, kitchen ranges, roasters, friers, broilers, garbage disposal units, large ironing machines, clothes driers and dishwashers.

The National Electrical Code, which forms the basis for practically all local electrical codes and ordinances, is a standard of safety. It deals primarily with the materials and methods of installation of wiring systems. However, these various codes cannot provide against the possibility of the wiring system becoming overloaded because of major additions to the home's electrical equipment. Code authorities recognize this limitation, and call attention to it in the introduction to the National Electrical Code, which states: ". . . an installation reasonably free from hazard, but not necessarily efficient or convenient. Good service and satisfactory results will often require larger sizes of wire, more branch circuits and better types of equipment than the minimum which is specified here."

Many people ask, "Why doesn't the local power company make sure the wiring in a house is sufficient? After all, the company is in the business of selling electricity and it's to their advantage to have a lot of appliances running properly."

The answer briefly is that your home is your castle, and what you do in it is your responsibility. If you chose to set it on fire by disregarding the limitations of its electrical system, the loss is yours. It may be yours alone, insurance notwithstanding, if subsequent investigation proves that your wiring was illegal and improper. Naturally, the utility companies don't like to lose customers, so many of them offer free wiring advisory service. Call the office of your local utility and find out. Note that this service is only *advisory*. The utility's actual responsibility ends with the power wires where they fasten to your house. **The service entrance wires and everything else then depend on you.** (The electric meter is the property of the utility but in

(Continued on page 26)

22

Fig. 2. Compare your main fuse box or circuit breaker box with the diagrams below. If it is the type shown at left, it is inadequate for present-day electrical loads. Consult your power company engineer.

BASIC CAPACITY: Probably 3,600 watts	BASIC CAPACITY: 14,500 watts	BASIC CAPACITY: 24,000 watts
 Typical 30 Amp. Fuse Type Main Switch	 Typical 60 Amp. Fuse Type Combination Main Switch and Branch Circuit Panel	 Typical 100 Amp. Fuse Type Combination Main Switch and Branch Circuit Panel
 Typical 30 Amp. Combination Main Breaker and Branch Circuit Panel	 Typical 60 Amp. Combination Main Breaker and Branch Circuit Panel	 Typical 100 Amp. Main Breaker
30 AMPERES May be only 120 Volt **OBSOLETE**	**60 AMPERES** 240 Volt **MINIMUM**	**100 AMPERES** 240 Volt **ADEQUATE**
This will supply: Lighting and a Few Plug-in Appliances.	This will supply: Lighting and Plug-in Appliances — Electric Range — Water Heater.	This will supply: Lighting and Plug-in Appliances — Electric Range — Water Heater PLUS any Major Appliances*

*With possible exception of Central Air Conditioning or Electric House Heating.

Typical Wattages of Some Lights and Appliances Normally Connected to General Purpose or Plug-in Appliance Circuits

LIGHTING watts

Ceiling or Wall (each bulb)	40-150
Floor Lamps (each)	150-300
Fluorescent Lights (each tube)	15-40
Pin-to-Wall Lamps	50-150
Table Lamps (each)	50-150
Ultra Violet Lamp	385

APPLIANCES watts

Baker (portable)	800-1000
Bottle Warmer	95
Broiler-Rotisserie	1320-1650
Casserole	1350
Clock	2
Coffee Maker or Percolator	440-1000
Coffee Grinder	150
Corn Popper	1350
Deep Fat Fryer	1350
Egg Cooker	500
Electric Bed Cover	200
Electric Fan (portable)	100
Electric Roaster	1650
Food Blender	230-250
Hair Dryer	235
Hand Iron (steam or dry)	1000
Heating Pad	60
Heated Tray	500
Ice Cream Freezer	115
Ironer	1650
Knife Sharpener	103
Lawn Mower	250
Mixer	100
Portable Heater	1000
Radio (each)	100
Record-Changer	75
Refrigerator**	150
Sandwich Grill	660-800
Saucepan	1000
Sewing Machine	75
Shaver	12
Skillet	1100
Television	300
Toaster (modern automatic)	up to 1150
Vacuum Cleaner	125
Ventilating Fan (built-in)	140
Waffle Iron	up to 1100
Warmer (Rolls, etc.)	100
Waxer-Polisher	350

**Each time the refrigerator starts it takes several times this wattage for an instant.

One each (230 or 240 volt) for: watts

Electric Clothes Drier	4500
Electric Range	8000-16,000
Electric Water Heater	2000-4000
Room Air Conditioner* (½ or ¾ ton)	1200-1600
Water Pump*	700-1500

One each (115 or 120 volt) for: watts

Automatic Washer*	700
Built-in Bathroom Heater	1000-1500
Dishwasher-Waste-Disposer	1500
Electrostatic Air Cleaner	60
Home Freezer*	350
Mechanism for Fuel-fired Heating Equipment*	800
Room Air Conditioner* (1/3 ton)	750
Summer Cooling Fan*	250-750
Waste-Disposer alone* (without Dishwasher)	500
Water Pump*	700
Workshop or Bench* (Total wattage will vary)	

*The wattage of motor-operated equipment will vary, depending on the size of the motor. Individual circuits are necessary, however, in order to avoid frequent "blackouts," poor TV and radio reception, constant dimming or flickering of lights when the equipment is operating; to assure continuity of service from such devices as the home freezer and the heating plant, and to permit the use of plug-in and major appliances at the same time.

GENERAL PURPOSE CIRCUITS	For Protection They Need Fuse or Circuit Breaker	You Can Connect All at Once
For lighting and general use in living and bedrooms; lighting only, in kitchen, laundry, dining area. Most homes built before 1940 still rely on one or two 15 ampere General Purpose Circuits for *all* lighting and appliance use. In many instances, even certain major appliances have been plugged in on these poor, overworked wires.	 One 15 amp. plug fuse per circuit / One 15 amp. breaker per circuit (Ratings imprinted on handle.) (20 ampere fuse or breaker permitted *only* when No. 12 wire is used.	1610-1800 watts

PLUG-IN APPLIANCE CIRCUITS		
To convenience outlets only (no lights), in kitchen, laundry, dining area — seldom found in homes built before 1940. Most homes built since 1940 have one or more Plug-in Appliance Circuits, but some do not. And, often, the one Plug-in Appliance Circuit has since been forced to substitute as a Major Appliance Circuit, to serve some new appliance, like automatic washer, dishwasher, or home freezer. Then, it becomes overloaded each time it is shared with any of the plug-in appliances shown on the list at left.	  One 20 amp. plug fuse per circuit / One 20 amp. breaker per circuit (Only No. 12 wire is permitted for 20-amp. plug-in appliance circuits.) Modern practice is to use 3-wire circuits. These are each protected by two plug fuses, like those shown above at left—or by a double-handled breaker: 3-wire circuits are rarely found in older homes.	2300-2400 watts on 2-wire circuits

INDIVIDUAL EQUIPMENT CIRCUITS		
Each of the major appliances and other equipment listed at left should have its own, individual branch circuit, in order to do its best work. If you have an electric range, water heater or clothes drier, you are sure to have a separate circuit for each one. They could not have been installed otherwise. However, in many homes, other major appliances have been connected to General Purpose or Plug-in Appliance Circuits which were already carrying more than their share of lighting and plug-in equipment.	2 Cartridge Fuses or   2 Plug-Fuses per circuit  One Plug-Fuse per circuit 1 Double-Handled Fuse per circuit  One Breaker per circuit Ratings of fuses and circuit breakers serving individual equipment circuits will vary — depending on what piece of equipment is to be served. Most of the 115 or 120 volt major appliances shown here are served by 20 ampere circuits.	Nothing more than the appliance or equipment served by each circuit

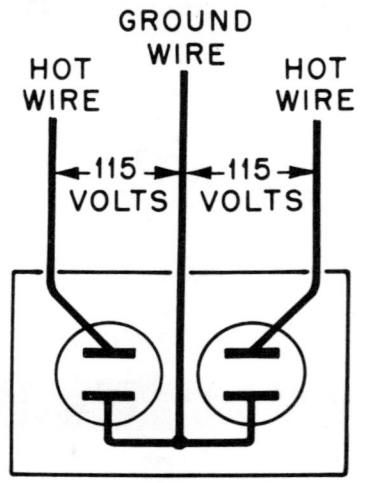

Fig. 3. As shown in diagram above, split outlet wiring permits use of two heavy-current appliances.

effect it becomes part of the permanent wiring installation in the home.)

In most older homes, the electric service entrance was planned to accommodate only lights and a few plug-in appliances, such as a toaster or an iron in the kitchen, radio sets in various rooms, and a portable vacuum cleaner. In such homes, certain newer machines cannot be used at all unless the entire service entrance is replaced by a larger one. Installing larger fuses than the present ones is no solution to the problem, and is an extremely dangerous and foolish practice.

A common mistake made by many people is to assume that the service entrance is "adequate" merely because it is "three-wire." Most homes built since about 1940 have three-wire service, which can accommodate an electric range and a water heater. However, few of them have three wires that are big enough to bring in sufficient electricity for today's needs. Wire of the No. 2 size is recommended as a minimum. Remember that you pay only for the electricity you use, no matter how large the service entrance may be. There-

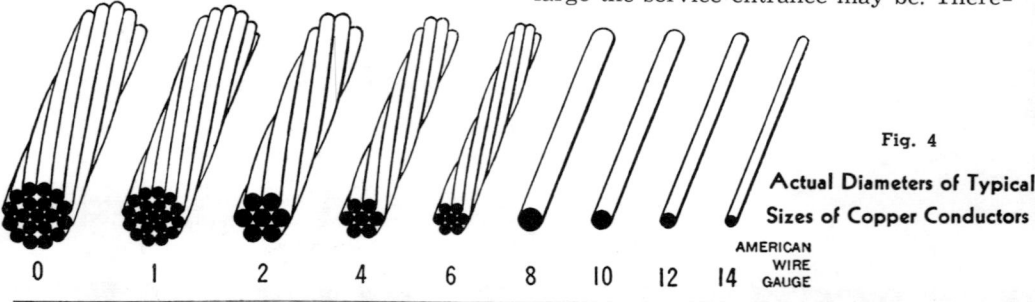

Fig. 4
Actual Diameters of Typical Sizes of Copper Conductors

Fig. 5. **PROPERTIES OF COPPER CONDUCTORS***

Size of Conductor AWG	Circular Mils	Ohms Per 1000 Feet 25°C—77°F Bare Conductor	Bare Conductor Diameter— Inches	Concentric Lay Stranded Conductors No. of Wires
14	4,107	2.575	.064	Solid
12	6,530	1.619	.081	Solid
10	10,380	1.018	.102	Solid
8	16,510	.641	.129	Solid
6	26,250	.410	.184	7
4	41,740	.259	.232	7
2	66,370	.162	.292	7
1	83,690	.129	.332	19
0	105,500	.102	.373	19
00	133,100	.081	.418	19

*From National Electric Code—1953.

fore, it pays in the long run to have it made big enough to permit future expansion. It can easily be too small, but it can never be too big.

It is difficult and risky for a layman to determine the actual size of the service entrance wires, as this usually means poking around the circuits while they are alive. Really the safest and cheapest thing to do is have the job done by a representative of the power company or by a local electrical contractor.

As a minimum, examine the main fuse box or circuit breaker box and look for an Underwriters' Label. If it is marked "Form 30," the service entrance is definitely obsolete. See Fig. 1, page 22. If the label has disappeared or if it has a different form number, compare your main panel with Fig. 2, page 23, and you'll get a fair idea of what you have.

According to modern standards, the service entrance in a 1000 square foot home should provide at least 4,500 watts for lighting and plug-in appliances (more in larger homes), *plus* any of the following permanently connected major appliances which are already in or are likely to be installed in the near future:

Automatic Washer	700 watts
Built-in Bathroom Heater (how many?) each	1000-1500 watts
Dishwasher	1500 watts
Clothes Drier	4500 watts
Electric Range	8000-16,000 watts
Water Heater	2000-4000 watts
Electrostatic Air Cleaner	60 watts
Home Freezer	350 watts
Mechanism for Fuel-Fired Heating Plant	800 watts
Room Air Conditioner, ⅓ ton	750 watts
Room Air Conditioner, ¾ ton	1200 watts
Water Pump	700 watts
Waste Disposer	500 watts

What can be done about inadequate entrance service and equipment? The power company engineer or electrical contractor will probably recommend one or more of the following:

(Continued on page 29)

Fig. 6

ALLOWABLE CURRENT-CARRYING CAPACITY, IN AMPERES, OF COPPER CONDUCTORS*

Based on room temperature of 30°C (86°F)

	In Raceway or Cable		In Free Air		
Size of Conductor AWG	Not more than three conductors in raceway or cable; if the number of conductors is four, the allowable carrying capacity is 80 per cent of the values given.		This generally covers open wiring on insulators, and knob and tube work.		
	Rubber Types R, RW, RU, RUW / Thermoplastic Types T, TW	Rubber Type RH	Rubber Types R, RW, RU, RUW / Thermoplastic Types T, TW	Rubber Type RH	Weatherproof Type WP
14	**15**	15	20	20	30
12	**20**	20	25	25	40
10	**30**	30	40	40	55
8	**40**	45	55	65	70
6	**55**	65	80	95	100
4	**70**	85	105	125	130
2	**95**	115	140	170	175
1	**110**	130	165	195	205
0	**125**	150	195	230	235

*From National Electric Code—1951.

Fig. 7 INSULATION TABLE*

Insulation	Type Letter	Maximum Operating Temperature	Suitable For
Code Rubber	R	60°C (140°F)	General Use
Moisture-Resistant Rubber	RW	60°C (140°F)	General Use and Wet Locations
Latex Rubber	RU	60°C (140°F)	General Use
Moisture-Resistant Latex Rubber	RUW	60°C (140°F)	General Use and Wet Locations
Heat-Resistant Rubber	RH	75°C (167°F)	General Use
Thermoplastic	T	60°C (140°F)	General Use
Moisture-Resistant Thermoplastic	TW	60°C (140°F)	General Use and Wet Locations
Weatherproof	WP	80°C (176°F)	Open Wiring by Special Permission

*From National Electric Code—1953.

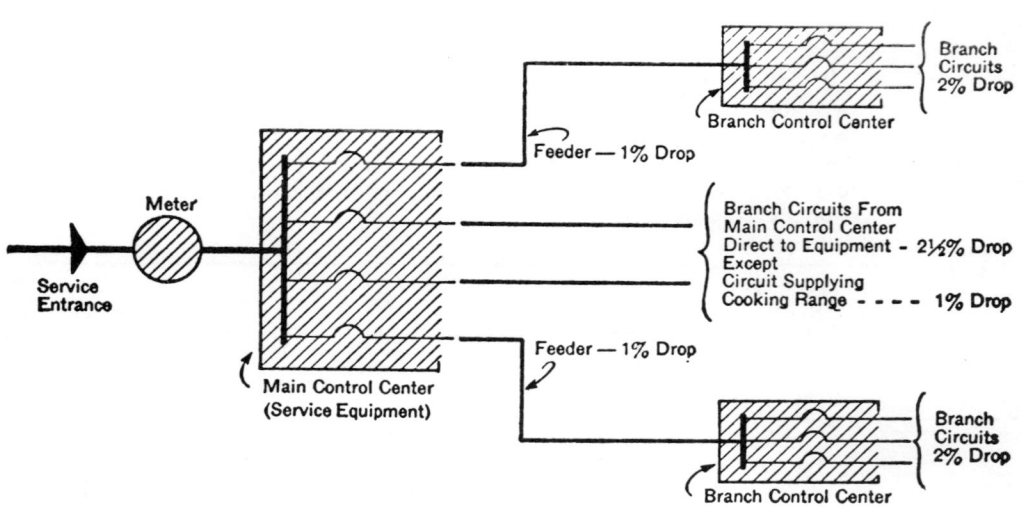

Fig. 8. This illustrates recommended allowable maximum voltage drops in a typical house wiring system.

1) Replace present service entrance wires with larger ones.

2) Replace outmoded fuse or circuit breaker box with one of larger capacity, probably a minimum of 100 amperes.

3) Retain present main panel as part of the service equipment and install a second main panel to increase the total capacity.

4) Replace old meter with a newer one.

This is only the beginning, of course. You have to work out from the fuse boxes into the branch circuits feeding the various parts of the house.

In some homes, a bad case of overloaded circuits can be relieved by having the automatic washer, dishwasher, freezer and other major appliances put on individual circuits. This may require some chopping of walls for the new wires and outlets, but it's worth the trouble. By the time a house needs new wiring it probably can also use a new paint job, and the two operations can be combined.

A modern and efficient method of increasing circuit capacity is to have one or more three-wire circuits installed, to serve convenience outlets into which you want to plug more than one high-wattage appliance at a time; for instance, a toaster and a coffee pot, at breakfast time, or a broiler and an iron, to permit a woman to press clothes while food is cooking. As shown in Fig. 3, page 26, this arrangement divides the openings of each convenience outlet between two different circuits, greatly reducing the chance of overloading. The wires should be No. 12 in size.

Three-wire circuits also permit you to control one section of an outlet from a wall switch, while leaving the other section permanently alive for any plug-in purpose.

Wires and Voltage Drop*

The "circular mil" is the unit of measurement of the cross-section of wire used in electrical practice. One circular mil, abbreviated cir mil or cm, is the area of a circle 1/1000 of an inch in diameter. If the diameter of the wire in mils is known, the figure is simply squared and the result is circular mils. Because electrical workers rarely if ever have occasion to put a micrometer on copper wires, and because the cm numbers are very large and unwieldy even for small wires, this method of designation is rapidly falling out of favor. Instead, much more convenient one- and two-digit numbers, forming the "American Wire Gauge," or "AWG," are used in practical work. The accompanying table, Fig. 5, page 26, gives the relationships between gauge numbers, circular mils, actual wire diameters, etc. The AWG is the same as the "Brown and Sharpe Gauge," or

---

*Part of the material in this section has been abstracted from the "Westinghouse Home Wiring Handbook," Westinghouse Electric Corp., Pittsburgh, Pa.

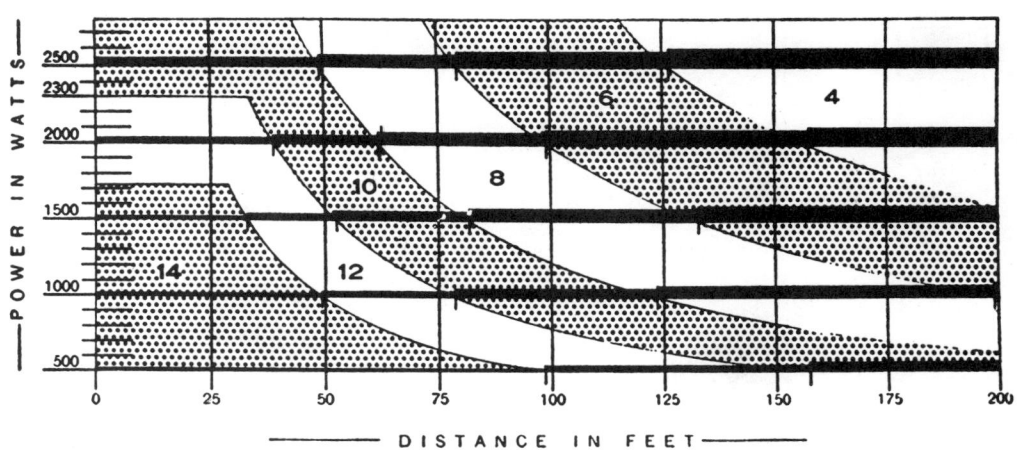

Conductor Size Based on Voltage Drop (115 Volt—2% Drop)

Fig. 9. With the aid of this chart and those on pages 28-29, you can determine what size wire you need.

"B & S." Fig. 4, page 26, shows the actual full-size diameters of typical power wires from No. 14 through No. 0.

The conductor sizes given in Fig. 6, page 27, are based on current-carrying capacity of wire having type "R" insulation, which is a rubber compound, and the wires are assumed to be in raceways or cables. There are many varieties of insulation, but the ones listed in Fig. 7, page 28, are the ones in common commercial use.

Each type of conductor insulation affords a given maximum safe-operating temperature. If this "safe" value is exceeded for

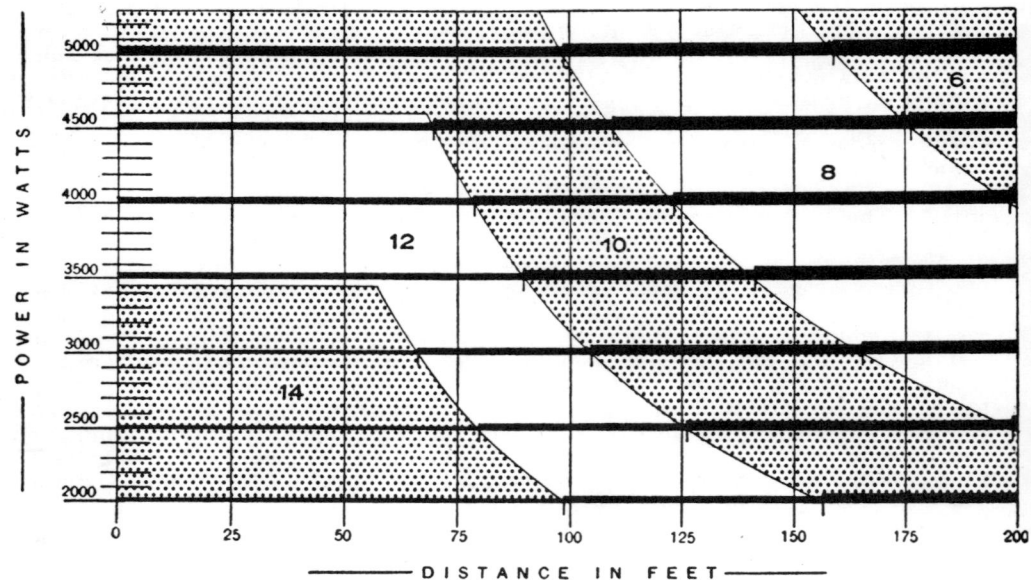

Fig. 10. **Conductor Size Based on Voltage Drop (230 Volt—2% Drop)**

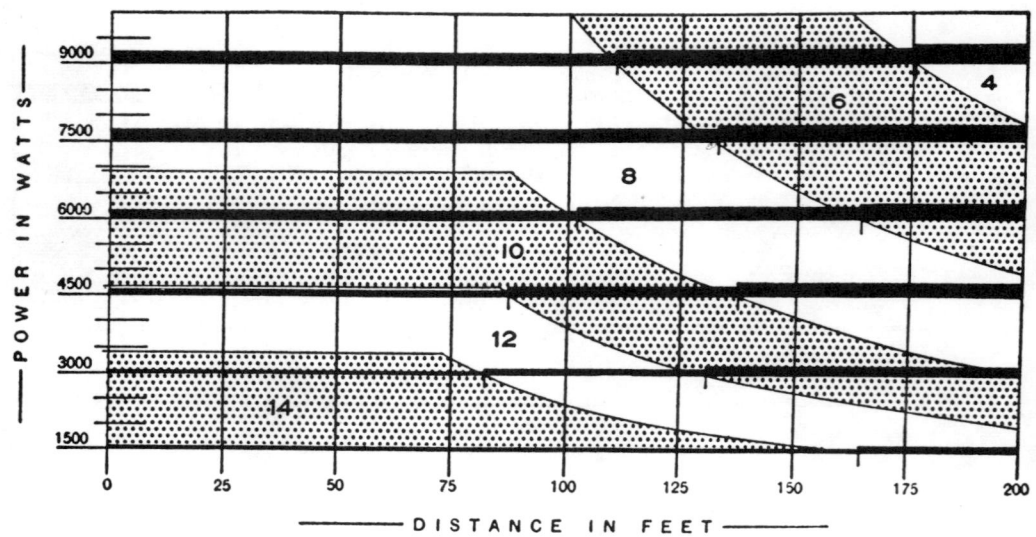

Fig. 11 **Conductor Size Based on Voltage Drop (230 Volt—2½% Drop)**

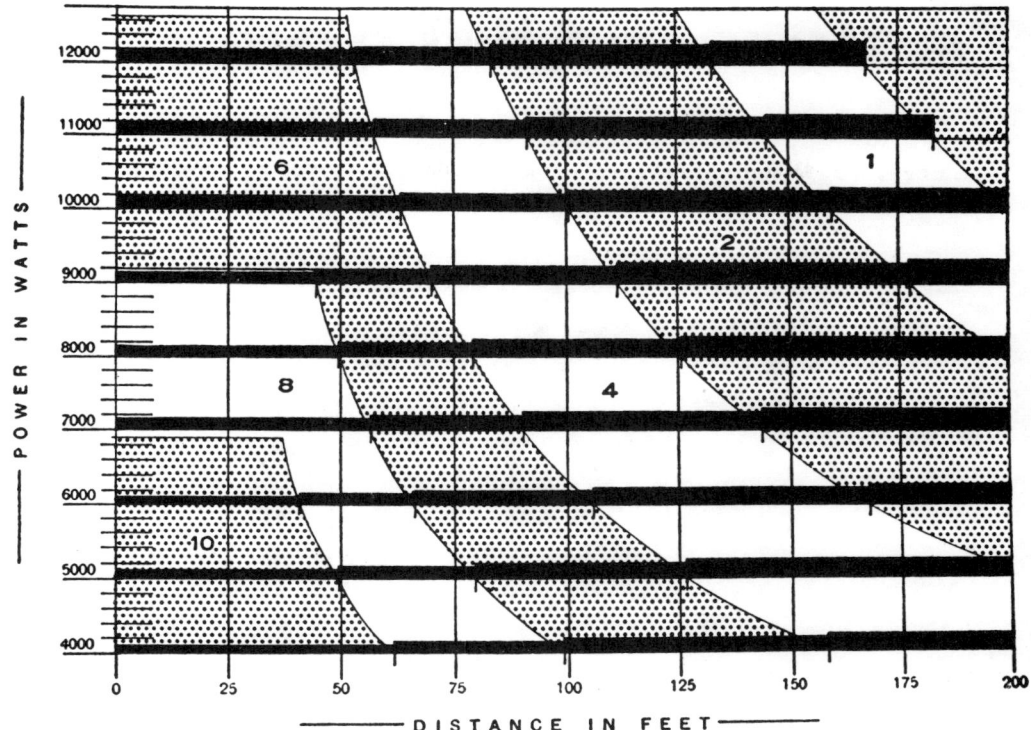

Fig. 12 **Conductor Size Based on Voltage Drop (230 Volt—1% Drop)**

any considerable length of time, the insulation will deteriorate rapidly; under heavy overload conditions it can readily melt or burn off, permitting the copper wires to touch each other or the grounded cable in which they might be encased. If the fuses or circuit breakers are functioning normally, they will open and cut off further current.

The conductors of a wiring system should be of sufficient size not only as a safeguard against overheating, but also to restrict voltage drop. It is impractical to avoid *all* drop, but it can and should be held to reasonable proportions.

The recommended allowable maximum voltage drops in the various portions of a typical house electrical system are shown in Fig. 8, page 28. It is good practice to have the conductors of such a size as to keep the drops within the percentage limits indicated. The heavier the wire chosen for a circuit, the lower the voltage loss in it and the higher the voltage delivered to the appliance.

To determine if a conductor sized correctly for current-carrying capacity will also keep the voltage within allowable bounds, check against Figs. 9, 10, 11, pages 29 and 30, and 12, above. Each of these covers a specific type of feeder or circuit. Based on economical voltage drop, load in watts and length of the circuit in feet, the proper size of conductor can be selected readily. Here's a practical example of the use of the charts:

Situation: A 115-volt branch circuit carries 1500 watts (13 amperes) a distance of 75 feet. It is desired to keep within 2% voltage drop, or 2.3 volts. Will No. 12 wire, having a carrying capacity of 20 amperes, do the trick?

Answer: No. Fig. 9 shows that No. 12 will carry 1500 watts about 53 feet with a 2% drop. To find the right size, start at the 1500-watt line at the left, and run your finger to the right until you meet the vertical line coming up from the 75-foot mark at the bottom of the chart. The point of intersection is clearly on the heavy line marked 10, which is the number of the needed wire. •

31

Testers and Tools

The Clicktester, Handitester and Lightester are simple projects to make; you'll find them invaluable for trouble-shooting appliances

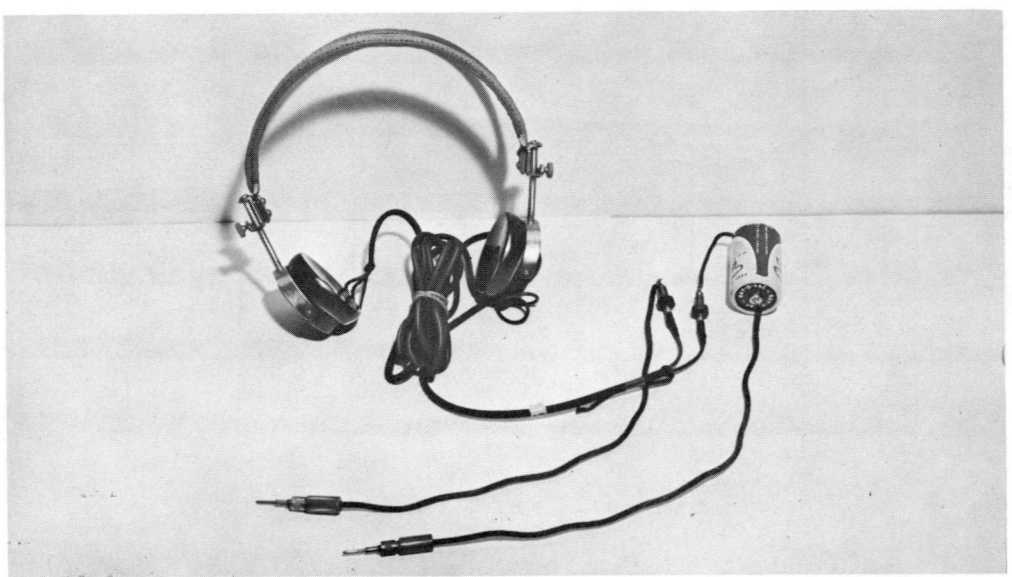

Here is the "Clicktester" wired but not assembled; the parts have been separated to show connections. The earphones, the single flashlight cell and the flexible test prods are connected in simple series.

ALL electrical appliances contain wire of one sort or another, through which current flows to perform a variety of tasks. In the case of heating devices, such as ordinary lamps, irons, grills, coffee makers, etc., the wire is purposely designed to resist or impede the movement of electrons. The latter, in pushing their way through this resistance, develop considerable friction, the outward effect of which is the desired heat. The most commonly employed resistance wires are alloys: nickel chromium, nickel copper, nickel chromium iron, nickel iron, and manganese nickel, which are sold under dozens of different trade names.

For most other purposes it is desirable to have wire of low resistance. Soft copper is universally used because it is cheap and workable. Only silver has a lower resistance value, and for this reason the contacts and sometimes even the wire of certain high-grade instruments are silver-plated.

In low-resistance wire, electron movement is converted into useful mechanical movement through magnetic effects, as in the case of motors, bells and buzzers, and other items.

Obviously, the wire path must be continuous, or no current can flow. Because wires do burn out in normal service or from accidental short circuits, or break from physical abuse, the basic test to be made on an appliance suspected of being defective is a "continuity" check. Fortunately, this can be done easily and quickly with some very simple and inexpensive testers, which you can make yourself either from "junk box" parts or a prepared kit.

The "Clicktester"

Consisting merely of an earphone, a single flashlight battery and a couple of pieces of wire, the "Clicktester" is entirely adequate for about 90% of all the trouble-

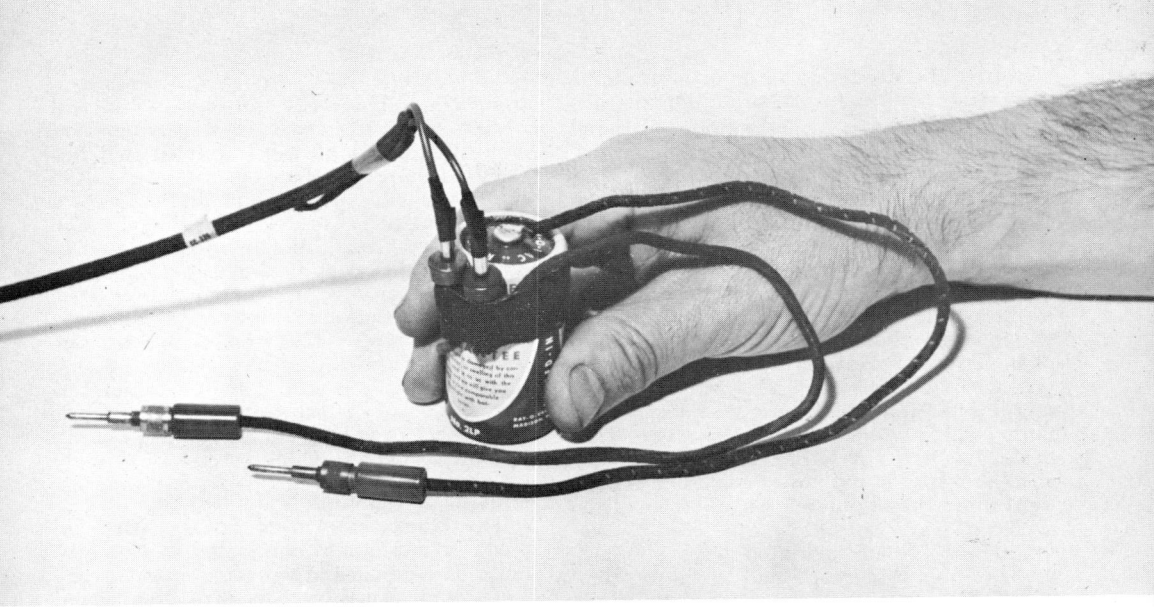

The two tip jacks for the earphone terminals are taped securely to the body of the flashlight cell. The length of the leads with the test prods is not critical; lamp cord between 12 and 18" is OK.

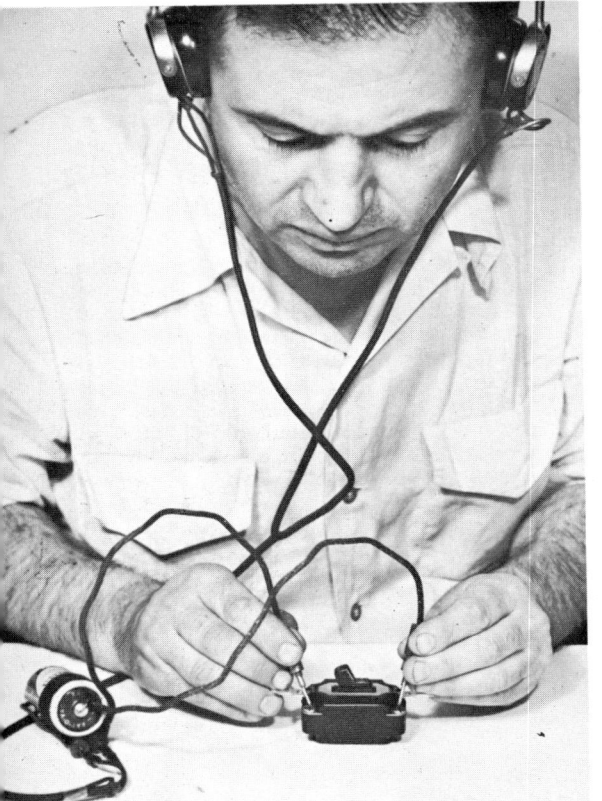

Check the condition of switches with Clicktester by tapping the probes against terminal screws.

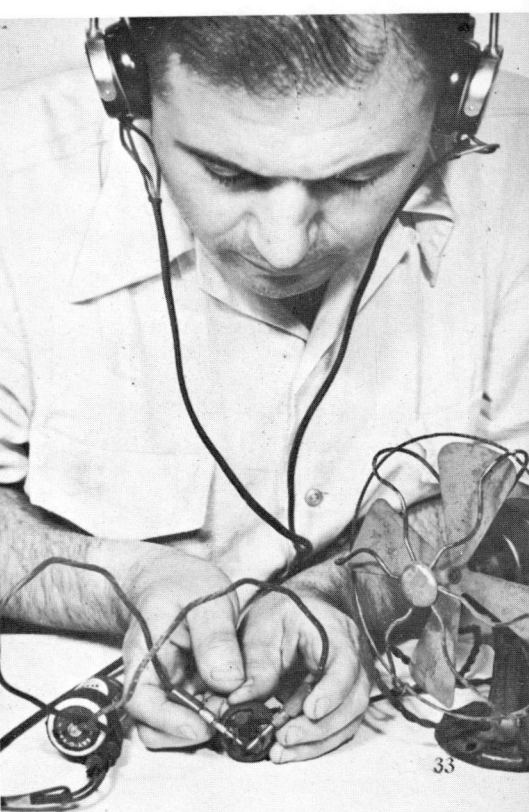

Is wiring in fan OK? A test with Clicktester will give answer; no sound reveals an open circuit.

shooting you are likely to do on household electrical devices. *Any* single or double earphone intended for telephone or radio work will serve the purpose. Astronomical quantities of very sensitive military phones are kicking around the surplus stores, at a fraction of their real value. The radio mail order firms sell a perfectly suitable single phone for only 96 cents!

To facilitate connection to the end pins of the phone cord, you need two pin jacks, which cost 9 cents each; also two tip plugs, at 14 cents each, for use on the ends of two test wires or "probes." The latter can be any flexible insulated wire . . . a section of lamp cord is fine . . . about a foot long. The battery can be of either the "C" or "D" size. One that is too run down for a flashlight might have enough juice left in it for a year of tester service.

Cut a piece of insulated wire about 3 inches long; solder one end to the bottom of the battery and the other to a tip jack. Solder one end of a probe wire to the top (center) connection of the battery. Solder one end of the second probe wire to the second tip jack. Tighten the free ends of the probes to the tip plugs. The latter do not require soldering. Push the bared end of the wire through a hole in the body of the plug and catch it under the threaded head nut. Tape the tip jacks individually with friction or Scotch electrical tape, and then tape the pair to the body of the battery. Push the tips of the phone cord into the jacks, and you're in business. It will probably take you longer to read this description of the Clicktester than to make the item.

With the phones resting on the table, touch the free probe ends together. You will hear a loud click when you make contact and again when you break it. With the probes pressed firmly together, you will hear nothing. Don't be afraid of the metal ends of the probes. You can touch them freely, as the 1½ volts of the battery isn't enough to shock a gnat.

Using the Clicktester

In using the Clicktester, it is usually convenient to wear the phones, just to get them out of the way. Don't put them directly over your ears, but push them forward slightly. The clicks can be strong enough to be uncomfortable when they are sounding.

To illustrate a basic application of the Clicktester, let's try it on an ordinary switch. In the latter's off position, touching the probes to the connecting screws should produce no sound. Snap the arm to the on position and try again. This time you'll hear loud clicks as you tap the probes on the screws. These are the results you will obtain from a switch in normally good condition, but don't think that all switches respond that way. Because of failure of the internal spring or fusing of the contacts, a switch is likely to test either open (no clicks) or closed (clicks) with the arm in either the on or off setting.

The more wire in an appliance, the higher its resistance, relatively. You might therefore expect that the clicks will be weaker with a device like a fan or clock, for instance, than with a switch, which has practically no resistance. Actually, the difference is not very great, as you can readily tell by trying the Clicktester successively on an electric bulb, a fuse, a fan, an iron, a mixer, etc.

The Clicktester must not be used on parts or appliances connected to live circuits. The devices to be tested must be disconnected entirely. Observe the usual safety precaution of unscrewing the line fuse before touching the wires or terminals of any outlet. In the case of common appliances such as fans, mixers, air conditioners, irons, etc., it is, of course, only necessary to pull the line plug from the wall receptacle.

A device as simple as the Clicktester can be expected to have some limitations. The clicks indicate that the device under test has a continuous or closed circuit; however, the tester cannot distinguish between a normal low-resistance circuit and an extremely low resistance such as created by an internal short circuit or other abnormal condition. To do everything the Clicktester can do, and its missing 10% also, you need a *measuring* rather than an indicating instrument.

The "Handitester"

The Heathkit "Handitester," made especially for electrical trouble shooting, is such an instrument. A complete kit costs less than $15 and makes up into a professional-looking meter that will prove extremely useful not only for household appliances but also for the electrical system of a car and for the simpler elements of radio and even television receivers. Assembly and wiring are an evening's work. In a shiny black molded case, the completed tester stands only 6 by 3 by 2½ inches overall.

The Handitester is a combined voltmeter, ohmmeter and ammeter, all in one. The various functions are brought into play by means of a 12-position switch on the front panel. Connection between the tester and the circuit or device to be tested is made by flexible plug-in wires. One wire terminates in a spring clip, which is hooked to one

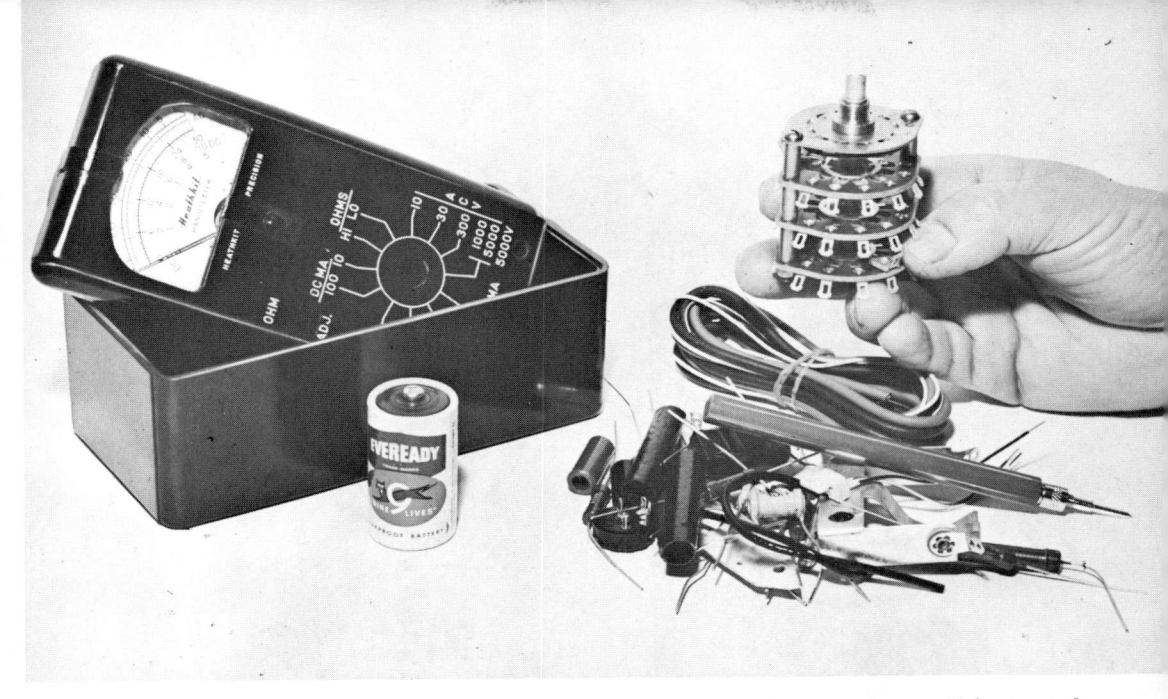

These are parts for Handitester as furnished in complete kit form. Meter unit is part of front panel. Hand holds three-deck "function switch," represented on front panel by control knob with pointer.

Inside view of completed Handitester. Battery on back of meter provides current for all resistance measurements. Wiring as seen here is compact.

terminal of the appliance; the other wire ends in a long insulated probe which is touched to the other terminal of the appliance.

Instruments of the Handitester type are known generally as "VOM's," for "Volt-Ohm-Meter." They are available in a large variety of both kit and factory-assembled models, from mail-order firms and from electronic supply stores everywhere.

As a voltmeter, the Handitester has 10 ranges, five each on DC and AC. Some of their possibilities for checking and troubleshooting are listed on this and the following page for your information:

DC:
- 0 to 10 volt scale: flashlight, lantern, radio "A," and doorbell batteries; one-, two- and three-cell storage batteries.
- 0 to 30 volt scale: hearing aid and radio "B" batteries; six-cell storage batteries.
- 0 to 300 volt scale: larger radio "B" batteries; radio set "B" voltages.
- 0 to 1000 volt scale: electronic photoflash batteries; radio "B" voltages.
- 0 to 5000 volt scale: same as 1000 volt scale.

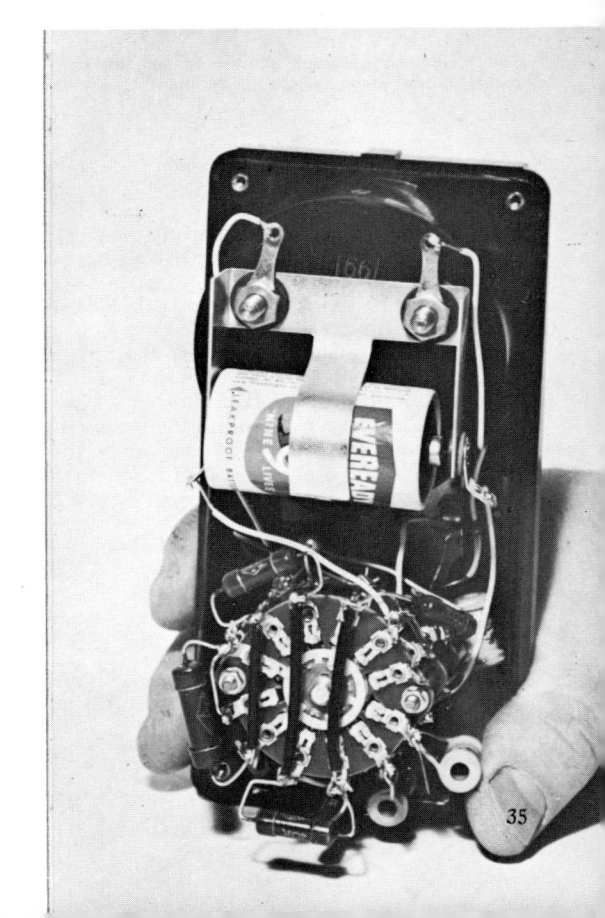

35

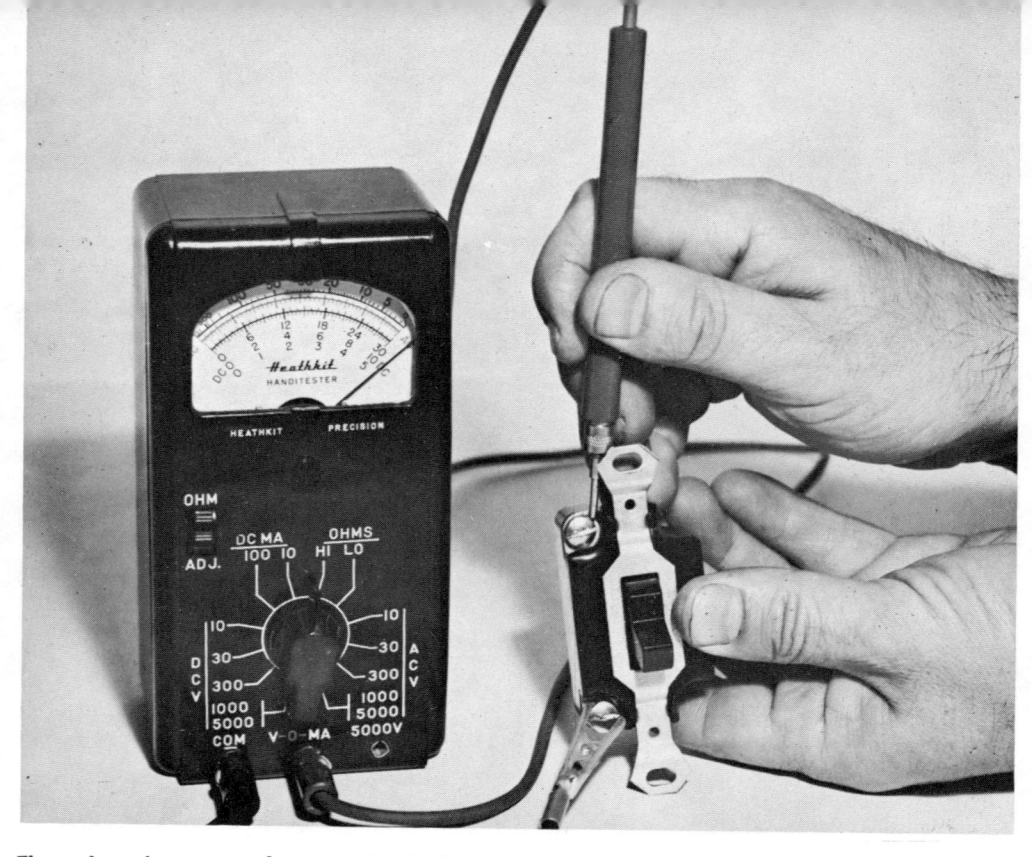

The value of a meter shows up in checking a switch for poor contacts. If they are poor, the meter reads an appreciable fraction of an ohm; if they are good, the needle bangs over to zero.

AC:

0 to 10 volt scale: some bell transformers.
0 to 30 volt scale: bell, toy train and house thermostat transformers.
0 to 300 volt scale: all two-wire, three-wire and four-wire power circuits.
0 to 1000 and 5000 volt scales: not much application.

As an ohmmeter, the Handitester is used like the Clicktester for continuity checking, except that it actually measures the resistance of the appliance in ohms instead of only showing a closed or open circuit. The meter has two resistance ranges: "LO," with easily read figures between 0 and about 500 ohms; and "HI," 0 to 50,000 ohms. Most appliances have normal resistance values well below 500 ohms. About the only ones running higher are small electric clocks, which measure between about 700 and 1000 ohms.

Zeroing the Meter

If the Handitester is set for LO ohms and applied to the same switch used experimentally with the Clicktester, the two extreme ends of the scale will come into play. First touch the probes together and turn the "OHM ADJ" knob on the front panel until the needle swings all the way over to the right or O position; this step is called "zeroing the meter." Separate the probes and the needle will fall back to the left end of the scale. Now touch the probes to the switch terminals. With the arm "off," the Handitester needle will not move, showing the switch to be completely open. With the switch "on," the needle will bang over to 0 ohms, or the equivalent of a dead short circuit. This is normal, as a closed switch should offer no appreciable resistance to the flow of electrons through it. If its contacts become loose or dirty, a condition that shows up on the meter as a slight value of resistance definitely above the O line, it can become quite hot and waste a lot of energy.

Ohmmeter readings have some significance in trouble-shooting only if you know the *normal* resistance values of appliances and machines. In this connection it is extremely interesting and instructive to make quick VOM checks on the usual devices found in the home or shop. Here are some actual readings:

Radio	5 ohms
Mixer	7 ohms
Toaster	11 ohms
Laundry iron	14 ohms
10-inch fan	22 ohms
⅓ hp drill-press motor	1½ ohms
7½-watt lamp	400 ohms
60-watt lamp	5 ohms
15-watt fluorescent heater	5 ohms
Small soldering iron	700 ohms
Large soldering iron	85 ohms
Gun-type soldering iron	7 ohms

As with the Clicktester, a VOM in its resistance-measuring function must not be used on live circuits. The current that makes the meter operate comes from a self-contained flashlight battery.

The "Lightester"

To determine if exposed wires and terminals in house power circuits are alive or not, it is very useful to have a simple "Lightester." This is nothing more than a lamp socket with a short length of flexible wire, the ends of which are fitted with insulated test prods.

The socket should preferably be of the "keyless" type, without a built-in switch. If only a common socket is on hand, tape or otherwise fasten the switch in its "on" position. The lamp can be of any size whatsoever. Because the tester is carried about, and because glass bulbs are fragile, it is a good idea to protect the lamp with a simple wire guard that clamps around the neck of the socket.

The test prods can be merely six-inch lengths of ¼-inch dowel. Solder the wires to headless nails about 1½ inches long, and tape them securely to the ends of the sticks. Touching the nails to a suspected power line tells you instantly if it is alive

With a switch in its off position, the ohmmeter needle should remain absolutely stationary when the test prods are applied to the terminals. A high resistance indication means internal leakage.

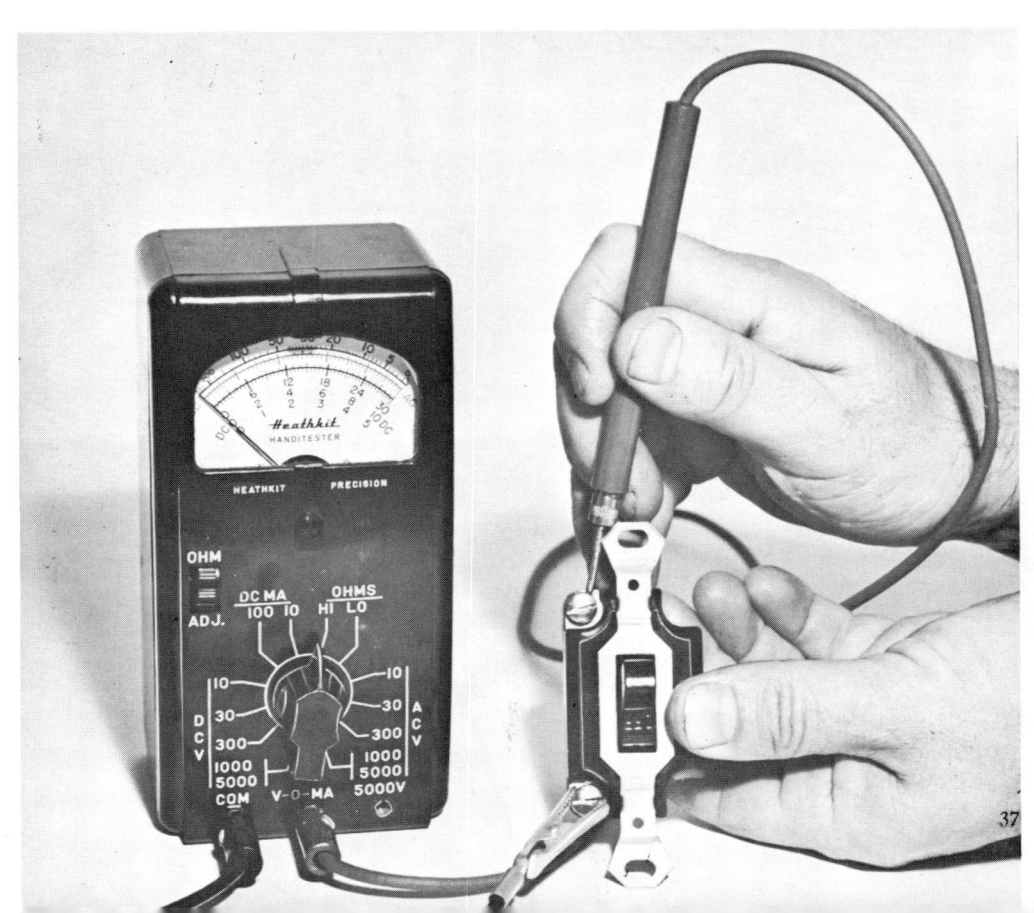

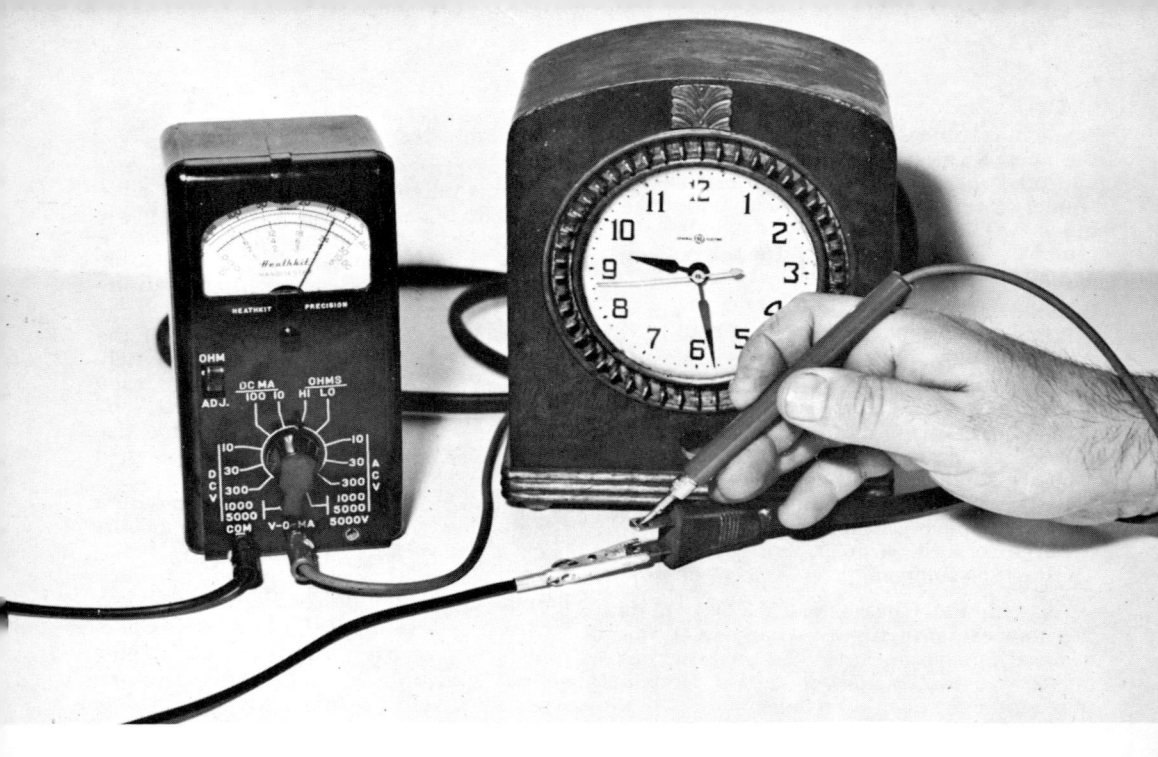

Above: With the Handitester set for ohms and connected to the prongs of a clock cord, the usual indication is several hundred ohms. No reading at all means that clock motor winding is open, or much less likely, that the power cord is open.

Below: The instrument shown in the photo is a VOM of a more advanced type (Precision Model 120), favored by electronic technicians and experimenters. Here it is being used to check the continuity and resistance of another clock motor.

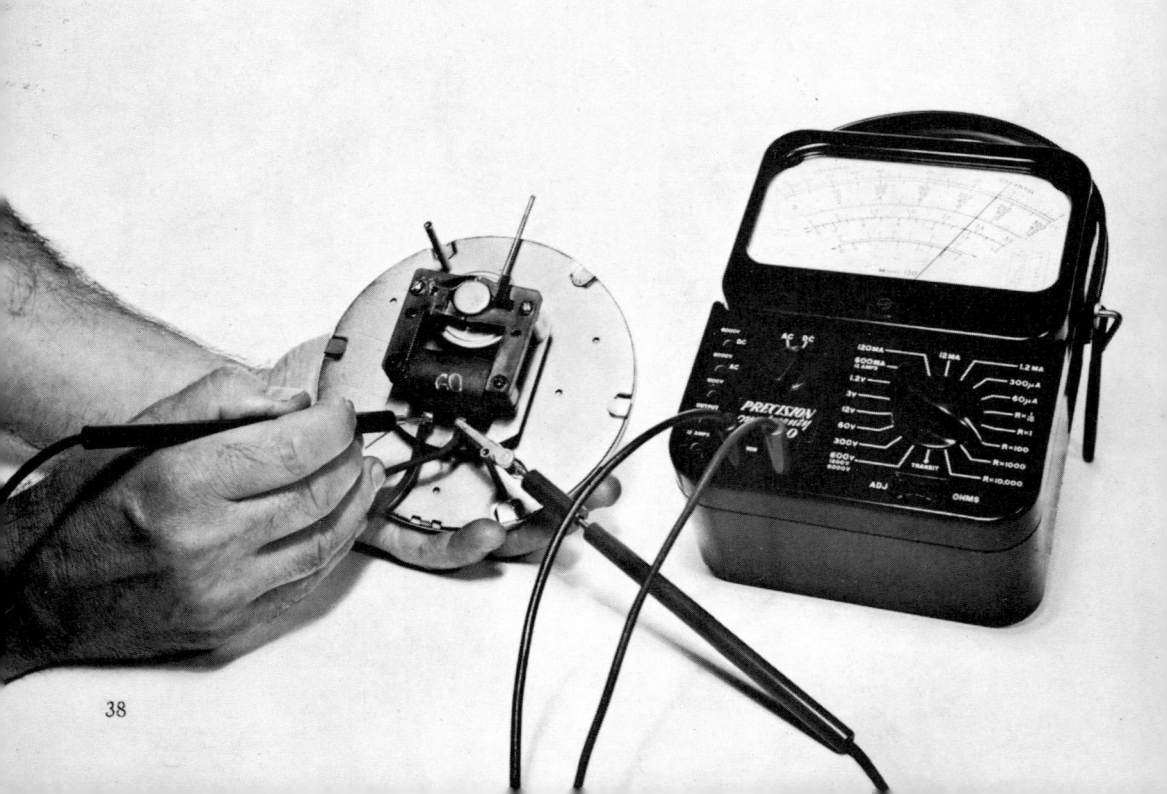

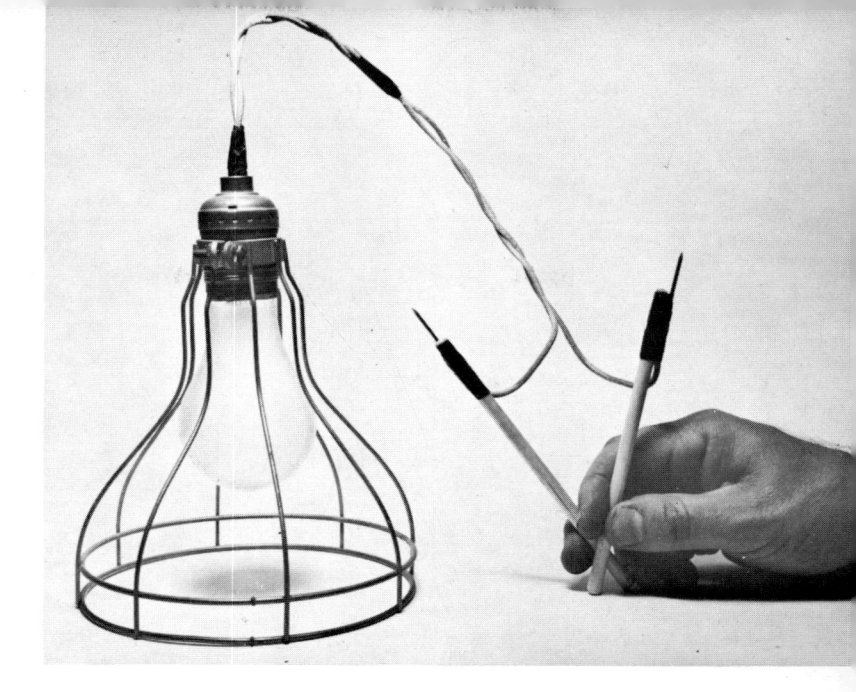

The "Lightester" consists merely of lamp and socket fitted with two test prods. The latter are dowel sticks with nails taped to their ends. Lamp can be any size. Protective cage is insurance against accidental breakage of bulb. This tester is very useful for quick check on 115-volt lines.

or dead. The wooden handles provide more than adequate protection against shock danger.

With a 115-volt lamp in its socket, the Lightester is, of course, limited to the checking of regular 115-volt circuits. If you're tempted to try it on 208- or 230-volt lines, you'll get a bright flash for half a second, and then you throw away the bulb. It is rather difficult to buy 230-volt lamps (impossible, in fact, in most parts of the country), so for checking these higher voltages it is better to use the 300-volt AC scale of a VOM.

Tools for Electrical Work

Any electrical repairs you can't make with the ordinary hand tools found in the basement or garage shop you probably can't make at all. Look at the picture on page 41 of some basic tools and compare it with what you have in your own tool box: soldering iron or soldering gun; rosin-core wire solder; side-cutting, long-nose and diagonal-jaw pliers; assorted screwdrivers; knife for trimming insulation and cleaning wires; tape for covering joints in wire; hacksaw for cutting BX; and extension cord for bringing juice from a distant outlet when the circuit in a room is purposely opened to permit repairs.

Of obvious value are also such standard tools as wrenches, hammers, nut drivers, files, etc.

Tools for soldering take two different forms, the soldering "iron" and the soldering "gun." In spite of its name, the "iron" uses a tip of copper. This is heated by a coil of resistance wire inside the body of the tool. Depending on its size, an iron takes from two to five minutes to reach operating temperature. It is ready for use when solder touched to the tip melts instantly.

The "gun," so called because of its resemblance to a pistol, is actually a step-down transformer. The primary winding consists of many turns of fine wire, and is connected to the house power line through a trigger switch. The secondary is a single loop of metal tubing or rod between about $3/8$ and $1/2$ inch in diameter, its exposed ends being terminated by a relatively thinner V-shaped loop of copper wire. Because of the large step-down ratio of the primary-to-secondary turns, the voltage across the loop is very low, in the order of two to three volts, and the current is very high, as much as 100 amperes. This heavy current causes the copper end loop to heat up. There is no danger of shock from the exposed secondary rods, because the voltage here is low and also because they are not connected directly to the house power line.

The big advantage of the soldering gun is that it comes up to operating temperature in about three seconds. It is especially handy for making just one or a few joints in a hurry. You can be all finished with most jobs in the time it would take a straight iron to warm up.

There are some soldering tools *shaped* like guns that are actually of the resistance-heating type.

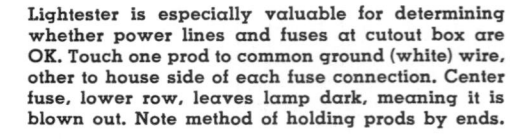

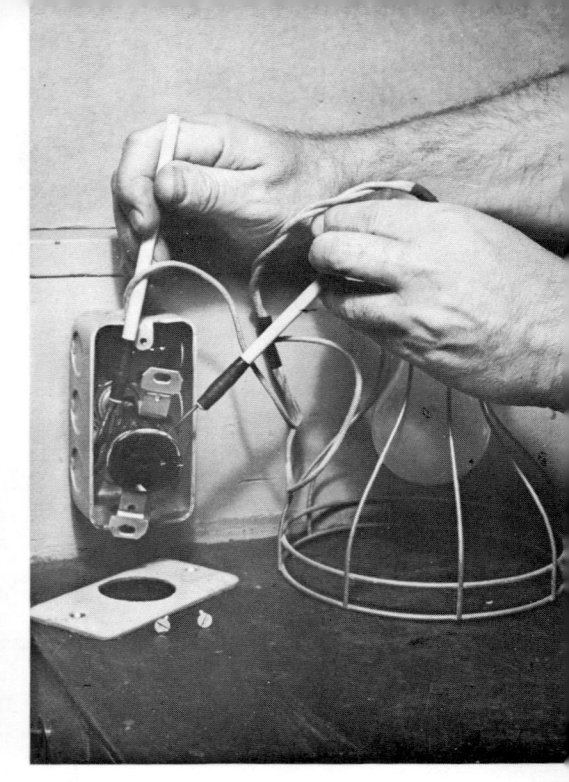

Is juice reaching prongs of wall outlet? Insert prods of Lightester. If no light, line is dead.

Is juice reaching terminals? If lamp goes on, one of contact springs in outlet itself is broken.

Lightester is especially valuable for determining whether power lines and fuses at cutout box are OK. Touch one prod to common ground (white) wire, other to house side of each fuse connection. Center fuse, lower row, leaves lamp dark, meaning it is blown out. Note method of holding prods by ends.

With test prod touched to terminal of lower right fuse, lamp lights up, showing that fuse and circuit are intact. Flickering of lamp often shows up loose or partially corroded fuses. Wire guard of Lightester provides convenient means of hanging the unit from any nearby edge that is available.

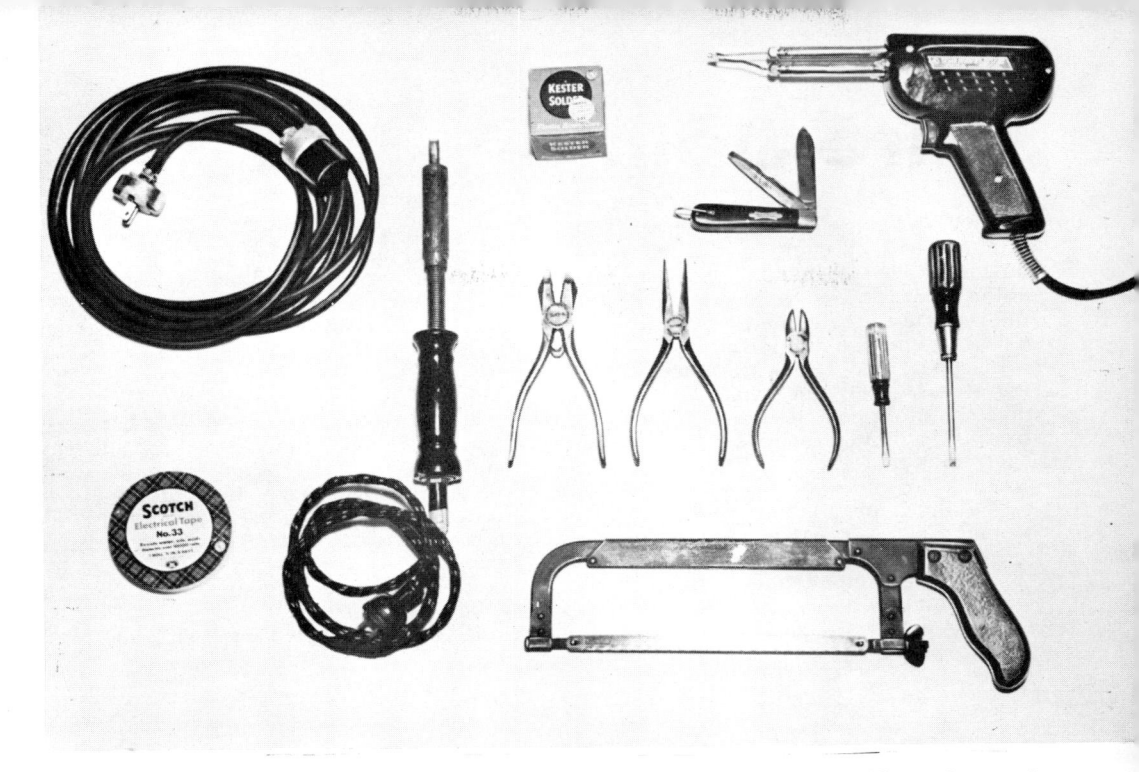

Basic tools needed for home electrical repairs are an extension cord, straight soldering iron, rosin core solder, knife, gun type soldering tool, a set of pliers, screwdrivers, plastic tape and a hacksaw.

Which type of soldering tool to choose? The answer is easy: *both*. For some operations one is preferable to the other. For instance, suppose you are working on a change in a power line, and want to solder a joint in it. Obviously, you can't use a gun if you kill the line first to make the latter safe to handle. The trick is to heat up a regular resistance-type iron, kill the circuit, and make the joint while it's still hot. A medium-size iron will hold its heat for about 30 seconds, which is more than long enough for several joints. A gun-type iron goes dead almost instantly when it loses its AC power.

Rosin-core solder is universally used for electrical connections of all kinds. The rosin is known as "flux," and its purpose is to prevent the formation of a layer of corrosion on the surfaces to be soldered when the hot iron is applied. Rosin, a derivative of turpentine, has no corrosive after effects.

Diagonal pliers are intend only for snipping wire, not for holding, squeezing or bending. Their jaws form a sharp V, and they can therefore be used in close quarters for trimming short pieces of wire.

Side-cutters combine cutting edges and flat, fairly heavy jaws. The latter are suitable for a wide variety of holding, turning and forming jobs. In the six-inch size, this is probably the most frequently used tool in all electrical work.

Long-nose pliers usually do not include cutting edges. They are intended for making loops in ends of wires and for light holding purposes. Do not use them for twisting nuts on bolts or similar heavy work. Once the slender jaws become distorted through this misuse, the tool becomes useless.

No one ever has enough screwdrivers. You need small, medium and large ones, because electrical appliances contain screws of widely varying dimensions. Fortunately, screwdrivers are cheap and last practically forever. If the ends become worn, they can be restored in a minute with a file or a grinder.

You will also need two or three sizes of Phillips-head (cross-point) screwdrivers. Handle these carefully and be sure to use the right size for the screw. When they wear out or are damaged they must be discarded, as it is virtually impossible to reshape them.

An excellent knife for electrical work is the Army tool known as the TL-29. This consists of a sturdy knife blade and a locking screwdriver blade in common handle. •

41

Wire Joints

Splicing wires is a simple chore

HAVE you observed that the cords furnished with many appliances seem to be just a trifle too short to reach the nearest outlet? An extension cord is a help, but the real cure is to add a permanent length of wire to the existing one.

Electrical and hardware stores carry a variety of cords and wires, and you can match the old and the new without much trouble. Joining them is a simple hand operation, and requires the use of only pliers, knife and soldering iron. If you are new at the game, it is a good idea, of course, to make a few practice joints with scrap pieces of wire.

Cords of all appliances contain flexible wire, which actually consists of a bunch of very fine wires held together by the covering of insulation. Solid wire is found in power conduits, bell circuits, intercom hook-ups and other fixed applications.

The secret of good electrical joints is merely cleanliness. The quickest and easiest way to brighten up wire is to scrape it very lightly with the *back* edge of a knife.

The wire inside most cords is bare copper. Depending on the age of the cord and the type of insulation, the metal might be of any shade from shiny bright to corroded black. In the better grades of cords, the wire is "tinned"; that is, covered in manufacture with a very thin layer of solder. This usually remains quite clean, and takes solder instantly.

Illustrations show typical splicing jobs. •

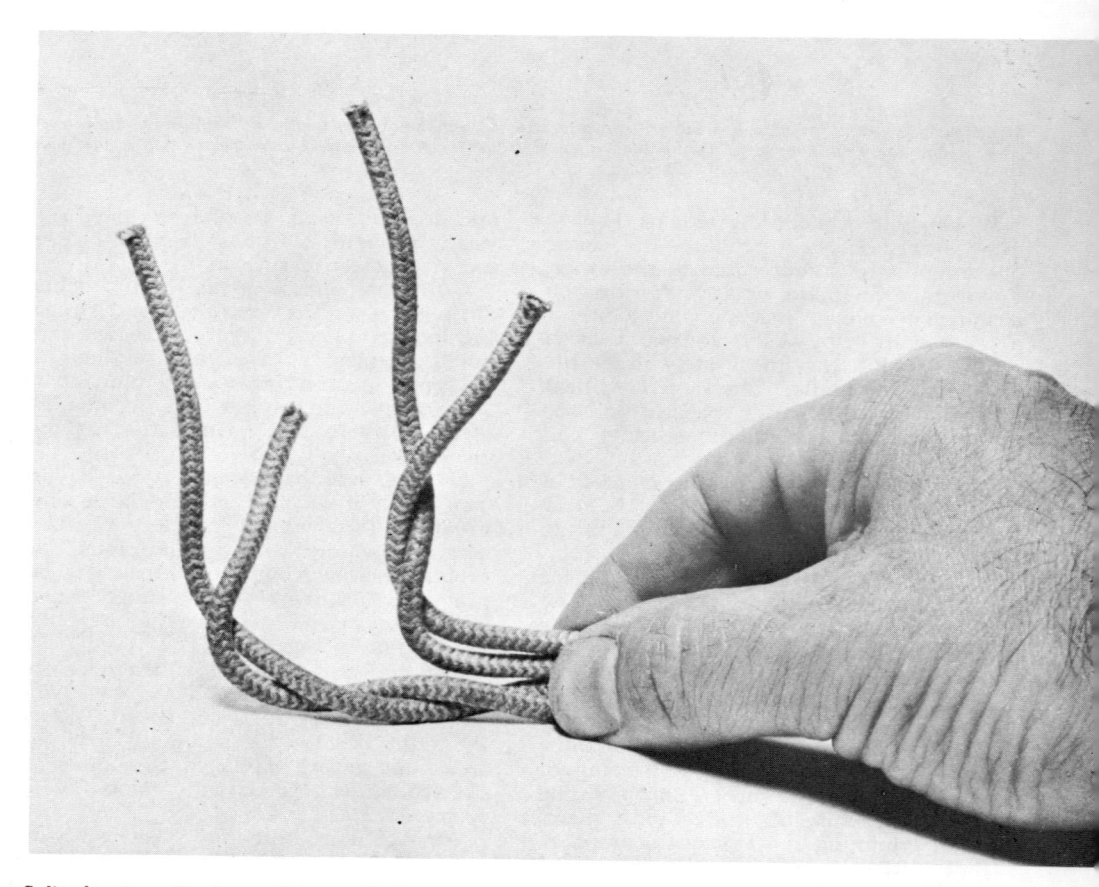

Spliced wire will show minimum thickness at points of joining if ends of the new and old wires are stagger-cut to length of about two inches. This is first step in splicing common twisted lamp cord.

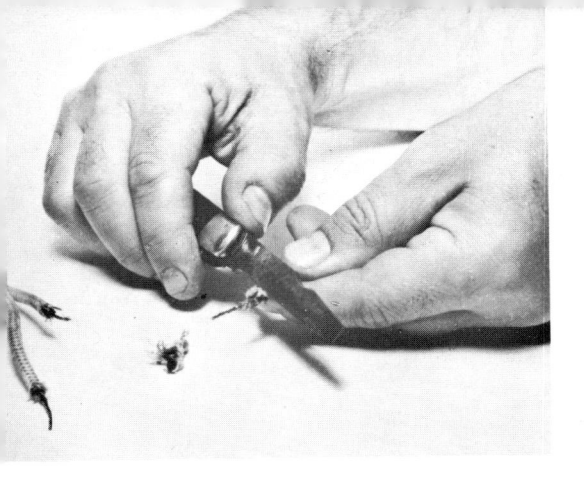

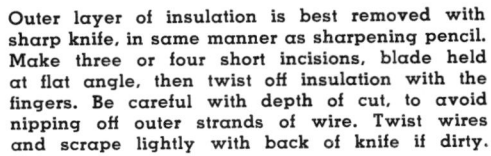

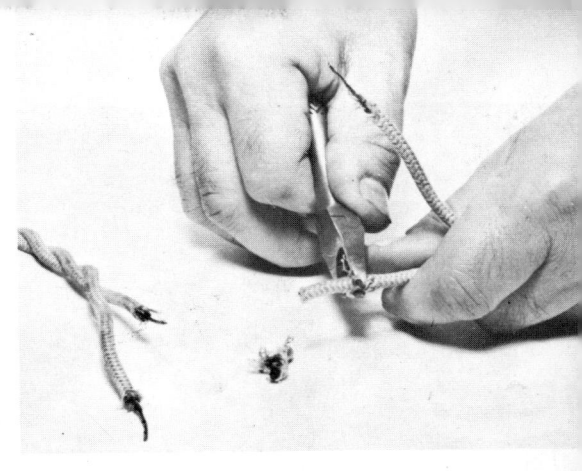

Outer layer of insulation is best removed with sharp knife, in same manner as sharpening pencil. Make three or four short incisions, blade held at flat angle, then twist off insulation with the fingers. Be careful with depth of cut, to avoid nipping off outer strands of wire. Twist wires and scrape lightly with back of knife if dirty.

With practice, you can remove insulation quickly with side-cutting pliers. Sever insulation by making a carefully controlled cut, and with jaws still partially closed, pull the covering off. The trick is to cut the insulation without nicking the wire. Some types of insulation do lend themselves well to this method, while other types do not.

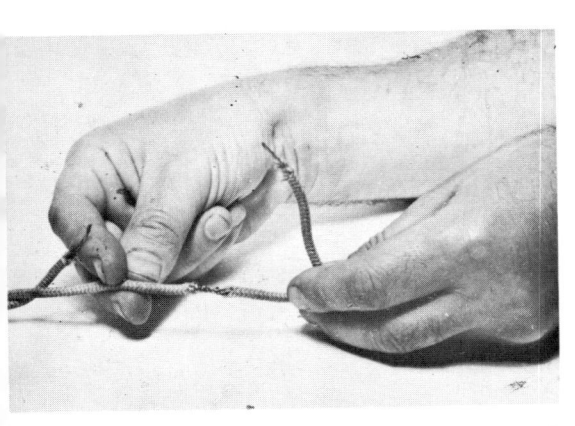

Twist together the long wire of one cord with the short wire of the other. Leave the other pair apart. The idea is to complete only one joint at a time. The job comes out neater in this manner.

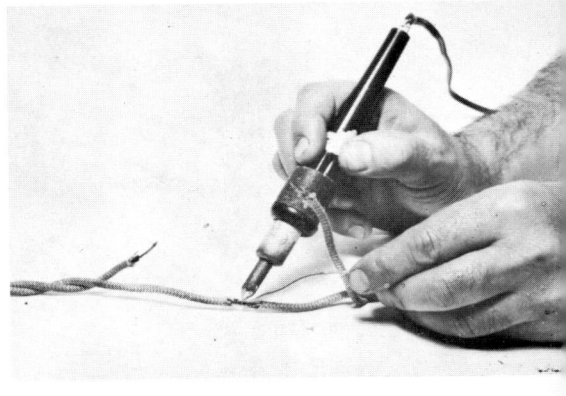

Using rosin-core solder, make first joint solid. Then leave the iron in contact with the connection until all of the rosin has boiled out and you have only a shiny coat of solder remaining.

The next step is to finish the first joint by taping it tightly. A good sticky tape for this purpose is sold as "friction tape," is obtainable in a width of about ¾ inch and color is black.

Staggering preserves general lines of the cord. If it is not convenient to solder the joints, make them about two inches long and tie them up with three or four strands from the cut-off ends.

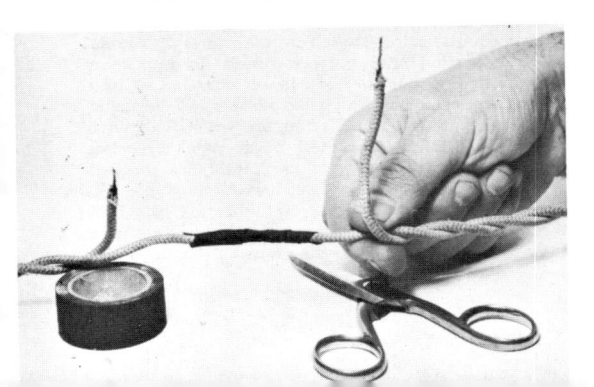

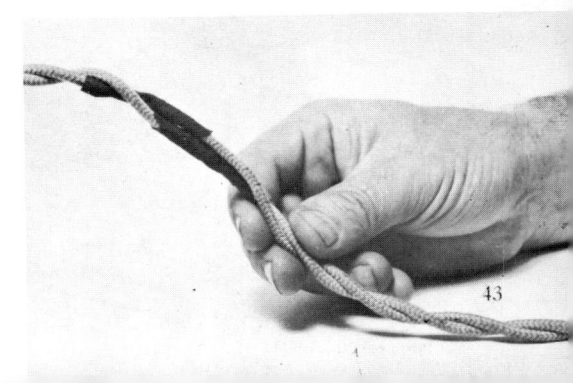

43

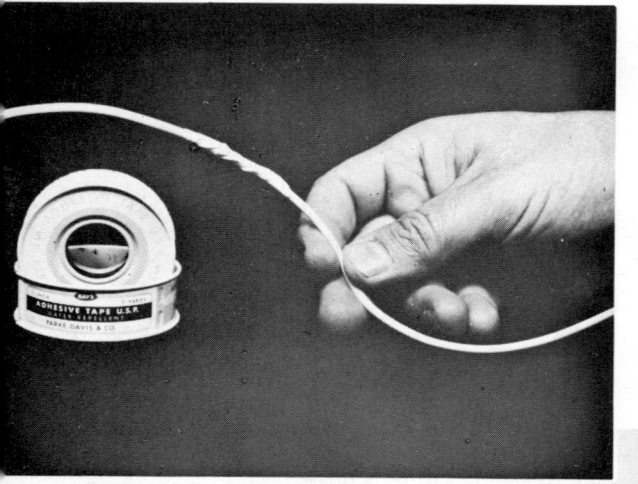

Light colored cords don't look attractive when spliced with black friction tape, so why not use white tape? Borrow some adhesive tape from the medicine chest. You'll find it sticks tightly and insulates well.

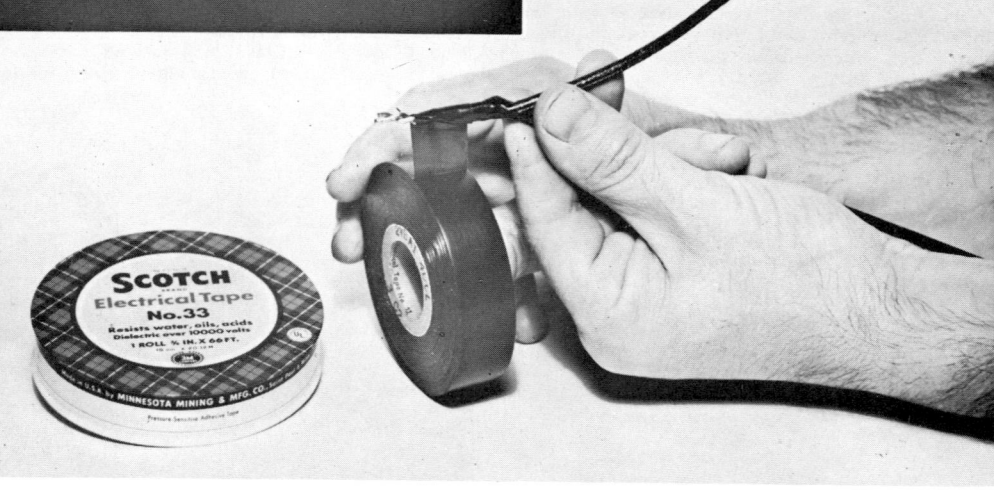

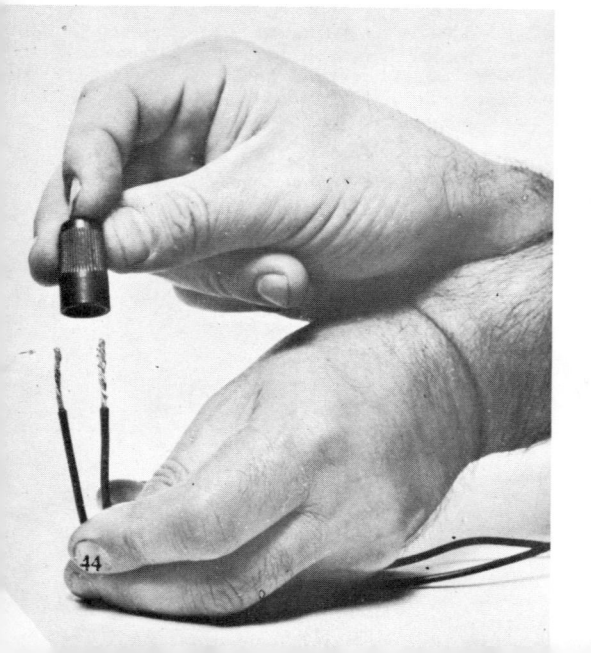

For splices that need protection against water, oils, acids, etc., an excellent tape is Scotch No. 33. It can be pressed with fingers to shape, and proves to be virtually air and liquid tight.

"Wire nuts" are widely used in both new and revamped electrical wiring because they offer quick and easy means of joining wires without soldering. This is an advantage when no current is available for a soldering iron (power circuit having been deactivated to permit work to be done on it) and when use of a blowtorch or other open flame is too hazardous (which is often the case). The wire nut comprises an insulated body with threaded metal insert. The wires to be joined are pushed into the latter and the nut turned in either direction two or three times; the threads bite into the wires and twist them together. Nuts are identified according to the wire sizes they fit.

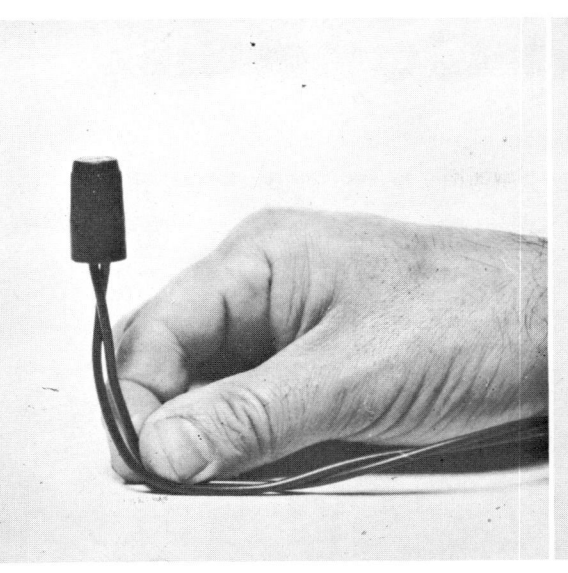

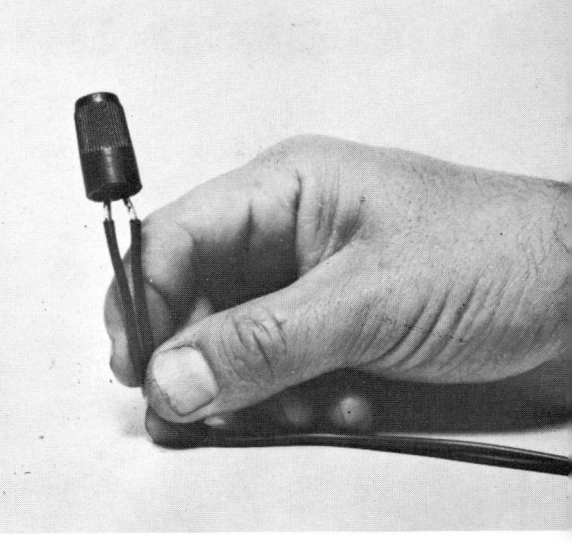

If the wires are bared to the proper length, a wire nut will be found to insulate your splice properly, and it is obvious that no additional covering in the form of tape is then necessary.

In this case, the wire ends have been bared too much and the unprotected sections remain exposed after the nut has been tightened. The joint can be easily opened and the wire then recut to fit.

Quick-heating soldering "gun" makes a fast job on wire splicing. Here, it is being used on single-conductor solid wire which is usually found in power conduits. See position of gun point and solder in relation to the joint. As the solder melts, the molten metal runs into the joint and forms a firm bond over the termini of the wires.

Solid wire in the No. 18 size, and smaller, is used for bell, buzzer, intercom and like low voltage applications. Easiest way to splice wire of this type is to twist the ends together with a pair of pliers. Soldering is advisable but not as important as in power circuits. Taping is necessary, of course, for prevention of short circuits.

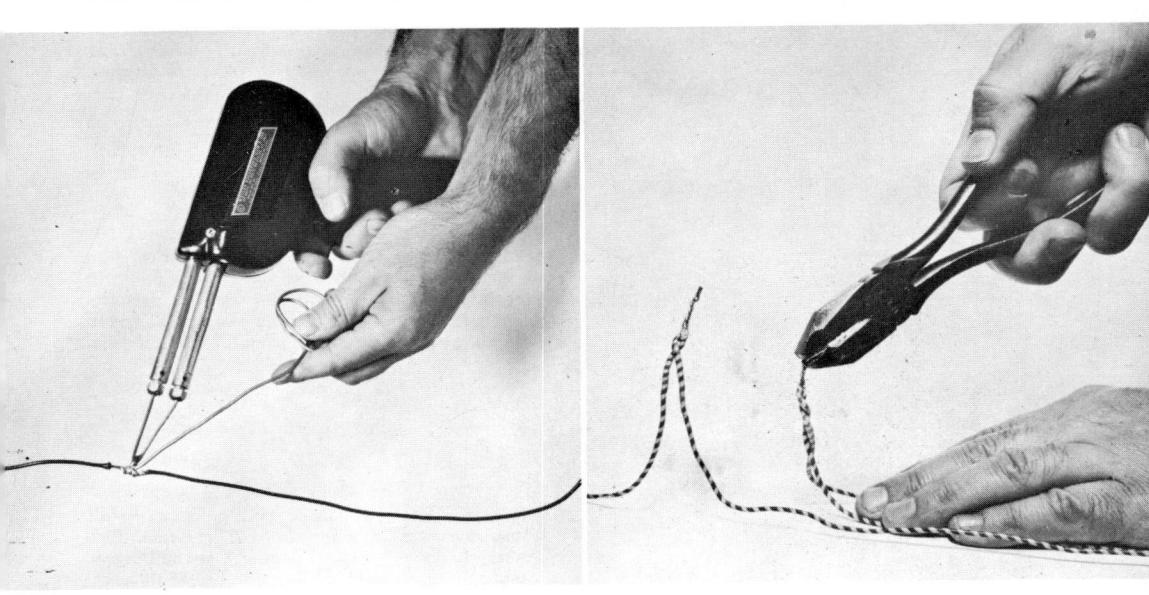

45

Cable and Conduit

Loom, BX and thin-wall are the most popular types for home power circuits

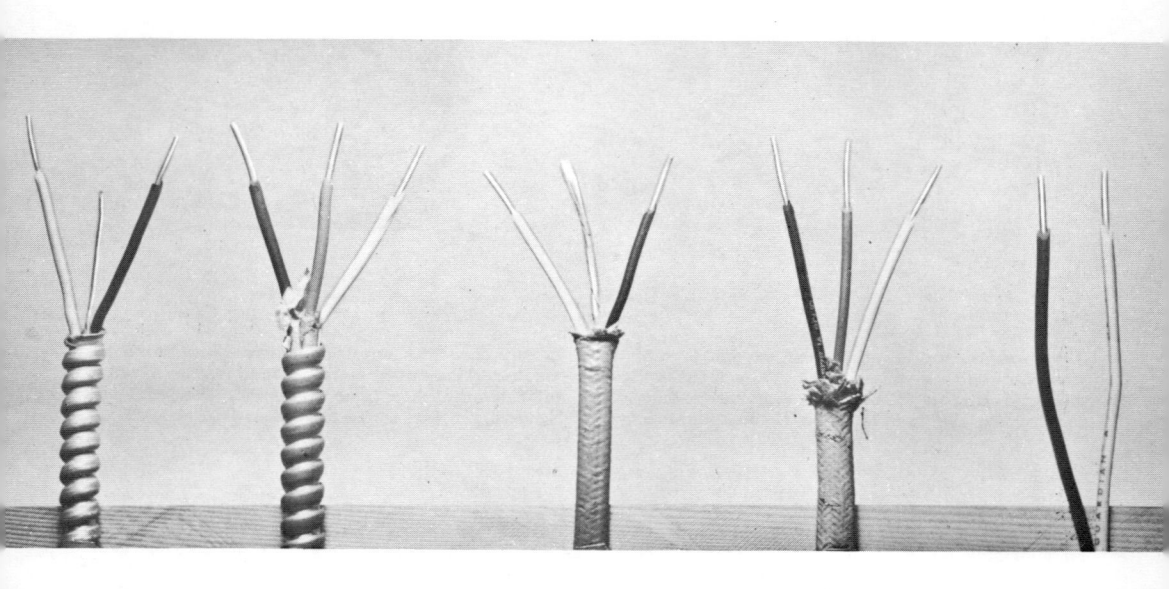

Some representative conductors of electricity: 1—Two-wire armored cable, or "BX," with extra grounding wire in the center. 2—Three-wire BX. 3—A two-wire nonmetallic sheath cable, with bare ground wire. 4—Three-wire, nonmetallic sheath. 5—Single insulated wires, colored black, white or red. These are used in thin-wall conduit.

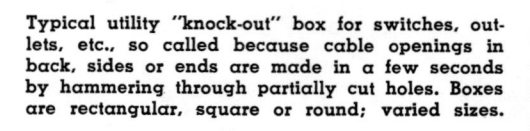

Typical utility "knock-out" box for switches, outlets, etc., so called because cable openings in back, sides or ends are made in a few seconds by hammering through partially cut holes. Boxes are rectangular, square or round; varied sizes.

Utility box at left has fitting at top for thin-wall conduit; the one at right, for BX or loom. The mounting lips on all boxes are spaced uniformly to take all outlets and other varieties of fixtures.

IF YOU expect to install new power lines or renovate old ones, you should know something about cable and conduit.

The most widely used type, because it is inexpensive, flexible, easy to handle, and permitted by many local building codes, is nonmetallic sheathed cable. This is also known as "loom," because of the woven appearance of its outer covering. It consists of two or three insulated wires, with or without a bare ground wire, laid parallel to each other in a common outer jacket. For indoor applications, a combination of thermoplastic and paper insulation is employed. For tougher service, both indoors and outdoors, a combination of thermoplastic, fiberglass and polyvinyl insulation is better.

Loom can be cut with pliers and trimmed with a knife. It can be mounted quickly by means of U-shaped nail straps, driven in with a hammer.

Some municipalities do not permit the use of loom, and require instead metal-clad wiring of some sort. The most popular is steel-armored cable, universally known as "BX" for no reason that makes sense. It contains two or three wires, and usually also has a bare bonding or ground wire running between them and the outer cable. The latter is spiral-made of thin steel, and the whole cable is flexible enough to be pushed around corners.

BX is tough stuff. Cutting the steel jacket without nicking the wires inside is very tricky and takes quite a bit of practice.

Both loom and BX are available in rolls from 25 to 250 feet.

Thin-wall conduit is merely galvanized steel pipe in various diameters and in standard 10-foot length. It is readily assembled to standard outlet boxes and other fixtures by means of threadless, clamp-type fittings. It can be bent at a rather wide right angle with a special tool. It makes an extremely neat and fireproof job. Some local building codes specify this type of wiring.

Thin-wall is distinctly different from both loom and BX in that it does not contain its own wires. These are pulled through during or after the assembly of a whole system, usually with the assistance of a flexible steel tape called a "snake."

An advantage of conduit for many purposes is that it can be shortened, lengthened, taken apart and put together both easily and rapidly. The wires themselves, being loose inside the smooth piping, can be pulled out undamaged and reused. •

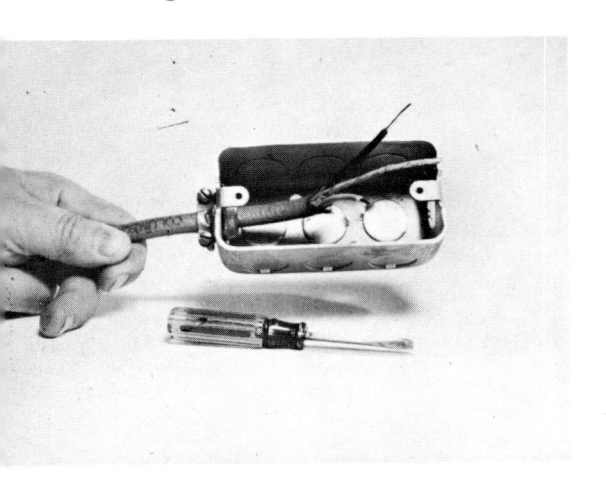

This is the method of bringing two-wire nonmetallic sheath cable into an outlet box. Clamp at left end of the latter holds the wire securely.

U-shaped straps, equipped with built-in nails, offer an easy means of fastening a nonmetallic cable to wooden walls. Fasteners of a similar nature are available for use on masonry walls.

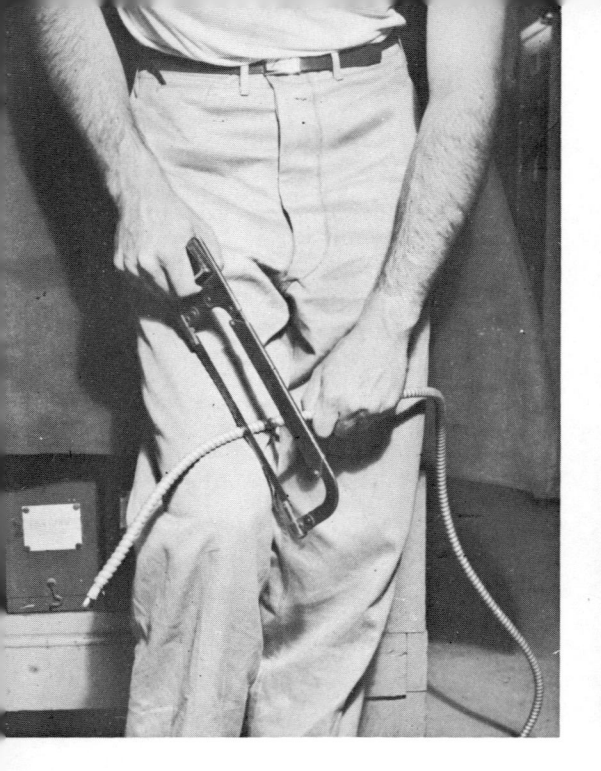

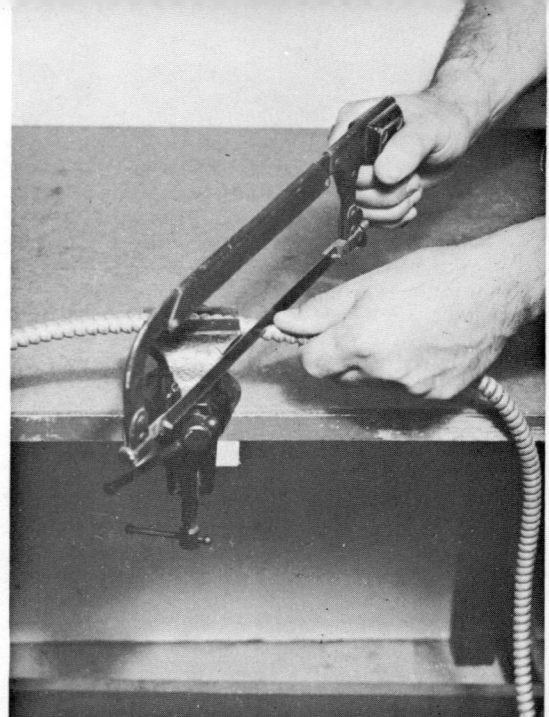

The BX cable is wiggly and difficult to hold by hand. Don't attempt to cut it this way; hacksaw is almost certain to slip or the cable to twist.

Best way to cut through the outer steel jacket of BX is with aid of vise. Hold the cable close to jaws; cut lightly at angle to the spiraling. Stop when inner paper insulation appears; twist off the cut section. This leaves wire ends free.

In the absence of a vise, a C-clamp and a block of wood will serve well to hold BX for cutting.

In a pinch, a large pair of pliers or a locking jaw wrench, when pressed hard against the workbench, will serve to keep the BX under control. Practice on scraps to acquire the knack of cutting a cable without touching the wires inside.

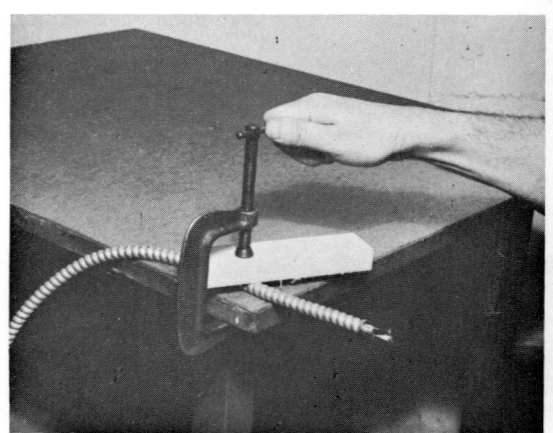

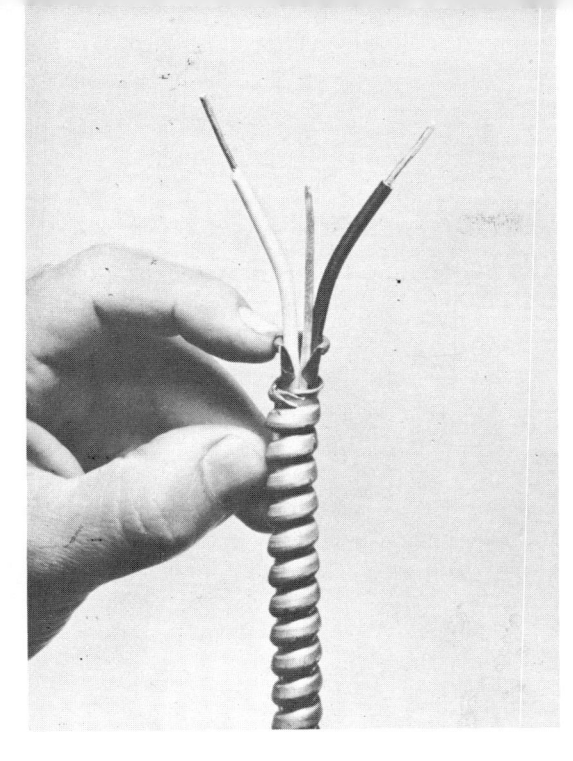

A special right-angle connector permits the BX to make a sharp entrance into the utility box. There are a great number of different fittings designed to ease assembly and wiring operations.

To protect wires of BX against possible chafing, push fiber bushing into cable. In photo at left, center wire is ground lead and rests against the cable. White wire in cable is always uninterrupted ground return; the white wire the "hot" side.

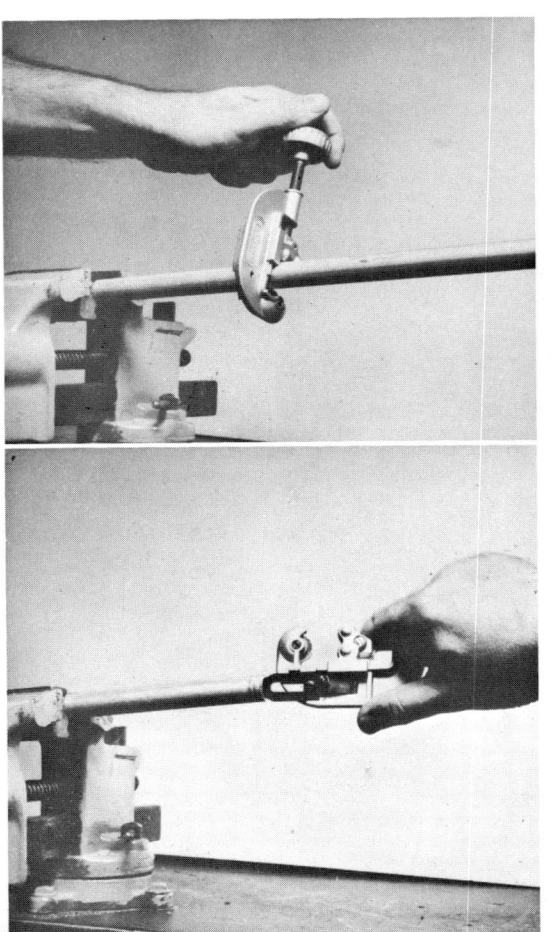

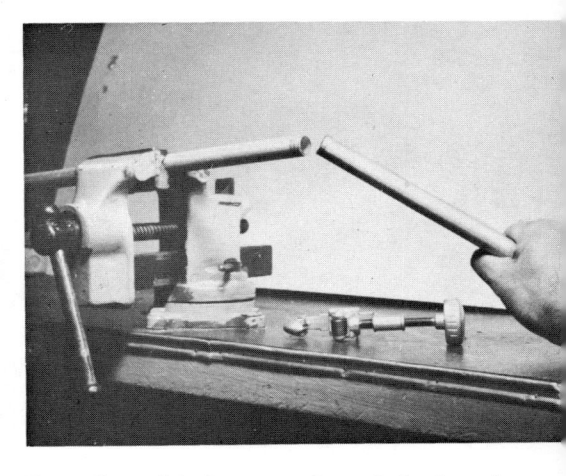

Thin-wall conduit is a seamless steel pipe of light weight. It can easily be cut with a hacksaw, but a much quicker and neater job is possible when done with a tubing cutter, as shown. Handwheel is turned as the tool is pulled around tubing and cutting wheel bites into the latter.

After only three or four revolutions of cutter, the sections of a conduit are easily separated.

Burr on inside of conduit must be removed to allow free passage of wires that will be inserted later. Simple reamer is part of tubing cutter.

"Persuader" puts round, even bend into thin-wall conduit. Tremendous leverage is applied through long handle of bender tool, a useful accessory.

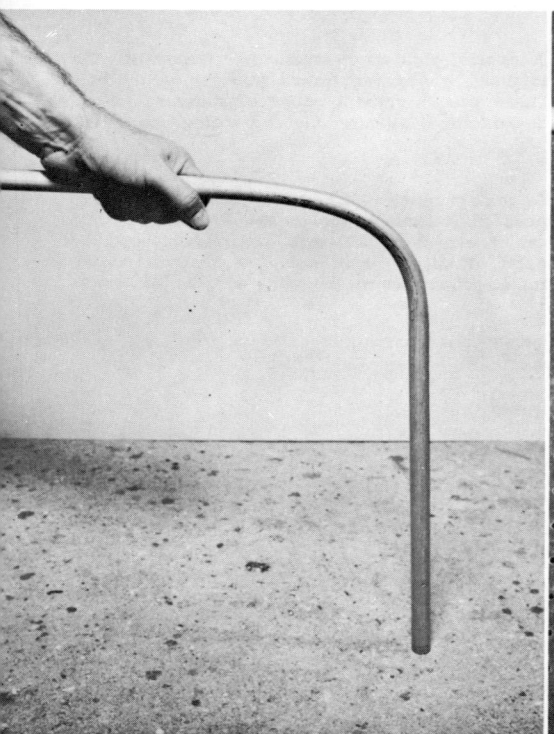

An uncramped bend in the thin-wall conduit is very essential to the passage of the wires. The smooth job results from the use of lever tool.

There is no difficulty when it comes to fastening a thin-wall conduit to a flat surface. This is solved by use of simple single-ended clamps.

The threadless ends of the thin-wall are readily fastened by a clamping-type connector, shown in the photo, right, attached to a utility box.

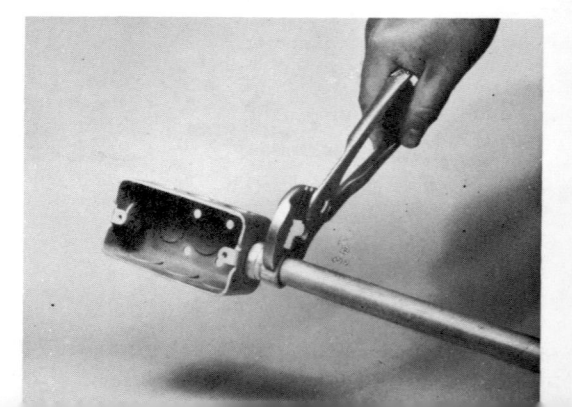

50

Right-angle fitting brings thin-wall close to outlet box. Hex nut on threaded shoulder tightens the internal split clamp against the conduit's end.

This double-ended connector, handled with use of two wrenches, makes a quick task of joining any two sections of the thin-wall conduit pipe.

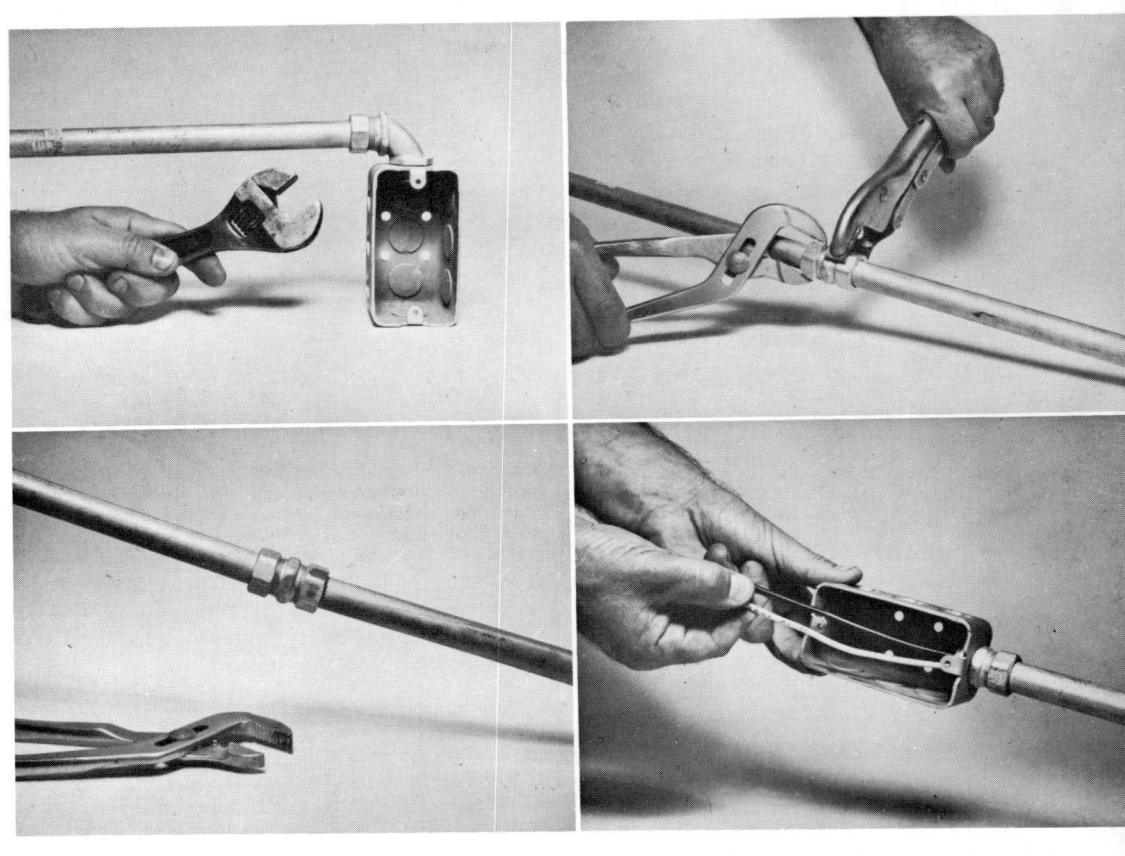

The desired result: This finished joint of two separate pieces of conduit is now neat and tight and allows free travel of wire through passage.

At this point, the actual wires are both pushed and pulled through the thin-wall conduit. This is usually the last part of assembly operation.

Neat, rugged and foolproof is this short installation of two duplex receptacles and thin-wall conduit on the back edge of a radio table. Outlet boxes are screwed down through their bottoms, so conduit does not require mounting straps.

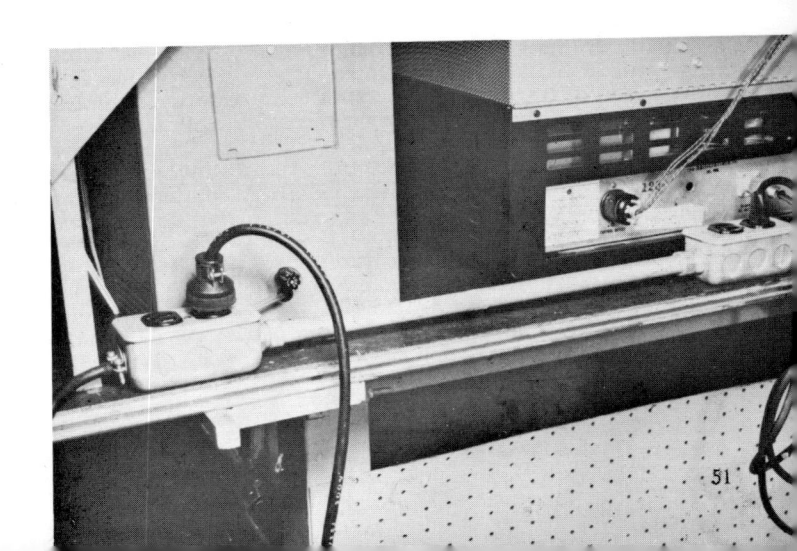

51

Play It Safe

Caution, common sense and proper grounding technique will prevent needless accidents

Opening the main switch kills current in all of the house wiring; however, this also means it will affect the refrigerator, furnace, etc. In many cases opening only a branch circuit is sufficient. A posted warning sign on an open circuit is helpful.

THE following item appeared recently in a New York newspaper. (Only the names of people and places have been changed.)

BUSINESS MAN KILLED WIRING FAN IN ATTIC

Townville, L. I.—John J. Doakes, 44-year-old business executive, was killed by electricity today while installing an exhaust fan in the attic of his new $40,000 home at 999 Shore Drive.

Members of the Townville Fire Department had to tear out part of the ceiling in an attic room to remove the body, which was crumpled in the space between the ceiling and the roof. An electric wire, which he was connecting to the fan, was clutched in one hand.

The accident occurred about 2 P.M. while his wife and their three children, two boys 19 and 15 and a girl 12, were on a shopping trip. His body was found about 3 P.M. by a neighbor, Joe Jones, who had been called by Mrs. Doakes after she was unable to find her husband when she returned.

Mr. Doakes was sales manager for a printing firm. He had moved into the house just a week ago.

This tragic accident was obviously the result of simple, unadulterated carelessness. The victim had forgotten or neglected to kill the branch circuit on which he was working, and he himself was killed instead.

There is a difference between "forgetting" and "neglecting" in cases of this kind. A man can be fully aware of the joltage behind power line voltage, and he can fully understand the importance of removing fuses or snapping circuit breakers open. However, while he may intend to open the circuit, he may simply forget to do so before he climbs into the attic with his hands full of tools.

There is the strong possibility that the victim of the fan accident left the power on deliberately, so that he could have light while working in the cramped attic space. He may have figured that there was no danger as long as he handled only one live wire at a time. This was sheer neglect. Maybe he did handle a single wire at a time, but maybe, when he held the "hot" line, he brushed against the grounded sheath of BX as he groped on the floor for a roll of tape.

Clearly, the moral to all this is: PLAY IT SAFE. It's easy to do so by following

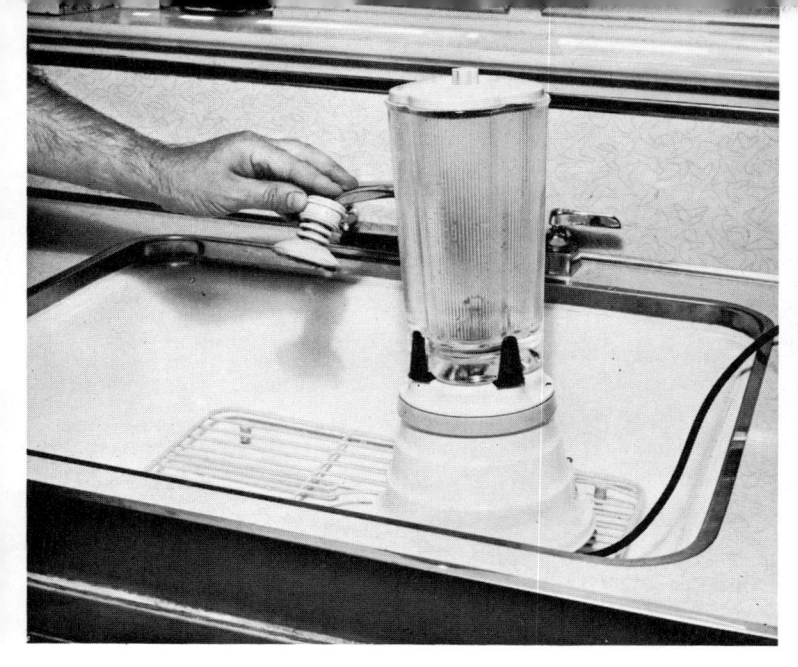

DON'T! Some housewives put mixers and blenders in the sink, while they are connected and running, to catch possible spillover. This is a dangerous practice, because the sink and the pipes near it are well grounded electrically, and there is always the possibility of a live circuit forming between them, the body, and one wire of connected appliance.

a few, common sense simple rules.

It would appear at first sight that the easiest way to avoid shock, when making repairs or installing new equipment, is merely to yank open the main switch. This deactivates all the wiring in the house and therefore you can touch *anything* with complete safety. This move is practicable if the work will take only a few minutes; say up to about 15 or 20. You must remember that pulling the main switch removes power from the kitchen refrigerator (and food freezer), which might be undesirable in warm weather; and also shuts down any modern heating plant, which might be undesirable in cold weather. With the main switch off you have no electric light, so you can work only in daylight in an area near a window.

Although an open main switch gives 200% safety, you can still have 100% safety, and the convenience of power for light, tools, etc., by removing the branch fuse only for the circuit that you want to touch. Presumably you have identified all the fuse or circuit breaker positions (see the chapter entitled "When Your Lights Go Out"), so this should take only a moment. Don't merely loosen the fuse in its socket; unscrew it completely and place it on the fuse box. Inform the other members of the family present in the house as to just what you are doing, and what outlets, lights, etc., will be inoperative while you are doing it.

With the line presumably opened by the fuse or breaker, give it a double check with the Lightester. If the bulb of the latter doesn't light, you can proceed.

Protect the Kiddies

An insurance company recently reported that about 40,000 electrical accidents in the home occur yearly in the United States. Considering the total population of about 170 million and the astronomical number of electric circuits and appliances in daily use, the figure is not a very large one. The sad part is that many of the victims who are seriously injured or killed are children. The fault is not theirs, but the parents'. Better protection in most cases calls only for a little common sense; in others for very inexpensive expedients.

The report listed these "bad actors": 1) open-type baseboard outlets; 2) lamp and other loose cords on the floors; 3) toasters and other appliances left connected after use.

Growing children are naturally inquisitive. They'll pick up hair pins, nail files, knives, forks, spoons, etc., and start investigating outlets and appliances. The metallic objects being perfect conductors of electricity, trouble is inevitable. Children have been known to pull out the two attachment plugs connected to a duplex wall outlet and to stuff the latter full of pins. Some of them stopped growing right then; others were more fortunate and escaped with nothing more than a strong jolt that threw them clear.

When the young son of Frank Bellek of Chicago had a narrow escape of this kind, papa decided to make a recurrence impossible. He designed a duplex outlet with a revolving cap over each section that turns automatically when the plug is removed

53

DON'T! Of all crazy ways of getting electrocuted quickly, this one is probably the best .. or the worst. The hand holding a metal knife, which is poked into the toaster to loosen a piece of bread, is resting on the metal frame of the appliance, which in turn is resting on a grounded metal stove. Keep toaster on wood table, and keep knives, and such, out of it.

and completely covers the live contact springs. To reinsert a plug, you merely place the prongs in the slots in the cap, twist a quarter turn to the right, and press in. Bearing the appropriate name "No-Shok," this self-thinking outlet is truly an inspired contribution to life and safety. It is simple, inexpensive, easy to install. Millions have been sold and it has proved foolproof.

No different in size or appearance from a regular duplex outlet, a No-Shok can replace the latter in any box. It shouldn't take more than five minutes per outlet. Follow exactly the procedure given for the installation of a mercury switch. (See "Silent Switch Lets Baby Sleep.")

Open toasters, broilers, etc., are another story entirely. You just have to get into the habit of removing the wall plug and tieing the cord around the appliance when a meal is finished. If possible, put the toaster in a kitchen cabinet, and close the door or cover of the broiler, to discourage tampering by children who may be about.

Junior isn't the only one who needs to be indoctrinated with good electrical safety habits. With appalling carelessness, many an adult sticks a knife into a "live" toaster to free a piece of bread. The toast pops loose, and the adult usually pops up about three feet himself. This practice is dangerous even if the appliance is "off," because it really isn't completely off at all. The internal switch opens one side of the line and this cuts off the current. However, and this is a very big "however", the *other* side of the line is still connected to one end of the heating wires. See Figure 1. If you poke a knife into the toaster you can very easily touch the latter and when you do you'll know it!

Loose cords on the floor are a menace mainly to toddlers who are teething. Children at this stage bite anything they can reach. Witness the edges of a crib or play pen, which looks as if they have been attached by hungry beavers. An infant

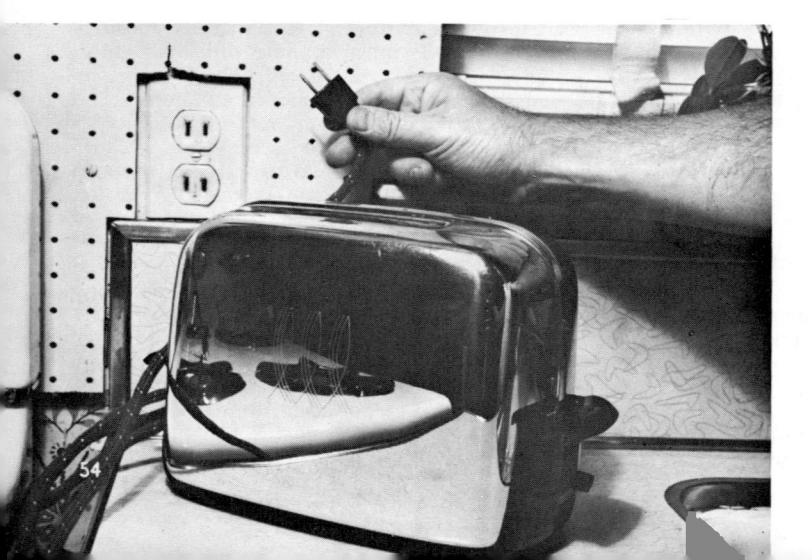

Want to save the life of someone in your family .. maybe yourself? Then do this every time before you allow anyone to put his fingers or a metal utensil of any kind into a toaster or other heat-type appliance with exposed elements. Also, store the toaster, when not in use, in a closet or on a shelf, out of the reach of children.

Figure 1

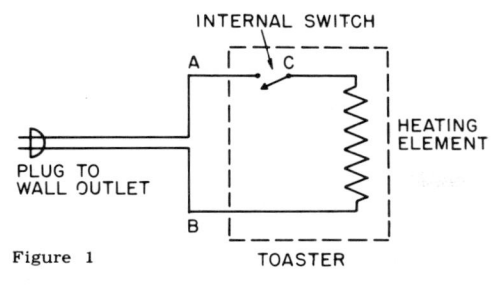

With the internal switch of a toaster "off," the line between the plug and point A is reasonably safe because it is isolated from the accessible heating element. However, any point in the toaster between C and B can readily become "hot" in relation to a ground if the plug should be in the wall outlet the wrong way. Moral: Don't poke any metal utensils or hardware of any sort into your toaster!

crawling on the floor is sure to discover all the flexible wires for lamps, radio and television sets, fans, air conditioners, etc., and to try them for taste. If the insulation is thin to begin with, or has worn through in spots (see "Don't Let a Cord Tie You Into Knots"), vigorous chewing by baby may quickly bare the wires inside. Add a little salty saliva to make the connection more conducting... the result is horrible to contemplate. Nowhere else does preventive maintenance pay off in better terms.

In any household having a toddling child, it is usually necessary to clear all small objects off tables during baby's waking hours. If you don't do the job, he or she will. At night you can restore the room to its natural state. At the same time you remove the ash trays, flower pots, etc., also unplug the loose electrical cords and curl them out of sight. All you'll have to be concerned about then is baby cracking his head against a table, falling off a chair, getting wedged under the sofa, pulling the curtains down on himself, and similar minor events.

Protection By and Against Grounding

Fixed wiring and appliances, once installed properly, continue to work for years without developing or causing the slightest trouble. The same cannot be said of portable or semi-portable appliances and tools which contain motors and which therefore are subject to vibration and movement effects. In clothes washing machines these are further aggravated by the presence of soapy water, an excellent conductor of electricity.

To make use of the protective feature of grounding, you must know how circuits are grounded. Figure 2 shows a fundamental branch circuit such as might be found in any home. The white colored wire is uninterrupted throughout its length. At the meter, where the power lines enter the house from the street, this wire is thoroughly "grounded" by means of a connection to the nearest cold water pipe, which is a good "ground" because it is actually in contact with the earth for a considerable length. The primary purpose of this grounding is to provide a direct return path to the earth of accumulations of static electricity in the sky before and during a thunderstorm. Picked up by the long, exposed wires from the generating station, this static can and often does burn out power distribution systems. A *heavy* burst of static electricity takes the spectacular form of a bolt of lightning. Good grounding saves countless homes from serious damage. All overhead telephone wires are similarly protected, by "lightning arrestors" with a ground connection; and all outside radio and television aerials are supposed to be fitted with equivalent devices.

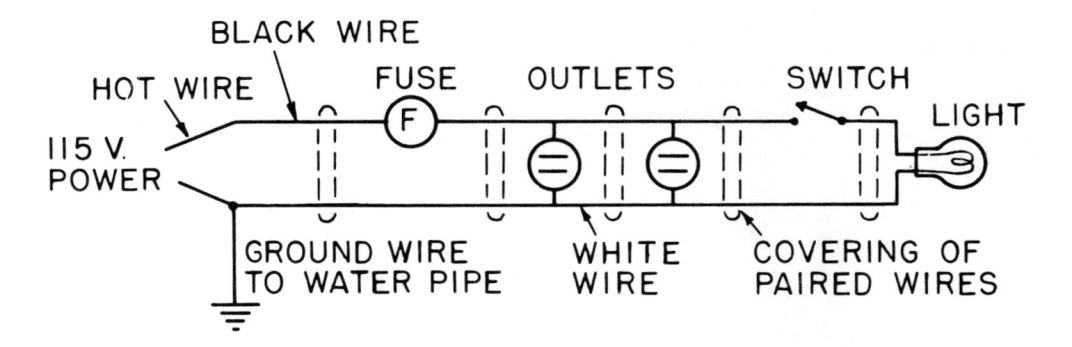

Figure 2

In house circuits, one side of the power line is grounded to a pipe; grounded wire is continuous throughout.

"BX" ARMORED CABLE

BLACK WIRE IS HOT

METAL SHEATH IS GROUNDED

WHITE WIRE IS GROUNDED

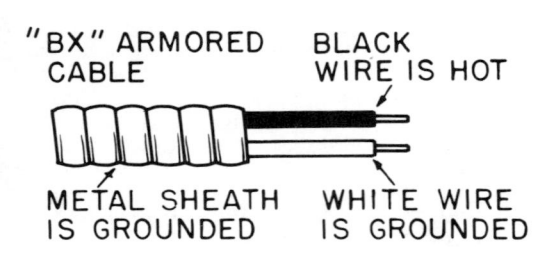

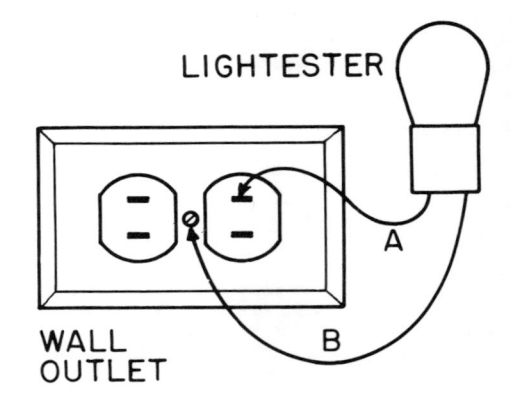

Figure 3

When power wires are encased in BX or other types of metal cable, the metal sheath is also grounded and becomes a parallel conductor to white wire.

LIGHTESTER

WALL OUTLET

Figure 4

A Lightester (see chapter on Testers And Tools) will demonstrate that a circuit can be completed through grounded frame of an electrical outlet box.

If the house is wired with metallic sheathed cable of one sort or another, this sheathing is likewise grounded. When wires are cut, the outer sheathing is clamped into holes in metal boxes containing switches, lamps, outlets, etc., and the continuity of the grounding circuit is thereby maintained. The white wire inside "BX" and other armored cable (see Figure 3) is thus actually part of the same common circuit as the outer armor. This is a very important but often overlooked fact, which some people find difficult to believe. If you want to be convinced, or need to convince others, a quick demonstration with the Lightester will do the trick conveniently and to your satisfaction.

As shown in Figure 4, place one lead A in the shorter slot of a wall outlet. If the fixtures have been wired correctly, this is the "hot" or ungrounded side of the 115-volt power line. First touch the lead B to longer contact of the outlet, which is the grounded side of the line. The bulb will light, showing that the outlet and the bulb are both OK. Now, leaving A in the short slot, touch B to the center screw of the outlet's cover plate. If it is reasonably clean of paint, the bulb will light again, showing that the lamp circuit has been completed to the grounded side of the line. It will also light if lead B is touched to any other

DON'T! Bringing any connected appliance to the sink can mean danger. Never fill steam iron this way.

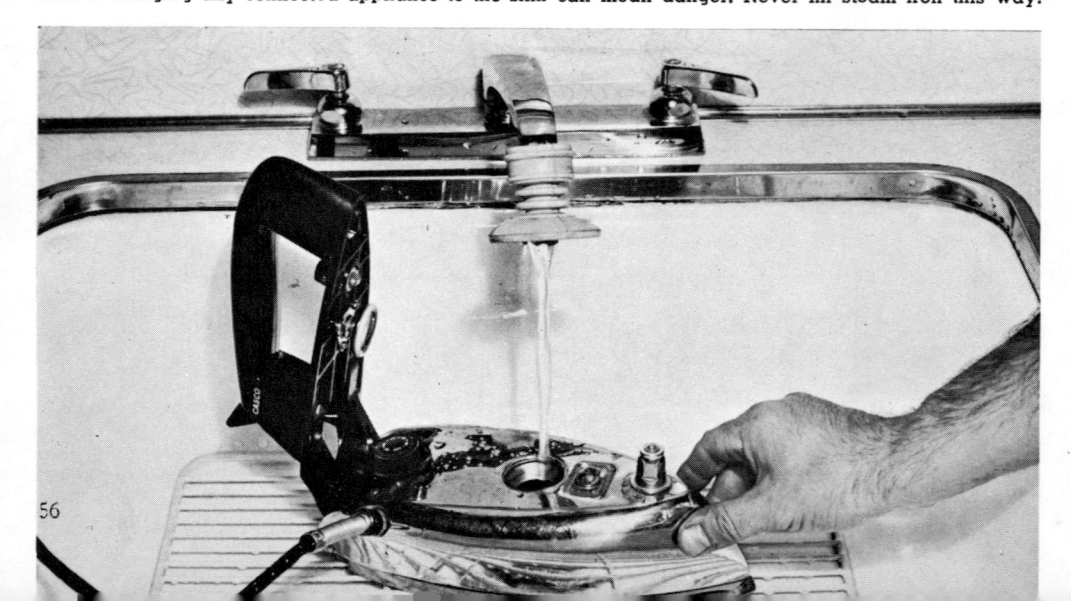

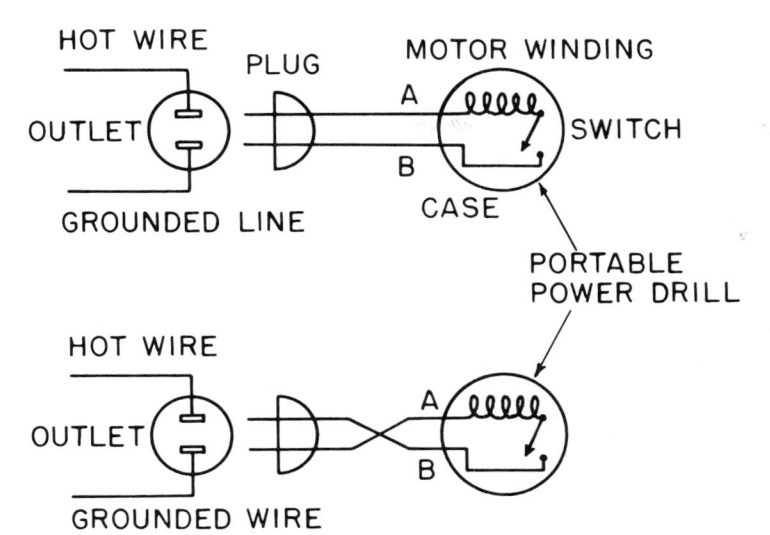

Figures 5 and 6
The two diagrams illustrate the wiring arrangement of a typical portable drill. The case of the usual drill is completely insulated from the wiring. Note that the drill works equally well with either position of plug.

grounded object, such as a water or gas pipe, a radiator or a heating register. Every metallic part of the water or heating system of a house is bound to be a good ground because of the interconnection of their various pipes and ducts.

Now let's consider a typical portable device and see how it behaves under normal and abnormal circumstances. The ¼-inch electric drill is a fine example because it is so widely used in the home, the shop and the garage for a variety of purposes. Figures 5 and 6 show it in simplified diagrammatic form. The motor itself is represented by a coil of wire, the switch by an interrupted line, and the metal frame or body by a heavy circle. The switch and the motor are connected in simple series and two wires A and B pass through the case and terminate in an attachment plug. The drill works equally well with the plug inserted in the wall outlet either way, as indicated in Figures 5 and 6. If the motor winding, the switch and the line cord are all normally well insulated from the case, the latter is "cold" from the electrical standpoint. Thus, if a person is using the drill in a garage, and is standing on the cement floor as shown in Figure 7, no part of the current in the drill passes to him, although his feet are in firm contact with the ground to which wire B is connected.

It is well known that motor-operated tools, especially portable ones that are knocked around a great deal, often suffer internal injuries. The insulation on some motor windings is rather thin, and can readily wear through if the tool is used frequently. Suppose that any worn part of the winding makes contact with the iron core on which it is wound. The core is part of the case, so a new connection C is established as shown in Figure 8. If the user plugs in the attachment plug and reaches for the drill, he will receive a surprise. Trace out the simple circuit and you'll see why. Current enters the drill from the hot side of the line through wire A, flows through the motor wire until it reaches the worn spot, bypasses from here to the metal case, through the arms and body of the user, through his feet and shoes in contact with the ground, and through the ground to make a complete path back to the grounded side of the power line. *The switch on the drill doesn't even have to be on.*

The severity of the shock depends on two main factors: 1) The condition of the skin. Clean, dry hands have a relatively high resistance and allow little current to pass through. Wet, dirty hands are much more conductive. 2) The effectiveness of the underfoot ground contact. Cement has a surprisingly low electrical resistance. The garage is almost sure to be close to a water pipe, so it is pretty well grounded. Cotton and woolen socks and ordinary shoes are good insulators if dry, and these items of clothing are what usually reduce the "shock" to a mere sting, which should be taken as a warning that the drill needs looking into.

Water Increases the Danger

Water on the floor enormously increases the danger, because it reduces the resistance of the floor itself, and, worse, that of the usually protective foot gear, if any is worn in the first place. Ignorance of this

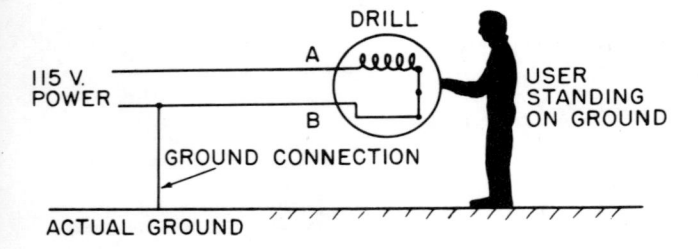

Figure 7

A portable drill in normal operation has switch closed; insulation protects user.

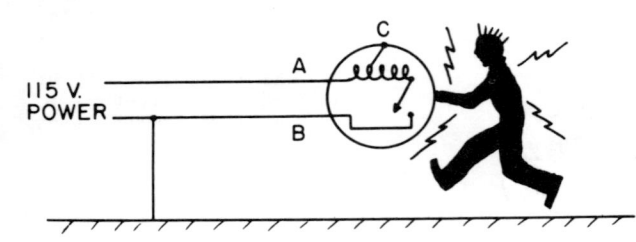

Figure 8

If motor winding should ground to case at point C, portable drill user is usually shocked because current will follow path through drill casing and through user's body to the ground and then back to the grounded power lead B as shown here.

fact was responsible for a particularly nasty fatality that occurred recently. A father and a young son washed the family car in the driveway of their home, in advance of shining it up. The boy, sloshing around in the water as all boys love to, reached for a power drill, which had been fitted with the usual polishing felt. The drill may not have even been defective. Water from the child's hands might easily have dripped into the case, making excellent contact with a hot connection inside. Brr .. cases like this give me the shakes.

Suppose that the partial grounding of the motor winding to point C occurred with the line plug reversed; that is, with A now grounded and B the "hot" side, as in Figure 9. What would happen to the user? As long as the switch is open, nothing. But the instant he closes the switch he establishes a good circuit from wire B, through the switch, through the section of winding between the switch and point C, and from there again through his body to ground.

Millions of small portable drills were bought by "do-it-yourself" enthusiasts, and numerous accidents occurred with them, before tool manufacturers got around to providing protection for them. This takes the form of a third wire in the flexible coil, with one end connected merely to the case and the other to any ground. In some drills the end of the ground wire is fitted with a threaded stud which is supposed to replace the cover plate screw of a duplex outlet; in others, it has a big spring clip, to clamp around BX or other metallic sheathing, or a nearby pipe. Newer tools now appearing on the market have their cords fitted with a *three*-prong plug which fits a new type of duplex outlet having three slots in a T-shaped formation. The two parallel prongs on the plug are the normal current-carrying connections; the offset third prong is for the grounding wire only. According to the National Electrical Code, all new power tools, workshop and laundry machines are supposed to have this three-wire system.

(For detailed instructions on installing new three-wire safety cords in older drills and similar tools, see the next section of this book, entitled "The Third Wire Is a Lifesaver.")

Figure 10 shows how a grounded case protects the user of any appliance. The ground wire, in effect hooked back directly to the grounded line B, has extremely low resistance, so much lower than that of the human body that it short-circuits the latter out of any circuit combination.

Protection Is Complete

Consider several very real accidental possibilities in Figure 10. Suppose wire A wears through at point 1, where it enters the case. It touches the latter. There is now a very low resistance path for the current to flow from wire A to point 1, to the case, all around the case, and out through the ground wire back to the grounded side of the line. This is a thorough short circuit on the power line, and will kick out the line fuse or circuit breaker almost instantly.

Suppose wire B touches against the case at point 3. If it touches without breaking off, the normal, safe operation of the tool is not affected, because this connection is grounded anyway! If it breaks off, and either touches or doesn't touch the grounded case, the circuit to the motor is

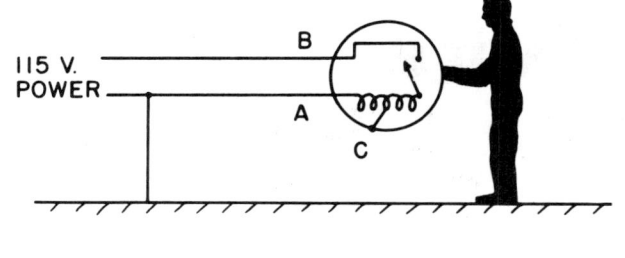

Figure 9

If grounded motor of the drill should have its line plug reversed, user will be safe—until he turns on the switch. He will then, of course, be shocked.

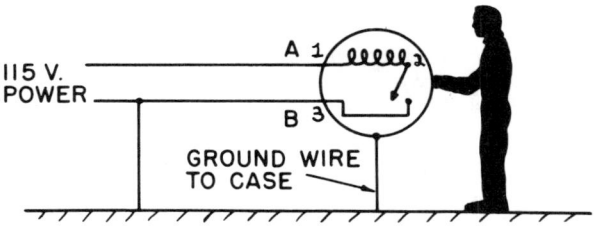

Figure 10

If metal case of the tool is well grounded with low-resistance wire, current flow under any accidental circumstances is confined between case and ground, and user does not suffer. If point 1 is grounded, line is short-circuited and fuse blows. If 2 is grounded, motor runs with switch open. If 3 is grounded, nothing will happen at all.

merely opened and the tool won't run when the switch is closed.

Suppose the junction point 2 of the motor winding and the switch becomes grounded to the case. When the tool is plugged in it will start immediately, even though the switch is still off. The power circuit from A is completed from 2 through the grounded case back to the grounded side of the line. The user still feels nothing because no current passes through his body; it's all going through the low resistance grounded case and ground wire.

More About Grounding

A separate grounding wire can easily be added to any tool or appliance not so factory-equipped. Fasten one end under any convenient screw on the case, tape the new wire along the present flexible cord, and attach a clip on the other end. It doesn't do any harm to remind you that this end must be grounded somewhere to do any good. The extra wire should not be any smaller than the wire in the present cord.

A separate grounding wire, with a screw-on clamp to fit on a water pipe, has been provided with most washing machines of recent manufacture. This wire should be placed so that it cannot be damaged or torn loose by clothes baskets, jars of laundry bleach, or other heavy objects. Loss of this grounding connection is invariably the reason some machines become "hot" and bounce their users across the room. (See section following.)

With some washers, the flexible rubber hose that goes to the cold water tap has a grounding wire woven into it. The machine thus is grounded automatically when it is hooked up.

Because water, gas and steam pipes are such good grounds, avoid contact with them when using *any* portable appliances. Certainly the worst place in this respect is the bathroom. With sickening regularity the newspapers report fatalities due to wet contact with exposed bowl heaters. A summer camper, a girl of 17, was killed recently when she tried to dry her hair with an electric dryer in a shower room. Radio and TV receivers of the AC-DC "hot chassis" type have shocked numerous occupants of bathtubs and have killed several children; all made the mistakes of twiddling the tuning or volume knobs with wet, soapy hands. Under more fortunate circumstances, the sets merely blew the fuses and plunged the bathrooms into darkness when the chassis made accidental contact with an exposed pipe or other fixture.

If electronic entertainment in the bathroom is important, at least make certain that the equipment is of the full transformer type. Better still for the purpose is a *battery-operated* transistor portable.

In the kitchen, get the family into the habit of keeping *connected* appliances away from the sink. One woman learned what happens when an electric frying pan is immersed in sudsy water for cleaning, with the plug still in the socket! She recoiled suddenly and gave herself a pretty thorough bath. Less funny was the experience of a mother who tried to give a six-month-old infant a quick cleaning off in the sink. Flailing its arms, the child pulled in a nearby toaster. Still connected, its exposed heating wires made a perfect return path to ground through the water. The baby was killed. •

The Third Wire Is a Lifesaver

Install grounding cords on motor-operated and "wet" appliances for safety

TO take the shock hazard out of any metal-body electrical appliance, you have to do only two simple revamping jobs: 1) Add a grounding wire to the present cord and replace the present two-prong non-polarized plug by a three-prong polarized plug; 2) Replace existing two-prong outlets by three-prong receptacles to take the new plug, or use polarized adapters.

Actually, the easiest way to add the lifesaving third wire is to use a length of new three-wire cord. In this the ground lead is colored green, and the current-carrying wires are black and white. Electrical and hardware stores now carry such cords in various lengths, with a polarized plug already molded permanently to one end. If you prefer, you can buy the cord and the plug separately.

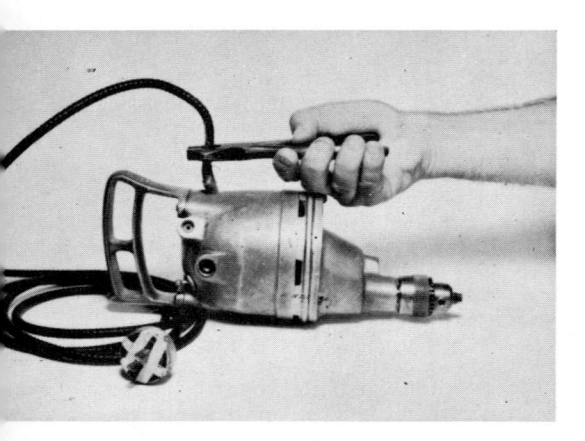

Portable drills, saws and other motor-operated tools are prime customers for three-wire safety cords. Old cord is probably torn, so cut it off.

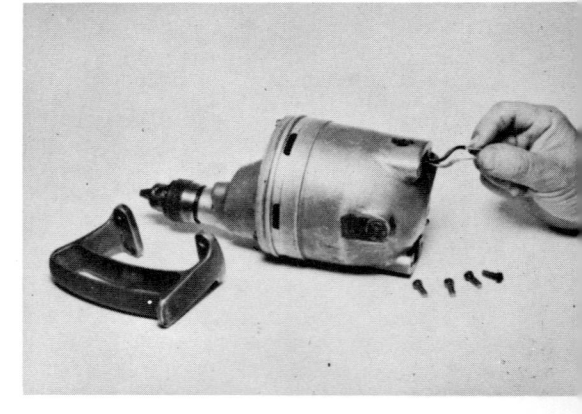

With handle removed or case opened, two leads from motor are located, pulled out carefully and cleaned off. Colors are usually black and white.

Grounding prong on a polarized plug is the long round one, represented at other end by a green wire. Run a continuity check with volt-ohmmeter.

Pull end of new three-wire cord through hole in body of tool and solder black to black, white to white. To green wire solder lug that fits screw.

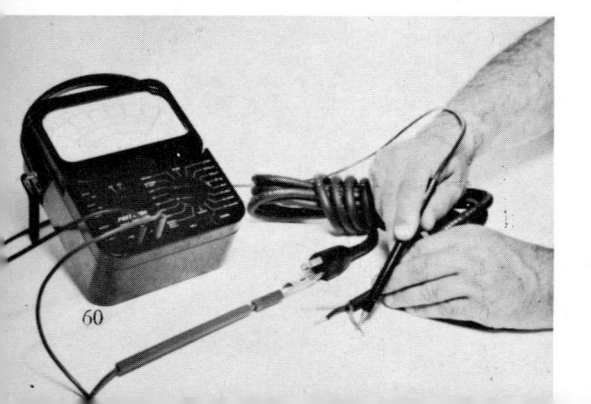

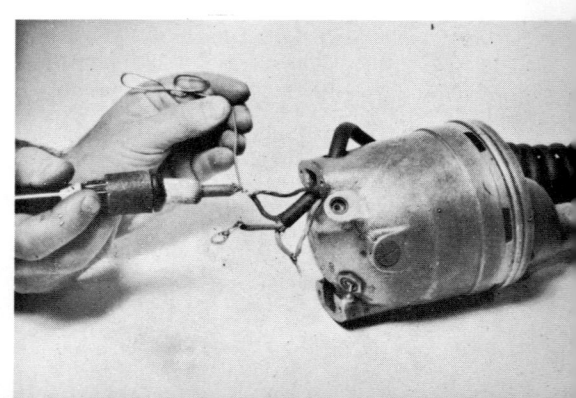

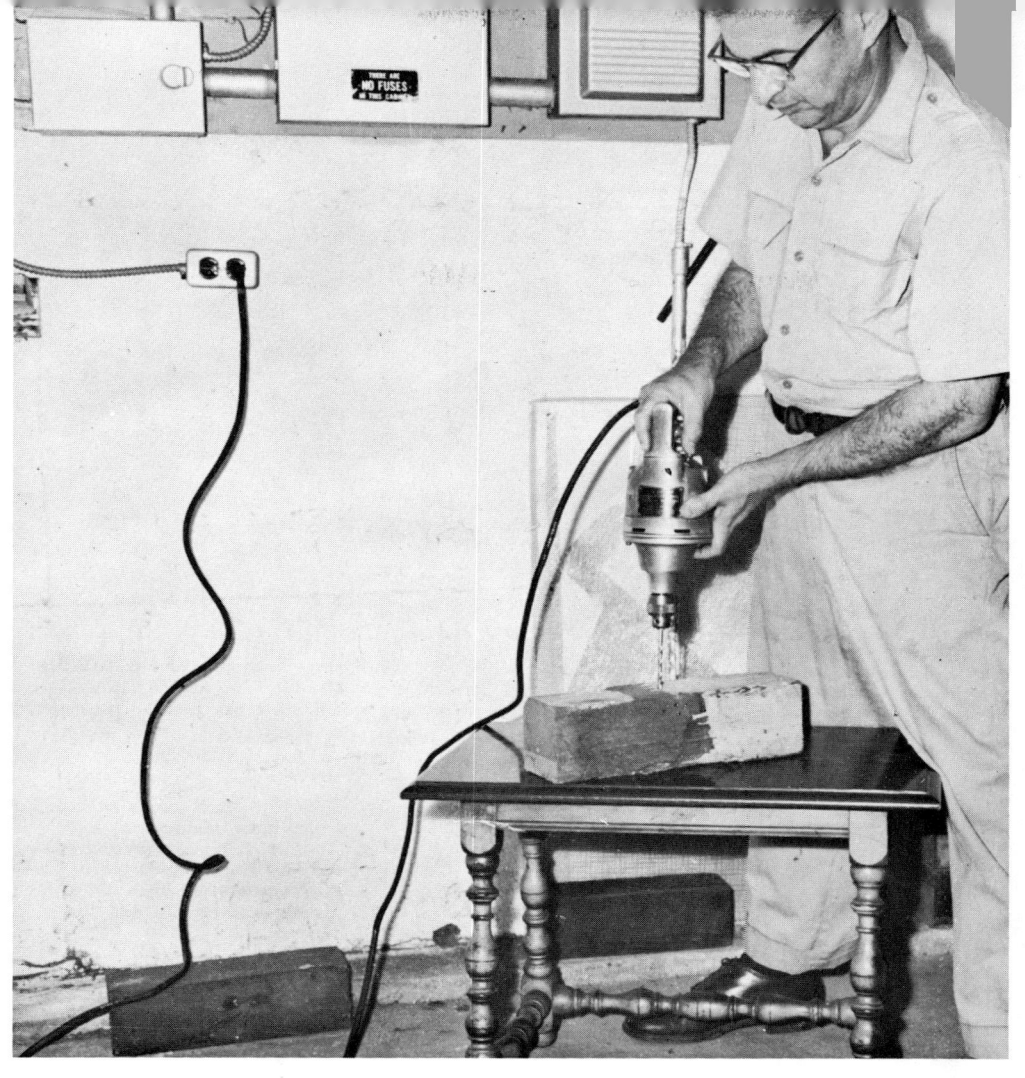

With your portable drill fitted with a three-wire cord, you can work in perfect safety even on a damp garage or cellar floor without danger of shock. In case of internal short-circuit, you only blow fuse.

After you tape the black and white splices, it is time to reassemble handle. Slip the ground lug over one screw and be sure to tighten well.

In order to take possible strain off your cord, as well as to increase its life, tape and then tie it securely to the under side of hand grip.

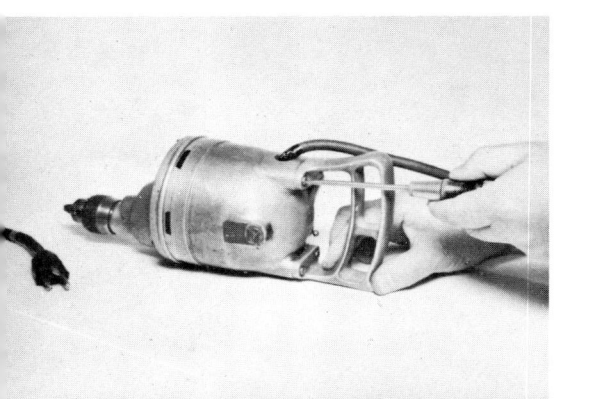

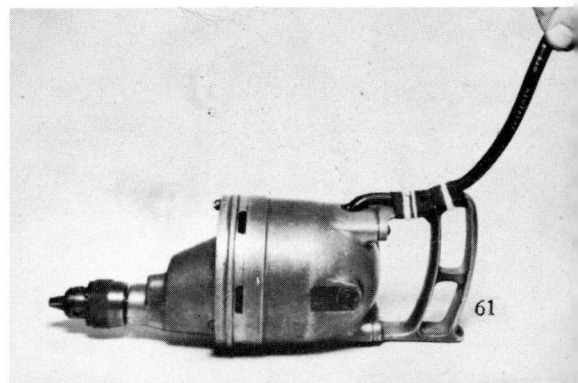

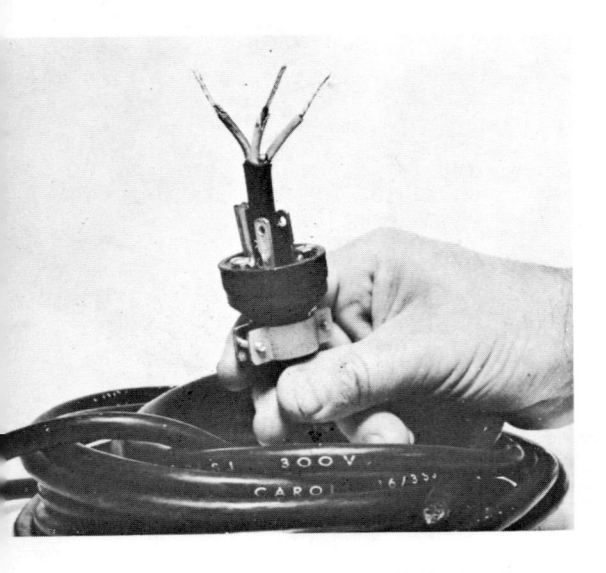

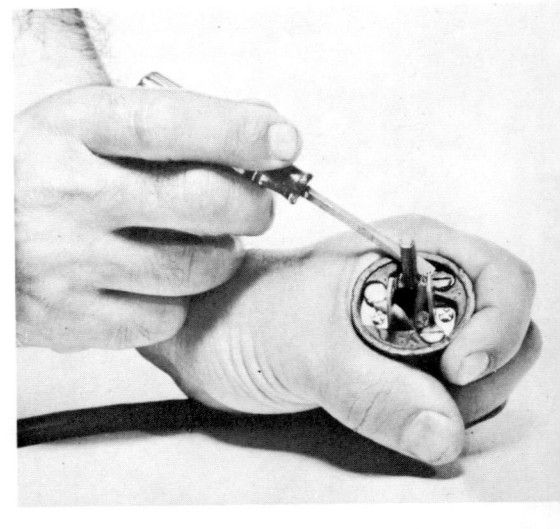

Make your own safety cord: Pull wire through polarized plug, trim off covering and insulation; clean and tin lightly to keep from coming apart.

Screwdriver points to green-colored terminal of ground prong of polarized plug. White lead must go to light prong and black lead to brass prong.

Old outlets in house or shop should be replaced by new polarized type to accommodate safety plug (left). However, satisfactory expedient, 75% safe, is in form of adapter.

For semipermanent use with a particular outlet, ground wire of polarized adapter can be fastened under mounting screw of receptacle cover plate, provided the box is grounded.

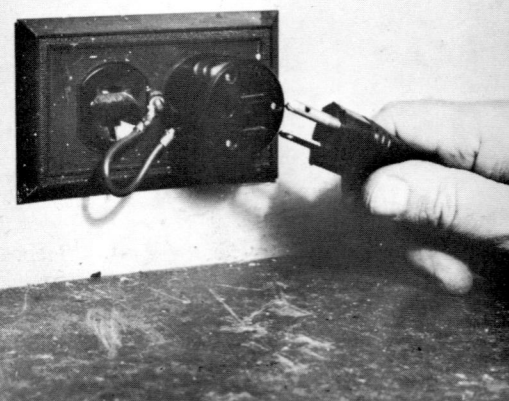

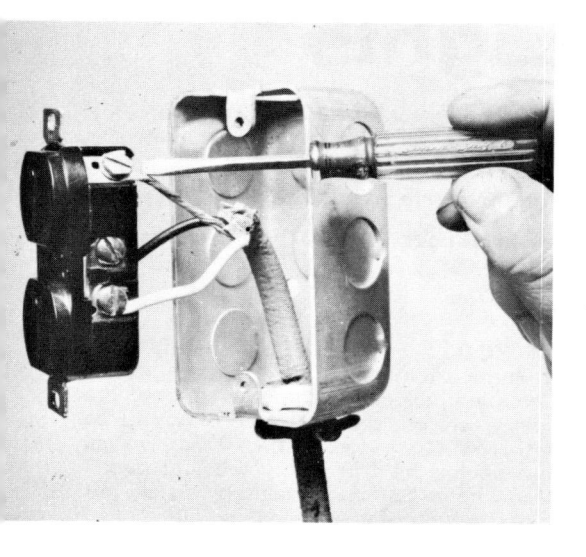

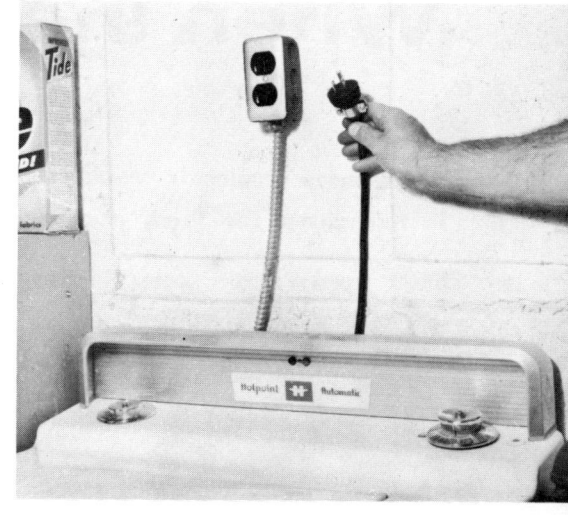

Screwdriver points to the green-colored ground screw of polarized outlet. Bare ground lead of non-metallic sheathed cable is shown connected.

Polarized receptacle and a polarized plug with three-wire cord mean complete assurance against power-line leakage when wet appliances are used.

The new polarized outlets look very much like the old ones except that they have three openings and three terminal screws. The one painted green is the ground connection. If metal outlet boxes are used with flexible armored cable ("BX") or rigid conduit, the ground connection to the green terminal is made automatically when an outlet is mounted, as this terminal is phyically part of the mounting ears of the outlet. If non-metallic cable is used, the bare ground wire woven between the insulated wires must be connected to the green screw. Replacing an old outlet is a screwdriver operation that takes a few minutes. Remember, of course, to pull the fuses first!

Study the accompanying pictures for practical how-to-do-it information on this important application of electricity. •

Pencil points to special tandem-blade polarized plug for 208/230-volt machines. Blades are in line but standard polarized plug's are parallel.

This is a "crowfoot" plug with matching outlet, also used for voltages higher than 115. Bottom (vertical) prong is used as ground connection.

When the Lights Go Out—

—the fuses or circuit breakers have been overloaded. The only cure is to lighten the load, not to invest in larger protective devices

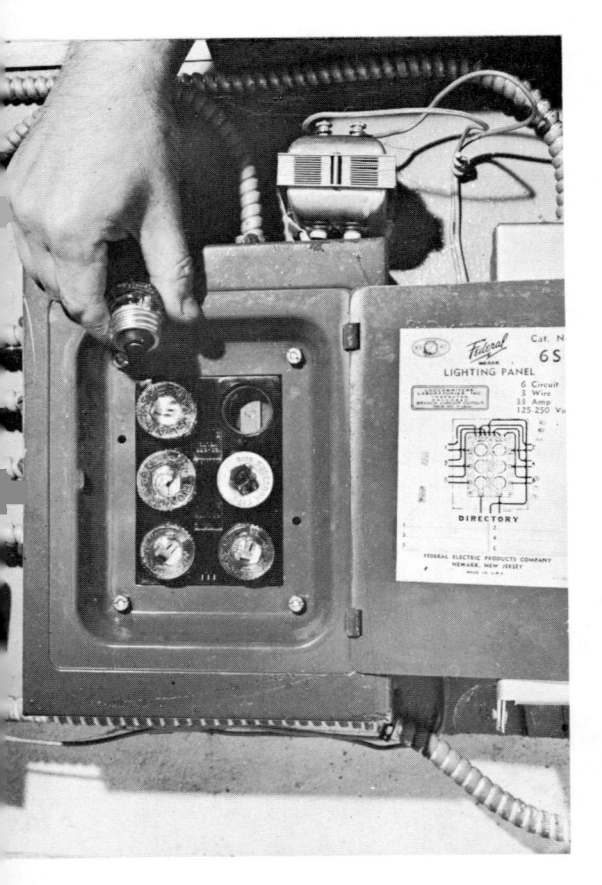

IF YOU have a headache, sometimes you can get temporary relief by swallowing a couple of aspirins. After the effect of the pills wears off, the headache may still be with you. If you feel so badly that you go to a doctor, he'll probably tell you that a headache is not an ailment by itself, but the symptoms of one.

To a large extent, the same goes for fuses. If fuses keep blowing out, merely replacing them with new ones is no cure for the overload somewhere in the house that is causing them to go "pfft." And replacing the original fuses with others of higher amperage rating is about as sensible as looking for a gas leak with a candle.

In some homes, in which no new heavy-current appliances have been added recently and everything is working satisfactorily, a fuse may go dead without apparent reason, and putting in a new one of the same rating restores operation to normal. In cases of this kind the original fuse itself was probably faulty. It may not have burned out at all, but merely devel-

Standard "plug" fuses have bases like lamps, and screw into receptacles in "cut-out" box. Keep a record on cover of latter of house circuits controlled by particular fuses to ease replacement.

"Cartridge" type fuses have exposed metal end caps, which fit tightly in spring clips in cutout box. Keep spares in latter. CAUTION: Even if fuse is blown out, end cap on side to meter is still "hot."

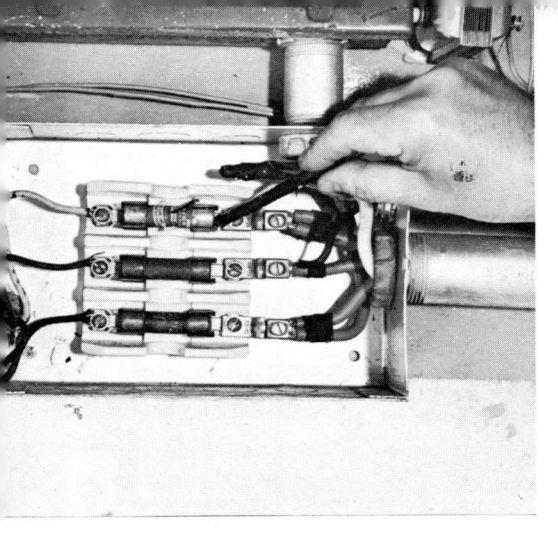

To remove a suspected cartridge fuse, first kill power by turning off main switch (have a flashlight handy if room is dark), then pry out with wooden stick. Turn on switch if light is needed during testing operation. Be sure to turn it off again before attempting to insert the new fuse.

oped an internal open circuit. The fuse wire may have become brittle and then broken under the influence of vibration from a passing truck, a slamming door, etc. I have examined many fuses that looked perfectly good yet showed positively and unquestionably as complete "opens" when given a continuity check.

Sometimes a fuse definitely blows out, and replacing it restores normal conditions. The burn-out may well have been due to a momentary short circuit which cleared itself, at least for the time being. For instance, a few strands of the flexible wire inside a cord for a floor lamp, a TV set, a fan, etc., might have worked against themselves because the cord has been stepped on a lot or otherwise abused. Enough current may have flown across these wires, during a second or so, to heat them and the fuse in the same circuit to the melting point. A new fuse holds, although the cord remains potentially dangerous.

Sometimes the touching wires, instead of flaring open, weld themselves together. New fuses then burn out as quickly as you put them in. Actually, it is better for this to happen, as then you know something is definitely haywire someplace and you are forced to go looking for it.

As a general practice, when troubleshooting the house power circuits, allow yourself *one* new fuse as a replacement for a blown unit. If this pops off, start shooting!

Heavy Starting Loads vs. Fuses

Blown fuses did not become a problem in most households until two highly desirable machines appeared on the market: first the clothes washer, which eliminates the most onerous of family chores; and then the air conditioner, which enables the family to sleep at night. The thing that puzzles owners of these machines is that they take less power than many other appliances that have been used for years without trouble. For example, a clothes washer takes only about 375 watts in normal operation and perhaps 800 or 1000 during a fast spinning cycle; a typical room air conditioner takes 800 to 1000 watts steadily. Compare these figures with the power consumption of a hand iron, 1000 watts; a bathroom heater, 1130 watts; a toaster, 1010 watts; a coffee maker, 830 watts; a frying pan, 1160 watts. If plugging in a 1000-watt iron doesn't bother the fuses, why does a 1000-watt air conditioner make them jump out of their skins?

The answer lies in the nature of both the fuses and the power load. An ordinary fuse, the kind you screw into a socket in a box in the basement, consists merely of a piece of wire of rather low melting point. As you probably know, electric current flowing in any wire must push its way through, and in so doing generates some heat. The higher the current, the higher the heat. For fuse purposes, an alloy wire is used that melts quickly if the current exceeds a certain value; the fuse wire is thin for low values of current and thick for high values. There isn't, and indeed there shouldn't be under ordinary circumstances, much leeway in fuse ratings. A fuse marked 15 amperes should not burn out with 14 amperes going through it, but it should be noticeably warm at 15 amps, pretty hot at 16 and just about melting at 17.

An 830-watt coffee maker plugged into a kitchen outlet takes about 7 amperes of current. For a fraction of a second after the appliance is turned on it takes more, but the interval is such a short one that the effect can be ignored for all practical purposes. A load of 7 amperes obviously places little strain on a 15-ampere fuse, which is

65

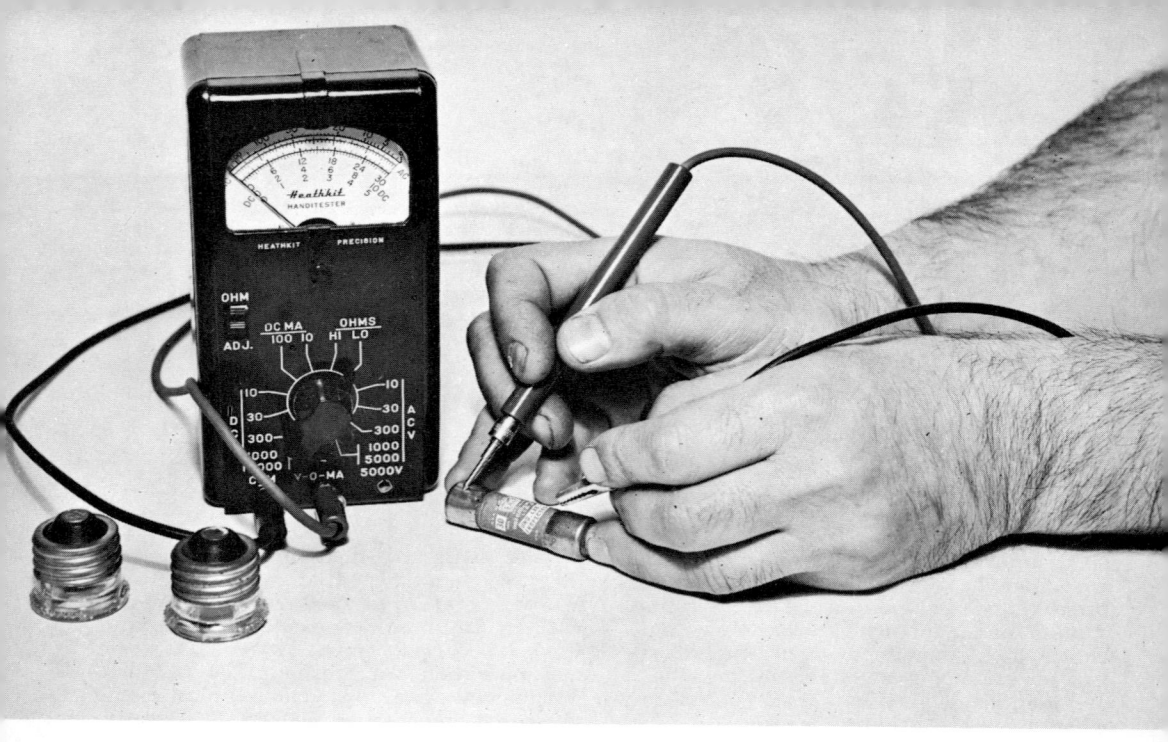

Quick test with Handitester shows condition of fuses. A good fuse registers 0 resistance, a blown one shows infinite resistance or open circuit. Check your fuses regularly and discard all defective ones.

the normal size for "branch circuits" in a home.

A standard size clothes washer is rated at 375 watts. While running it takes between 6 and 7 amperes of current. (For the arithmetic of volts, amperes and watts, see the section entitled "Power Is What You Pay For.") A 15-amp fuse should therefore afford plenty of latitude. It would, except for an important physical consideration.

Into a large steel tub you dump eight or nine pounds of clothes and then add water almost to the top. If this loaded tub were out of the washer, I doubt if you'd be able to carry it more than a few feet without straining a muscle or two. This is the stationary, dead weight the motor in the machine must get into motion. When you turn the dial to "wash," the power circuit to the motor closes. During an appreciable part of the first second following, the motor struggles to develop the necessary torque, and in so doing *draws 25, 30 or 35 amperes of current from the line.* If the line is protected by an ordinary 15-ampere fuse, the motor usually doesn't even have a chance to turn over once; the fuse merely goes "pfft," as it should with an overload of 100% or more, and you're stuck with a washer full of dirty clothes.

Appliance dealers and customers alike developed high blood pressure before they discovered a vital bit of information in the instruction sheets that came with washers. This stated quite clearly that ordinary fuses cannot be used, but must be replaced with special ones of the "slow-blow" type, which cost only a few cents more. These fuses are designed specifically to handle motor loads. They get a bit warm during the starting period, but they hold up long enough to permit the motor to overcome the inertia of the tub and to get it rolling. The motor current then drops quickly to its normal running value 6 or 7 amperes. A slow-blow fuse rated at 15 amperes does the job.

The time delay in slow-blow fuses is pretty delicately adjusted to give a safe balance between convenience and protection. If the tub is overloaded with a few extra towels and a bedsheet, and is just so heavy that it locks the motor, the continuing flow of 30 or 35 amperes kicks out the fuse in a second or so. If it didn't, the motor and the wiring to it would start to smolder. Similar stalling sometimes occurs in slightly overloaded machines that have a fast spin cycle for drying the clothes. If slow-blow fuses of the recommended size for a particular washer blow out, you can be pretty sure that the tub merely is being piled too high.

Slow-blow fuses are so important to the satisfactory operation of washers that some manufacturers tape an actual fuse to the prongs of the attachment plug of the machine, as an inescapable means of calling the buyer's attention to it.

Exactly the same problem presents itself with air conditioners, except that it is more acute because these machines usually contain two motors: a pretty big one for operating a stiff compressor, through which the refrigerating liquid flows; and a smaller one, for a fan that pushes the cold air out. The starting current of a medium size cooler working on 115 volts can be as much as 50 amperes. A slow-blow fuse, of a size depending on the running rather than the starting current, is again the answer.

Actually, fusing is a relatively minor problem with air conditioners. Much more serious trouble is caused by the steady hour-after-hour flow of the running current through house wiring that is too thin to handle it without heating up. (See the section entitled "Is Your Wiring Adequate for Your Load?").

The motors used with home workshop power tools range between ¼ and 1 horsepower and they, too, have fairly high starting currents. However, except in the case of lathes (and then not always), the load is not applied until the tool reaches full operating speed, so blown fuses are not too frequent. A slow-blow fuse in the shop line is the cure if one is needed.

Types of Fuses

Most of the fuses found in homes are of the "plug" type. This term is somewhat misleading, as plug fuses have threaded bases exactly like those of lamps, and they screw into threaded sockets. Fuses that really plug in are called "cartridge" fuses. These have a fiber body and metal end caps, and fit into spring clips. Slow-blow fuses, which are sold under a variety of trade names, have screw bases like ordinary plug fuses and can be distinguished from the latter by their more complicated internal spring mechanism.

Plug fuses can be removed and replaced with little danger of shock, because the ends are completely insulated and are not part of the circuit. Cartridge fuses, how-

Cutaway view shows internal construction of Westinghouse thermal type circuit breaker, a fine safety device. Contacts are open. When handle is pushed to right, circuit is restored and handle is latched.

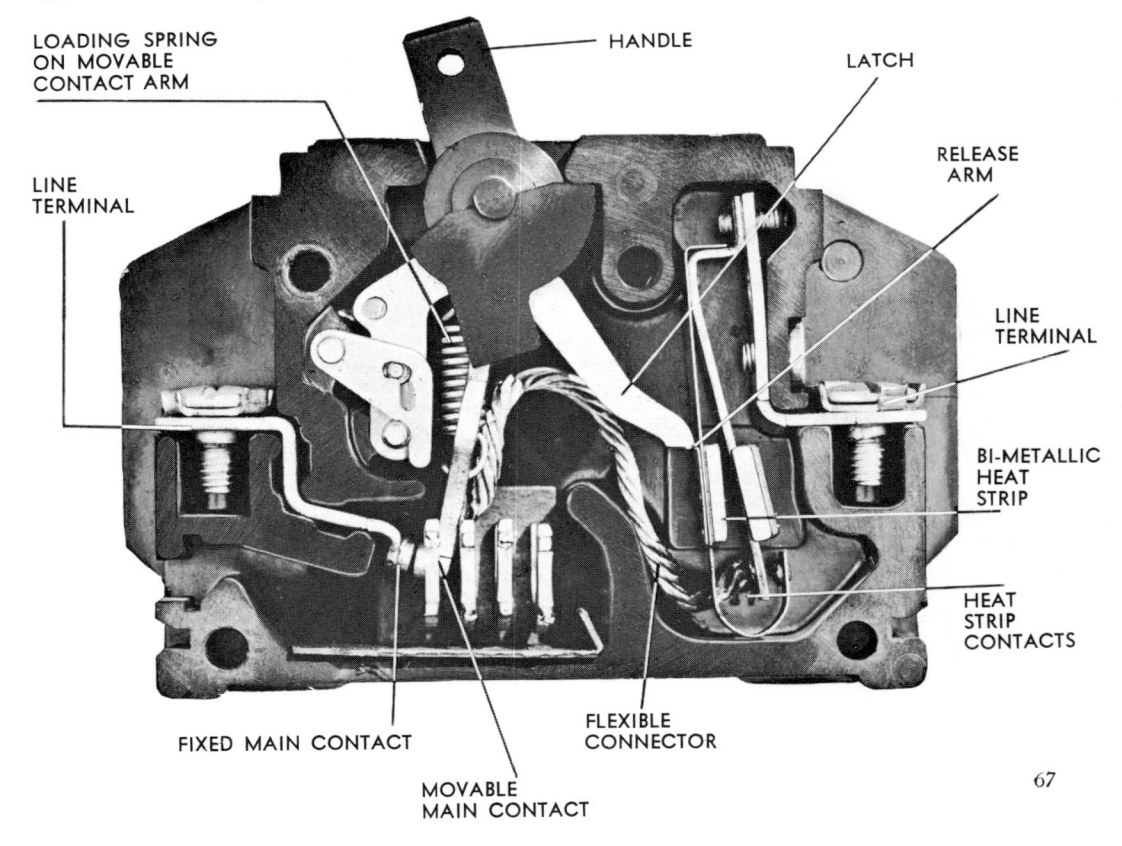

Even a child can operate the circuit breakers used to protect electrical circuits. Double bank of 14 breakers (Westinghouse) is completely safe because all "hot" connections are inside wall box.

This heavy-duty two-pole circuit breaker is intended for use on 3-wire, 115/230 volt circuits. A Westinghouse "De-Ion" type, it is rated at 50 amperes. Breakers are more convenient than fuses.

ever, must be treated with great respect because of the exposed end caps. Even if such a fuse is blown out, the end on the power line side is still plenty "hot." The picture on page 65 shows a safe method of handling cartridge fuses.

Testing fuses for condition is very simple. They are either open or closed. With the Clicktester, you will hear a loud click if the fuse wire is OK, or nothing if it is gone. With the Handitester, a good fuse shows as zero resistance; a dead one doesn't even move the needle of the meter. If intermittent contact inside a fuse is shown by an irregular clicking or a fluctuating meter needle, chuck it out. Fuses are so cheap that it doesn't pay to retain questionable ones.

Chart of Fuse Positions

The "cut out" box in most homes contains six fuses; more in many newer houses. It is highly advisable to know which fuses control which outlets and lights all through the dwelling. Have an assistant turn on all the lights in one room at a time, and also activate the wall outlets with portable lamps, a radio set, etc. Start removing fuses and let the assistant shout down or stamp on the floor when the juice goes off. Make up the data in chart form and cement or tape it to the cover of the fuse box. Also, keep a handful of spare fuses, of the right sizes for your power installation, within easy reach of the fuse box. You'll con-

gratulate yourself on your foresight in this regard the very first time a circuit goes dead unexpectedly, as it always does.

Circuit Breakers

In all but the lowest price brackets, the tendency in new home construction is now definitely toward the use of circuit breakers rather than fuses for protection against excessive current surges. A circuit breaker has a handle like a switch and looks very much like one; it is in fact a self-tripping switch that goes open when the current passing through it exceeds its rated value.

The breakers now coming into home use work on either a thermal or a magnetic effect, or a combination of the two. The thermal type employs a bi-metallic strip which flexes and trips one or more sets of spring-loaded contact points when the rated current value is passed. The magnetic type contains an electromagnet which does the same job. Most breakers incorporate a time delay feature like that of slow-blow fuses, and for exactly the same reason.

When a circuit breaker trips open on an overload, it can be reset in an instant; you merely push the handle back up. If the overload is still on, it will trip again. Like a good switch, a breaker will last a long time and rarely if ever will require replacement.

Because circuit breakers cost from 4 to about 25 times more than fuses, many people have gotten the impres-

New circuit breaker has screw base and can replace conventional fuses in regular cutout box without requiring changes in wiring. When current overload exceeds rating of breaker, center button pops up and circuit is opened. To reset breaker after overload is cleared, it is only necessary to press button down. This type of protective device is especially useful in homes and shops where occasional motor overloads at times occur.

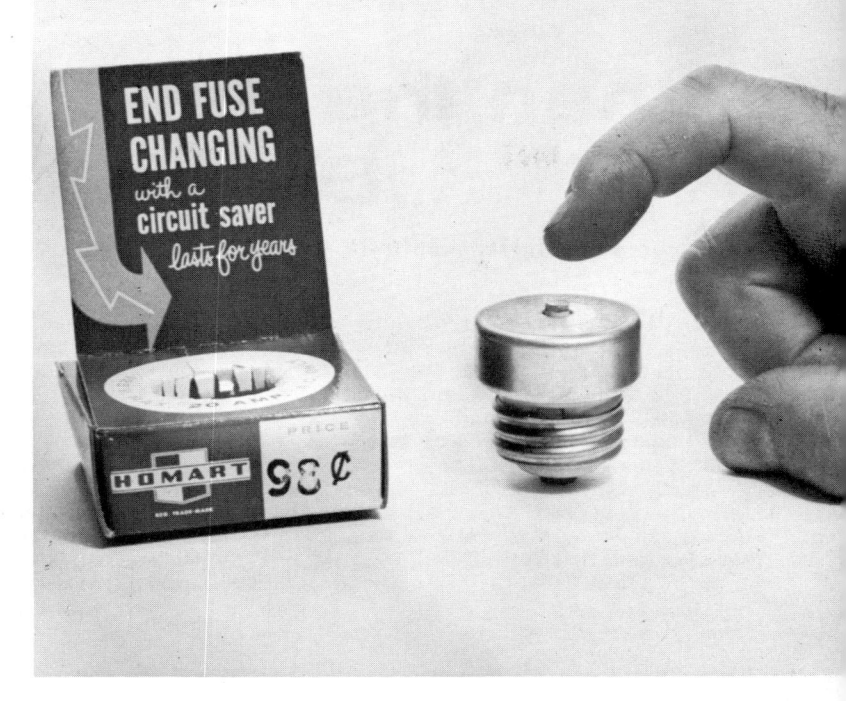

sion that circuit breakers in general have magical properties and offer more protection than fuses do. This is not so. An overload that trips a $2.50 breaker will also burn out a five-cent fuse, and just as quickly and thoroughly. The most obvious advantage of breakers is convenience. A far more important feature, which is not as widely appreciated as it should be, is that in many cases they prevent a thoughtless homeowner from deliberately overloading his power lines.

Consider a "standard" house having branch circuits protected by regular 15-ampere plug fuses. A new table-top broiler arrives one day and all the members of the family gather round while it is unpacked, admired, and then, of course, plugged in to see how it works. Many such broilers take pretty close to 15 amps all by themselves. If current is being carried on the same line for lights or other purposes, there is a very good chance that the 15-amp fuse will evaporate. Great disappointment registers on the faces of mother and the kids. So what does pop do? Nine times out of ten, he will not resist the temptation to replace the 15-amp safety valve with a 20-amp plug. Result: the broiler goes on and his reputation as Mr. Fix-It is saved. What happens to the power line is another story. Sooner or later this practice leads to disaster.

If the house is equipped with 15-ampere circuit breakers, the breaker feeding the broiler line will flip open on the overload just as the fuse did. But this breaker is permanently bolted into the distribution box, with its connections out of sight. There's *nothing* you can do to it except push the handle back to "on." Every time it trips open it is warning you that the broiler is just too much for that line. You might swear at it a little, but the sooner you realize the significance of the tripping of a circuit breaker, the longer will your house last.

I have heard people say they don't like circuit breakers because "they don't allow any flexibility in operating certain lines in the house." This is cockeyed reasoning of the worst sort. The fact that breakers do not permit any such "flexibility" is the greatest argument in their favor. Probably 90% of all actual cases of fires, charred wiring, sluggish air conditioners and freezers, etc., would not have occurred at all if uncorruptible breakers had been used instead of easily "fixed" fuses, which are a danger in ignorant hands.

In this section the value of 15 amperes has been used in describing fuse and breaker protection for branch circuits in a house. This is the safe allowable carrying capacity of No. 14 wire, the size most commonly used in homes. However, much greater values are permissible with heavier wires, as explained in the section "Is Your Wiring Adequate for Your Load?" An overload is an overload, regardless. •

69

When the Bell Doesn't Ring--

—corroded button contacts or loose connections are usually at fault

YOU'RE finishing your morning coffee, and are disturbed by a loud pounding noise from the vicinity of the front door. You rush to open it and find the postman with a package in his hand.

"Whassamatter, Bill?" you ask. "Why didn't you ring the bell?"

"I pushed the button about a dozen times, but nothing happened. Saw your car in the garage, so knew you were still in. Here, sign for this, will you?"

"Bell doesn't work?" you mutter.

"Lemme try it." You do, and it doesn't. That evening you have a small repair job to perform. That is, it'll be small if you know your bell wiring arrangement.

In many older houses the general scheme of Fig. 1, page 72, prevails. The source of power is a bank of No. 6 size dry batteries, usually three or four of them connected in simple series. The front door "button" is merely a momentary contact switch which, when pressed, closes the circuit to a bell. If a side or rear door is customarily used for

Bell-ringing transformer invariably is located close to the fuse box; to make a quick check on it, set Handi-test (see Testers And Tools) to 30-volt AC range and connect test leads to binding posts. This one reads OK.

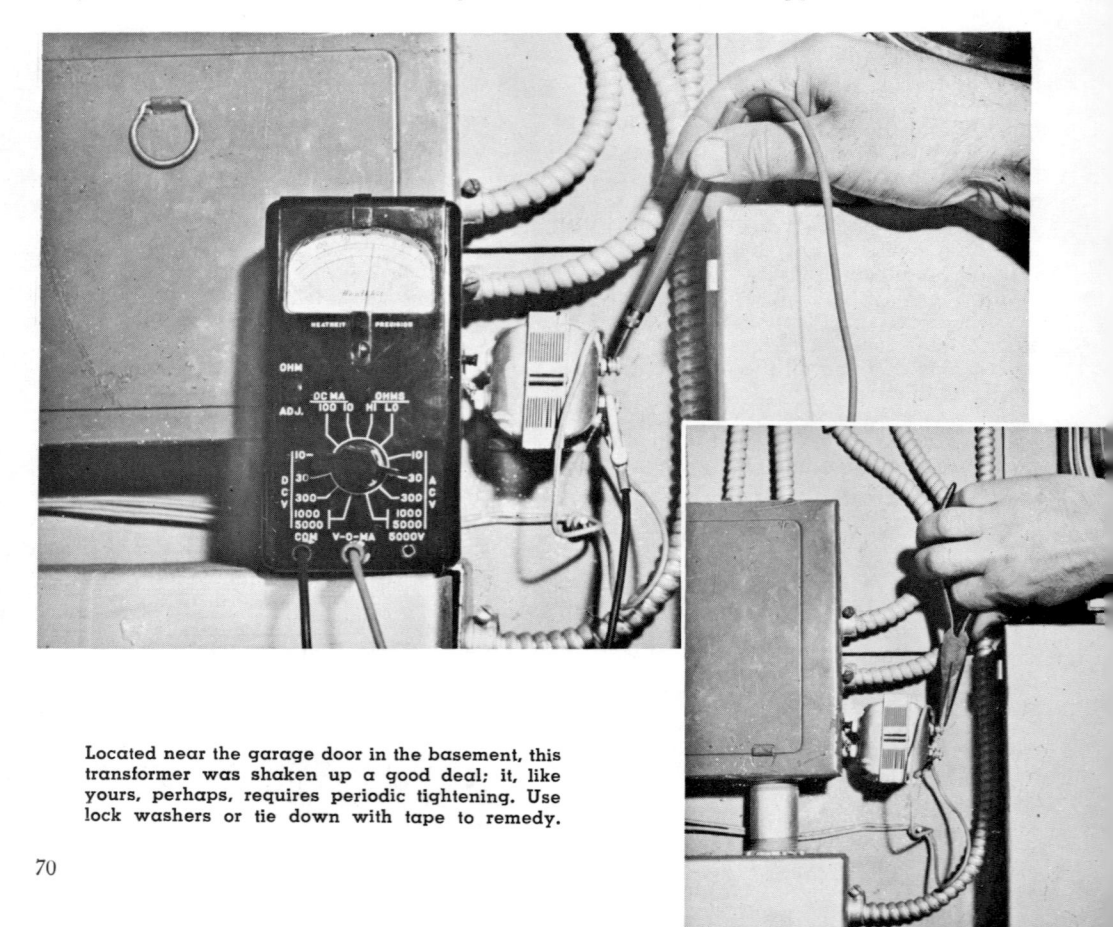

Located near the garage door in the basement, this transformer was shaken up a good deal; it, like yours, perhaps, requires periodic tightening. Use lock washers or tie down with tape to remedy.

Exposed bell buttons are usual cause of failure of the signalling system. Inspect frequently; to get at connections, remove two mounting screws.

If short-circuiting button terminals with screwdriver makes bell ring, internal contacts are defective; new button is the simplest way of restoring service.

deliveries, access to a yard or driveway, etc., another button is located here and it operates a buzzer. Any number of bells or buzzers can be hooked in to work off a single bank of batteries.

In most houses built during the last couple of decades the batteries are replaced by a small step-down transformer. The primary side, identified by its heavy black and white covered wires, is connected *permanently* to any of the branch circuits supplying power to the house. The secondary side, identified by its two knurled head binding posts, is connected to the bell, buzzer, or chimes through door buttons, exactly as in the battery arrangement. See Fig. 2, page 72.

The transformer reduces the 115-volt line voltage to values ranging between 6 and 16. These have absolutely no shock danger, so it is not necessary to "kill" the transformer circuit, by opening the branch fuse to which it is connected, when you shoot trouble in the bell and button wiring.

"If the transformer is connected permanently to the line, doesn't it draw power all the time?" This question is probably framing in your mind. Yes, it does, but the amount is so small that it hardly overcomes the friction of the bearings in the watt-hour meter. When a door button is pressed, a bell or a chime takes a few watts, but for such a short time that they add virtually nothing to the monthly electric bill.

The case of the transformer may feel very slightly warm to the touch. This is normal. It does not indicate overloading, but only the internal molecular friction of the iron core of the transformer as the alternating current goes through its periodic reversals. (See "The Power System in Your Home.")

Because they are activated for only a total of perhaps minutes over the course of a whole year, the bells, buzzers and chimes themselves rarely give trouble. If one fails to work, check these points:

1) The source of power. Dry cells last a long time, but they do dry out eventually. The usual sign of impending failure is an outcropping of a white chemical around the case. A dry cell in good condition measures 1½ volts. Three in series should check to 4½ volts, four in series to 6 volts. The Handitester, set for DC measurement, is fine for the job. If the batteries are more than a year old they should be suspected

71

Fig. 1.

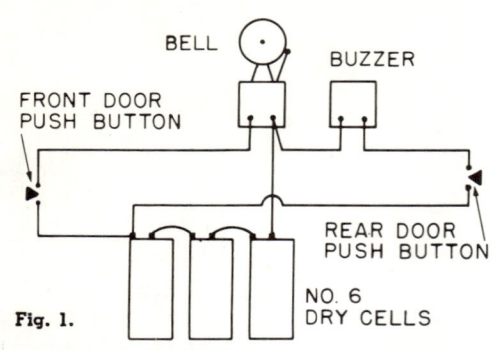

Above, a common arrangement of bell and buzzer in older houses using dry cells as source of power.

of weakness and then checked for voltage.

The rated secondary voltage of the step-down transformer is usually marked on the case. Set the Handitester for AC on the 30 volt scale, connect the test leads to the brass binding posts, and you'll know in an instant if the transformer is putting out juice. It isn't necessary to disconnect the existing wires to the posts for this test.

If the meter shows no voltage, disconnect either of the wires to the binding posts, open the primary power line circuit by removing the line fuse, set the Handitester for LO ohms, and try a continuity check on the secondary winding. If it's OK, it will show either zero ohms or a barely perceptible fraction of an ohm. If the needle doesn't move, the secondary winding is either burned out (an unlikely prospect), or one of its connections inside has corroded loose. A replacement transformer is then the obvious answer.

If the secondary is OK, you can run a similar test on the primary. To do this, leave the line fuse out, open the cutout box and find the primary wires, and then remove either one from its present connection. With the Handitester still set for LO ohms, again make a resistance measurement. If the primary winding is intact, it will register perhaps 25 ohms or so; if it is open, the meter needle won't move. Now you know positively if the transformer needs to be replaced or not. If it checks OK, reconnect the primary wire, close the cut out box, and replace the fuse.

Of course, it is assumed that the fuse in the transformer circuit is a good one, not that this is always the case! I once spent a frantic and thoroughly frustrating hour checking every inch of a simple bell circuit, until I had the inspiration to test the fuse. There was no reason for it to be open, but it was.

2) Loose connections. The nuts on many bell-ringing transformers do not hold very well, and are known to loosen if the unit is near a much-used door. Reinforce them with lock washers, or tie them down with strips of tape of any sort. Also inspect the screw terminals on the bells and buzzers.

The wire universally used for bell connections is No. 18 solid, with cotton or plastic insulation. Handle it carefully, as it has a tendency to break off if nicked or bent too sharply.

3) Push buttons. If the contacts are made of iron, as they are in many cheap buttons, they are bound to rust; if they're of brass they can still corrode and get dirty. If the batteries or transformer tested OK, unscrew a suspected button from the door frame and carefully pull it away so that you can get at the terminals. If they're rusty and pitted, don't be surprised. Scrape them off a bit, and short circuit them with the blade of a screwdriver. If the bell comes to life, you know what's at fault. •

In newer homes, a step-down transformer is permanently connected to the 115-volt line and supplies voltages between 6 and 16 for signalling devices. The transformer itself draws little current from the line.

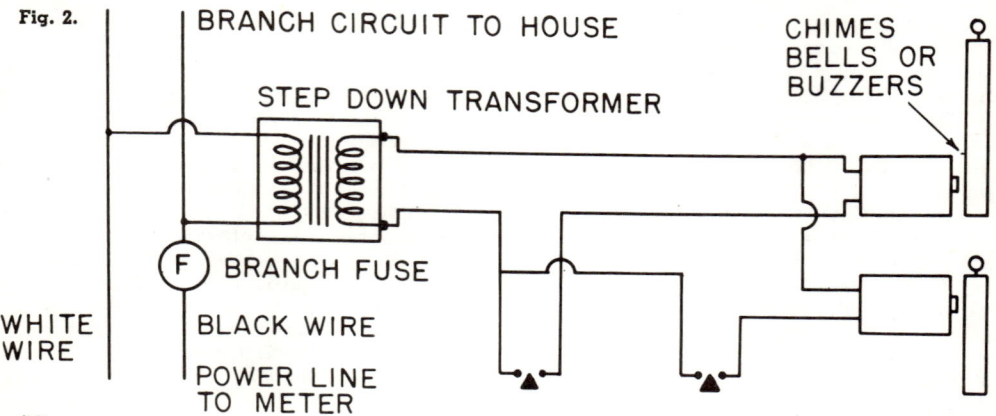

Fig. 2.

Coffee Maker

A COFFEE maker, like a toaster, is used only intermittently, and therefore enjoys long life. What usually requires replacement, during normal kitchen service, is the little light that comes on when the brewing process is completed. In most pots this is single-contact, miniature base lamp of the kind widely used as pilots in radio and television equipment. The method of getting at this light in a typical coffee maker is illustrated herewith.

Eventually, the main heating element might burn out. Putting in a new one is not always feasible, because of the sealed construction of the water chamber. In fact, it is often cheaper to buy a brand-new maker than to attempt to pry open the old one. •

Top right, turn pot over and remove knob of brew strength adjustment; tiny screw is on underside.

Above, remove any screws on the bottom plate and put these in a safe place, free from a loss hazard.

Center right, with cover removed carefully, thermostat mechanism, pilot light assembly are in view.

Right, fold bottom over. If bulb is faulty, replace with No. 47 lamp. Check connections for tightness, but don't bend or disturb the thermostat arms.

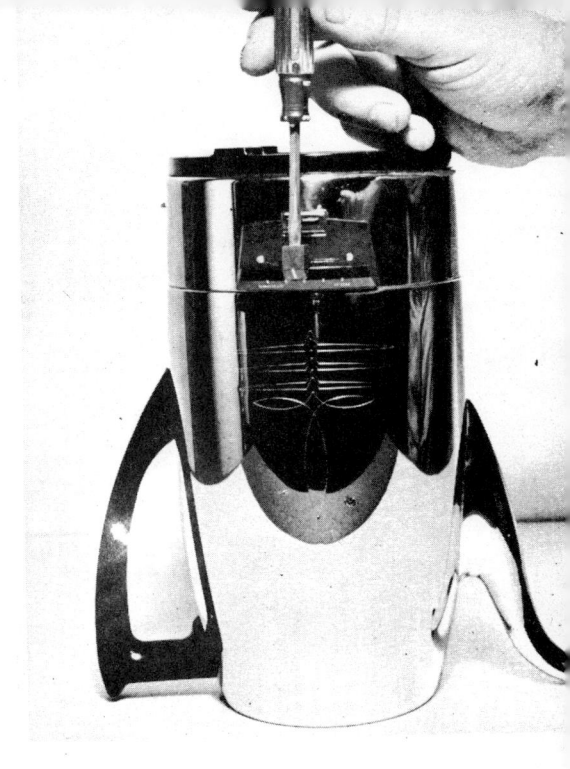

This practice more than any other puts an appliance out of commission. Neither the No. 18 stranded wire nor the molded attachment plug has the strength to withstand repeated yanking. Grasp the plug itself.

Don't Let a Cord Tie You into Knots

A mistreated connecting cord is often the cause of an appliance's breakdown. See that wires are well-insulated and don't abuse them

MANY common household appliances stop working unexpectedly not because of any internal breakdown but only because their connecting cords are stepped on, crushed, broken, cut, chewed by animals or otherwise mistreated. It seems rather obvious to say so, but an appliance can't operate if it doesn't receive power from the wall outlet.

Safety is strongly stressed by all elements of the electrical industry, but equipment manufacturers apparently have a blind spot when it comes to connecting cords. They produce appliances with strong, well-engineered bodies, and then, to save a few cents, they hook on flimsy cords with insulation so thin you can puncture it with a fingernail. Once installed, most appliances are not subject to physical abuse, but their loose cords often take a beating. Pay some attention to them and their life span will increase. And if you have to replace one, use heavily protected wire. •

When a plug is removed from its outlet, a knot often forms in the cord because of the curl in the wire. Open it before reinserting the plug. If knotted cord is yanked, it can sever the wire within the cord.

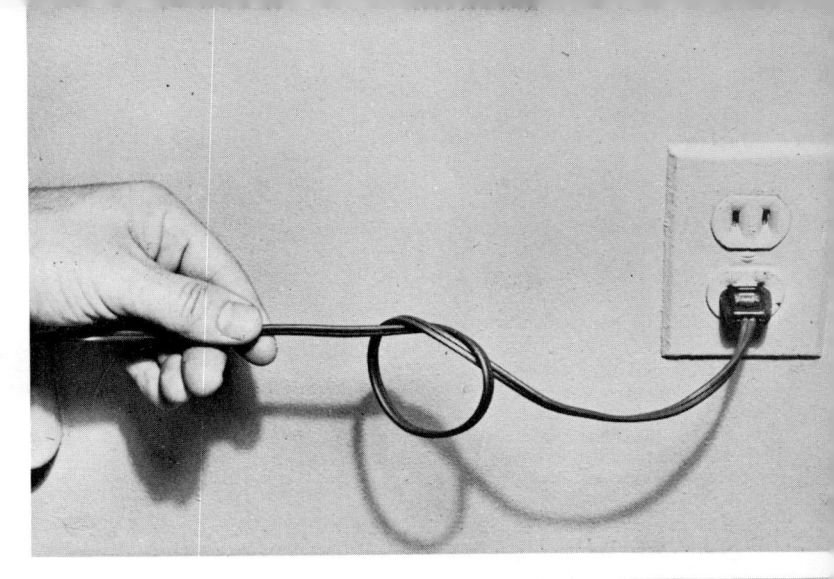

Some floor lamps provide no protection for the wire at point of emergence. Moving the lamp just a few times when cleaning the room will cause a short circuit. A layer of tape is an effective preventive measure.

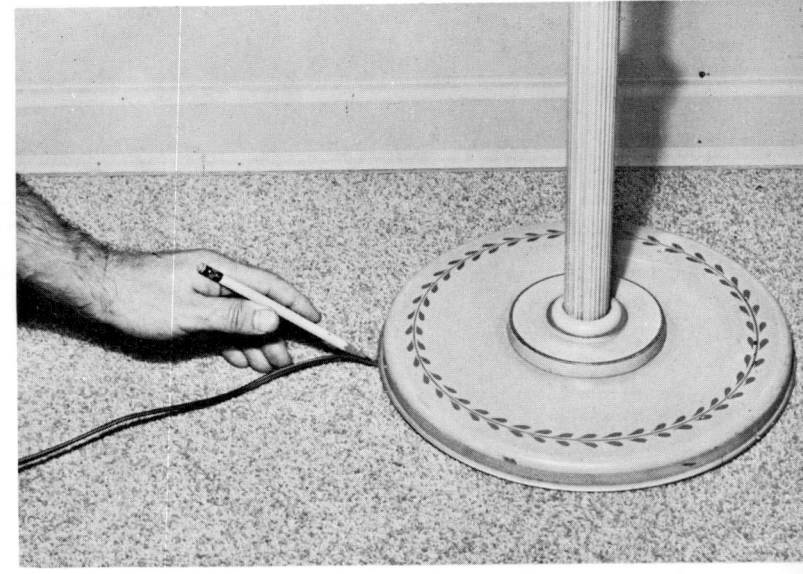

You can walk on a flexible cord only so many times before the insulation gives way. The bare wire is then both a shock and fire hazard, especially to the children. Place loose wires as near as possible to the wall.

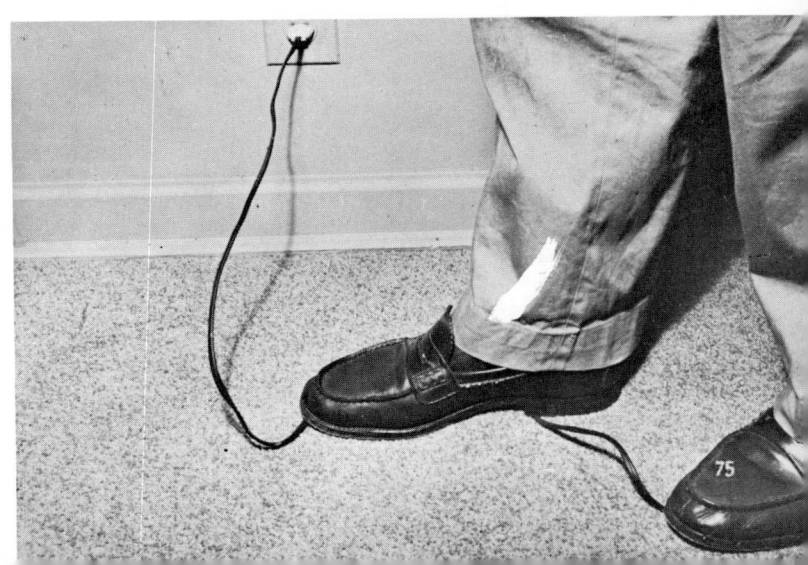

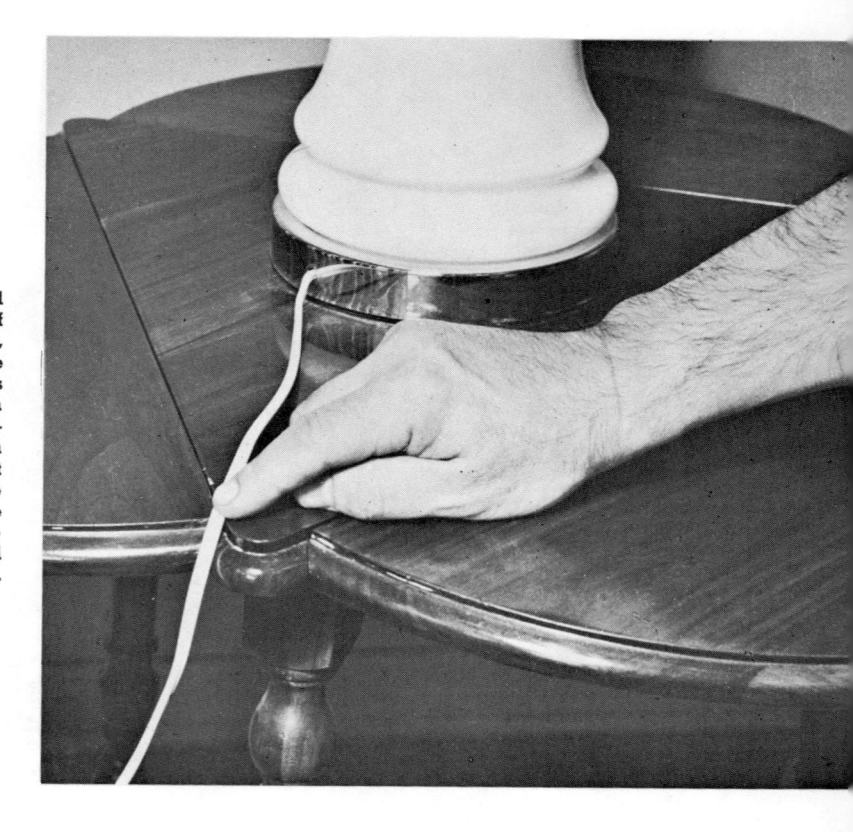

Don't let a cord get pinched in a section of a dropleaf table; if the wire is crushed, remove wall plug before touching it because strands sticking through insulation might well be "hot." Reinforce damaged section with layer of tape of nearest matching color. For white cord, white adhesive tape from the family medicine chest is ideal. Colored "Scotch" tape is also OK.

Vacuum cleaner cords take a particular beating because the appliance has to be moved around a lot. Try to keep the wire from under the wheels.

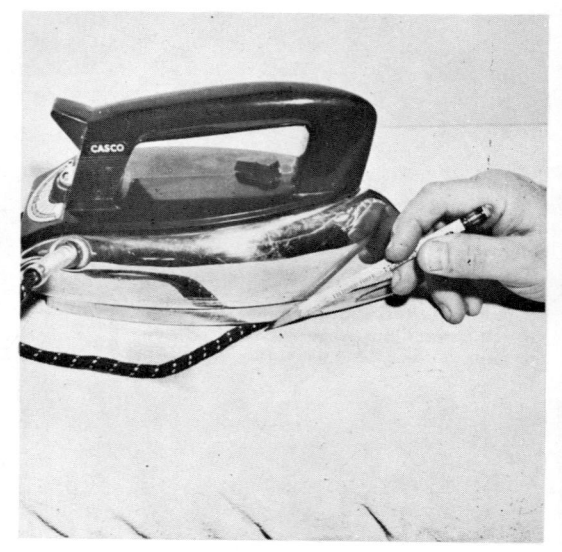

The sharp edge of a heavy pressing iron can do a lot of damage to the flexible cord. Keep the wire clear by hanging it over the back of ironing board.

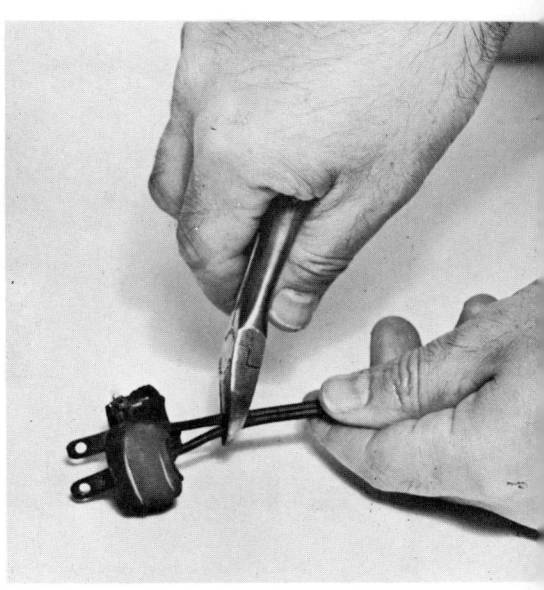

Many attachment plugs are made very cheaply of fragile compositions known in the trade as "molded mud." It is little wonder that they break up when stepped on or burn up when subjected to heavy current overloads. When buying replacement plugs, look for smooth, well-formed bodies, securely fastened prongs, terminal screws with broad heads, and fiber protection washers to fit over prongs and terminals, for your protection.

Never attempt to salvage a damaged plug by fastening the pieces together with tape or string. If the connecting cord is still in good condition, cut it off close to the plug, and discard the pieces of the latter. Use diagonal cutters, as above, or heavier "electrician's pliers." Examine wire carefully and trim off any sections near the end that show signs of crushing or bruising; these can be dangerous when you use the plug in the future.

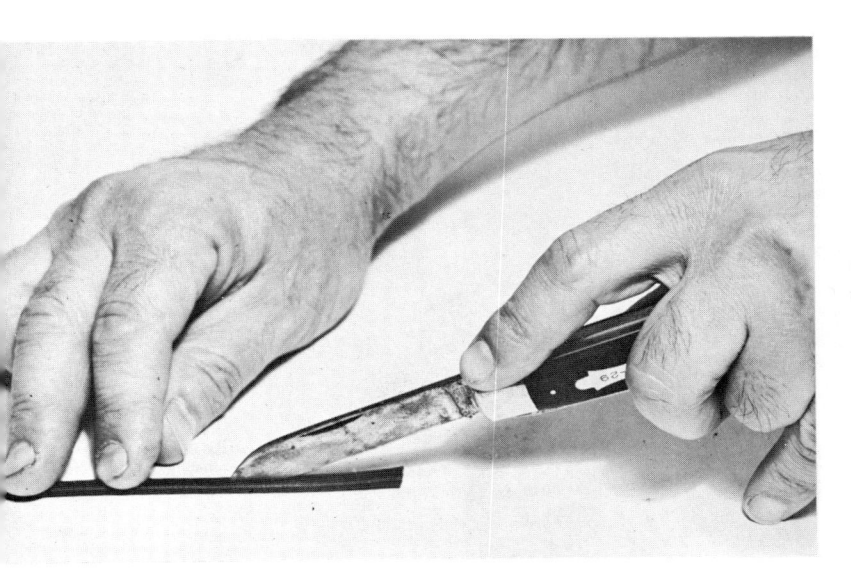

In preparing old cord for new attachment plug, first separate the ends a distance of about an inch and a half. Some cords require a sharp knife for this job; others in common use can be "zipped" apart without tools. Be especially careful not to damage insulation covering on each one of the individual wires.

Using the sharp edge of knife, pare off insulation on each end of wire a distance of about a half inch.

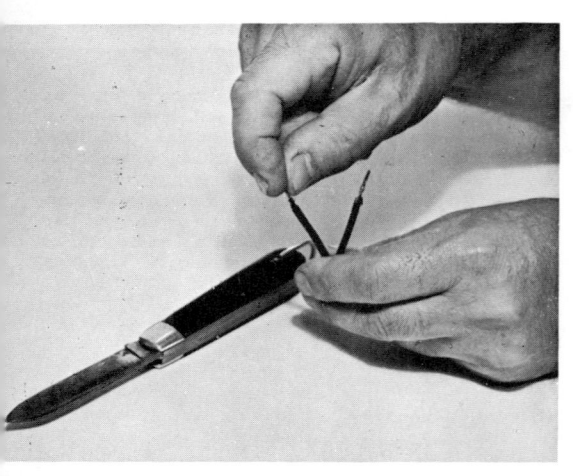

The next step in attaching a new plug is to twist together the loose strands at end of wires.

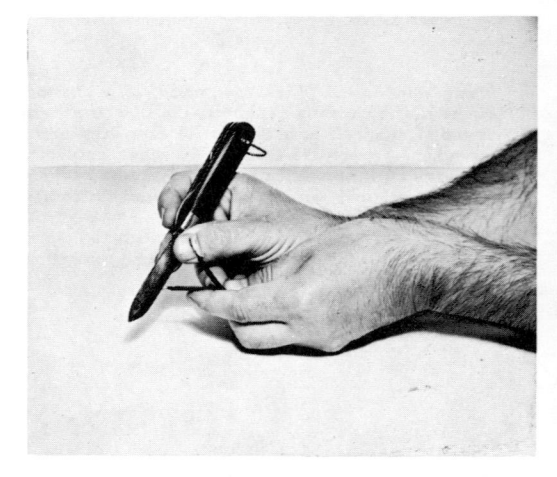

With back edge of knife, scrape end of wires clean and bright. Don't touch with fingers after this.

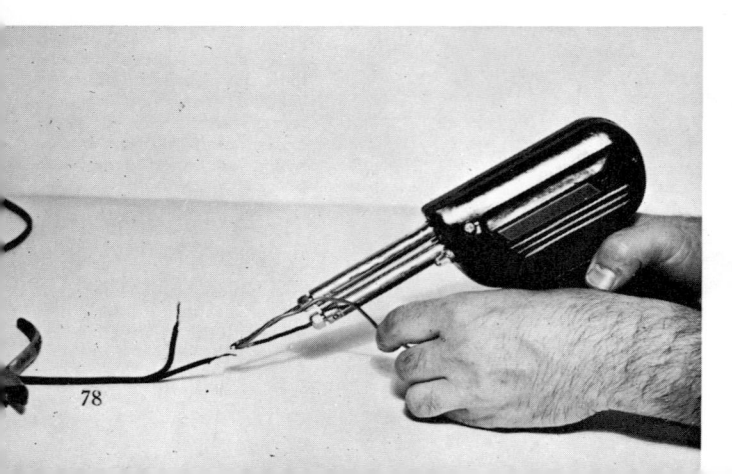

Apply thin coat of solder to each wire. This stiffens wires and makes them easier to fasten under the plug.

Immediately after soldering the loose end strands of the wire, poke the cord through the attachment plug. The one shown in the photo has a long neck or handle, which is very convenient for removing purposes.

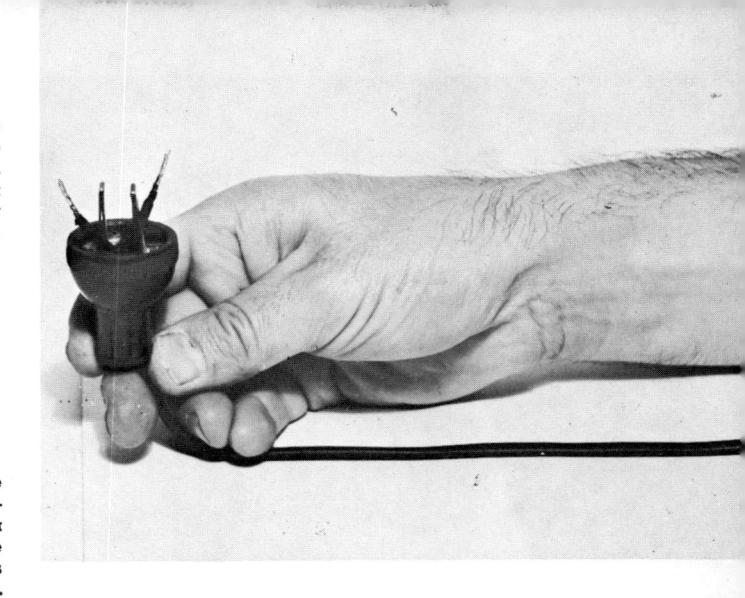

Starting from the pared ends of the wires, apply a layer of strong electrical tape back along the cord a distance equal to the length of the plug plus about a half inch. This tape will reinforce the insulation.

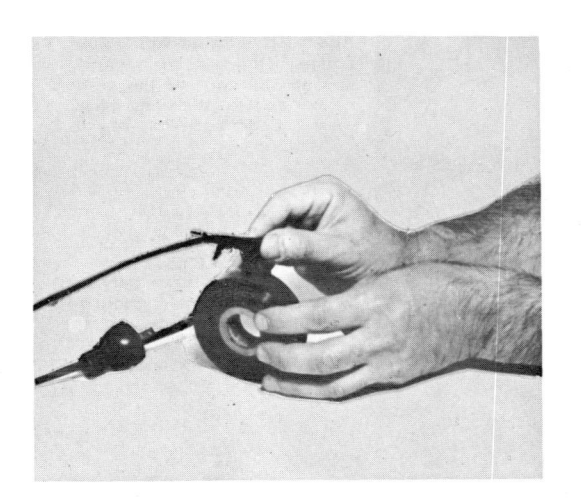

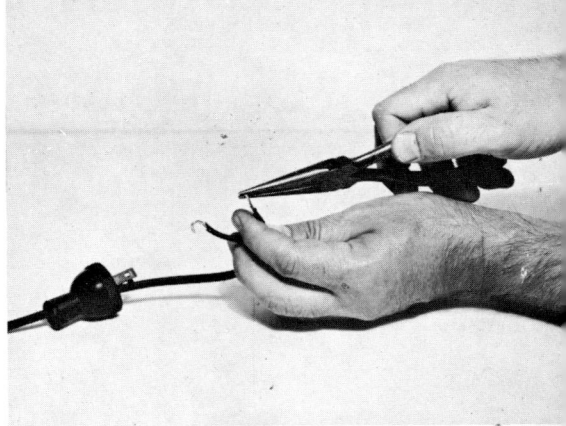

The wires are much easier to connect under the terminal screws of the attachment plug if they are first formed into U-shaped loops. Use long-nosed pliers to close the loops under screws and tighten.

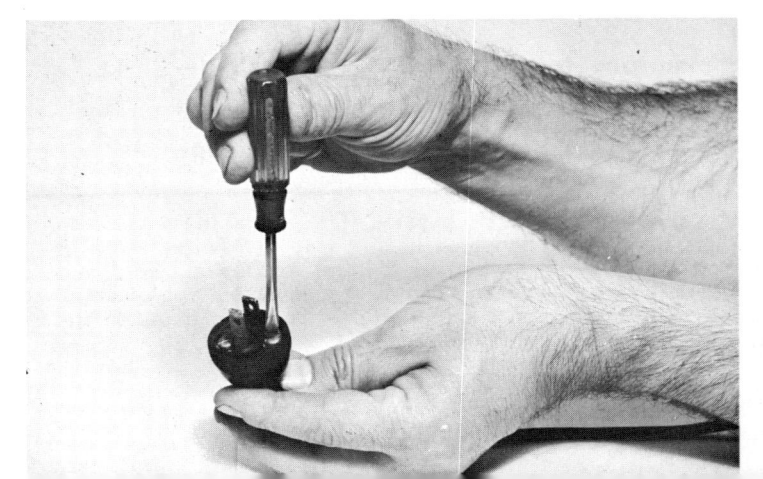

When securing the wires under the terminal screws, make certain that no loose strands stick out. These are often the cause of overheating at the plug or of blown-out fuses. If appliance is of portable type and plug is inserted and removed frequently, make periodic examination of terminals and tighten again if necessary.

Above, a sign of impending danger is the torn, worn insulation on the cord at the point it rubs against the lamp base. New cord makes neatest repair.

An old unused lamp may be restored to service by following simple directions in replacing the cord. Often, that's all there is wrong with lamp.

Re-cording a Lamp

The extent of the damage to your present cord will determine whether or not it needs replacement; with luck all you may need to repair it is a piece of electrician's tape

THE flexible cords of table and floor lamps usually show the first signs of wear at the point where they emerge from the base. If there is any leeway in the wire, sometimes it can be pushed into or pulled out of its hole, taped over, and then put back into place. If the rest of the cord is also damaged in any way, it's better sense in most cases to take out the old cord and put in a completely new one. A typical job on a table lamp is shown in detail in the photo sequence. •

Remove the shade for safekeeping; it's usually held in place with a decorative nut or stud, which unscrews readily. Following this, obviously, the bulb is removed and then actual repair work begins.

Next, snip off the old wire at the base of the lamp. Save good sections for other uses. Below right, to disassemble socket look for word "press" on shell near switch. Insert blade of small screwdriver, twist slightly, then press end of socket downward. This opens the toothed joint between the halves of lamp socket.

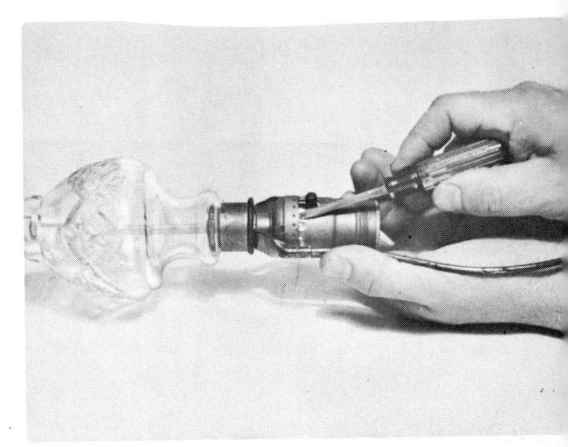

Next, remove old section of wire, inspect and clean socket, and tighten small screws inside shell as needed.

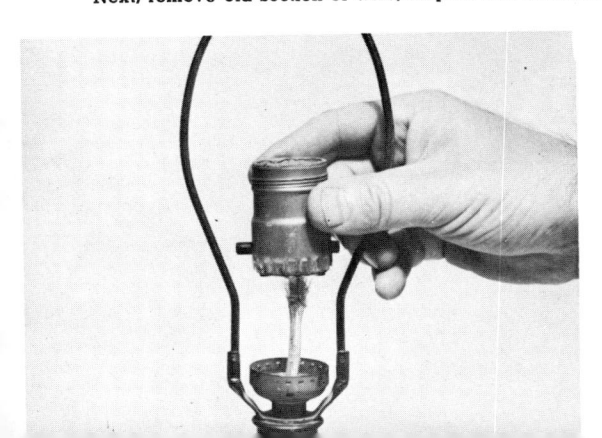

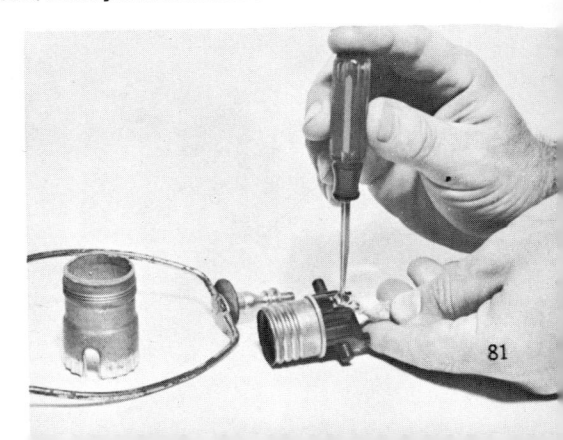

Next, check fit of socket and shade holder on neck of lamp; twist to right to tighten. Then, below right, feed the length of the new wire through the fixed part of the socket, down through base of the lamp.

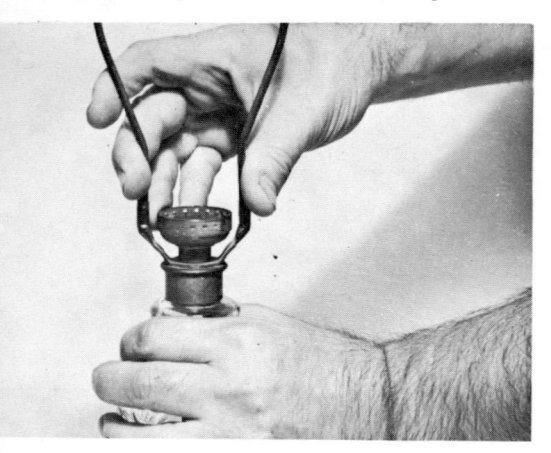

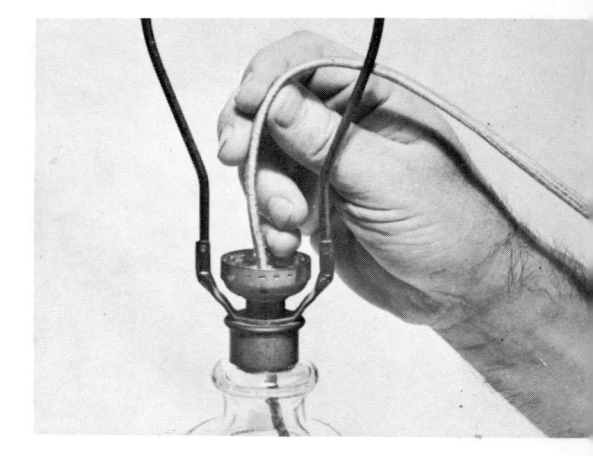

Separate ends of new wire, remove insulation, scrape clean and tighten wires under two screws of the socket shell. Then (below right) from the bottom pull wire down carefully till socket is in position.

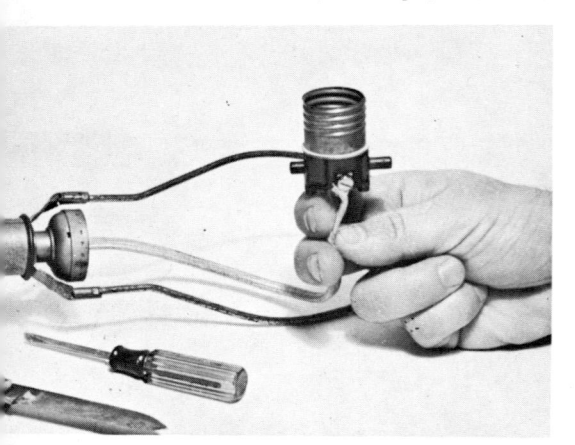

Now snap other section of socket back into position; start it at a slight angle and then squeeze along the bottom. Finally, protect new wire where it passes through base with ordinary white adhesive tape.

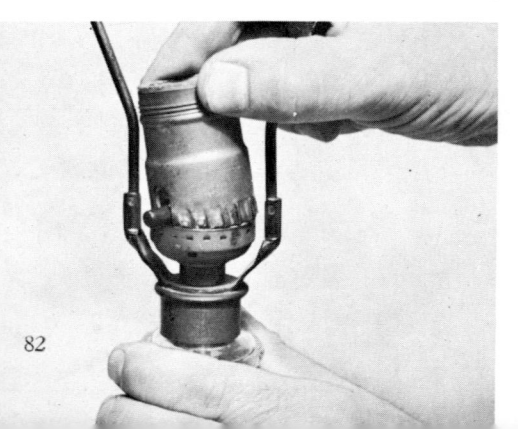

Bowl Heaters

Make a habit of testing your heater often to prevent accidents

Check for "grounding" by connecting Handitester to frame, each attachment plug in turn.

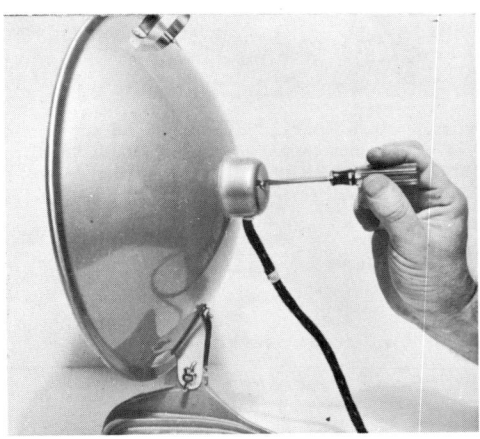

To get at connections to heating element, remove screw through the cap on back of heater's frame.

Check connections for tightness, insulation for breaks. Repair wire by twisting ends together.

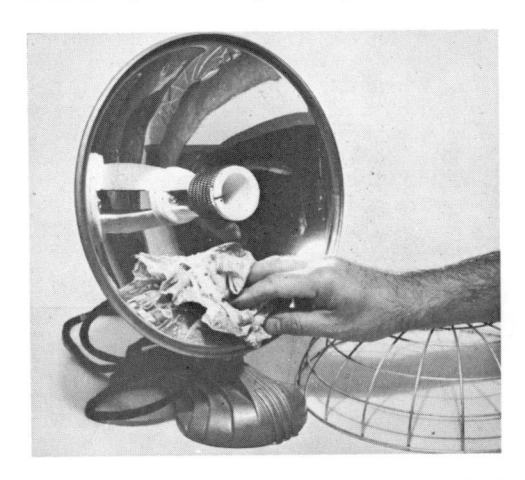

Effectiveness of heater depends greatly on shininess of reflector. Remove the line plug to clean.

A PORTABLE electric heater is often used in a bathroom or bedroom. Because people are likely to brush against it with bare limbs, it should be checked carefully and frequently for a "hot" frame, a condition resulting from accidental contact between the metal body and any part of the power circuit. This can be very dangerous, as explained in the section entitled "Play It Safe!"

For picture purposes, I bought a brand new heater. When I set up the Handitester for a simulated grounding test, I was astonished to see and hear the meter needle bang over to low ohms, indicating an actual ground! When I took off the end cap and examined the wiring, I discovered that the single screw holding the resistance wire element was rubbing through the insulation of one wire of the flexible cord. I fixed that in a hurry with a bit of tape. •

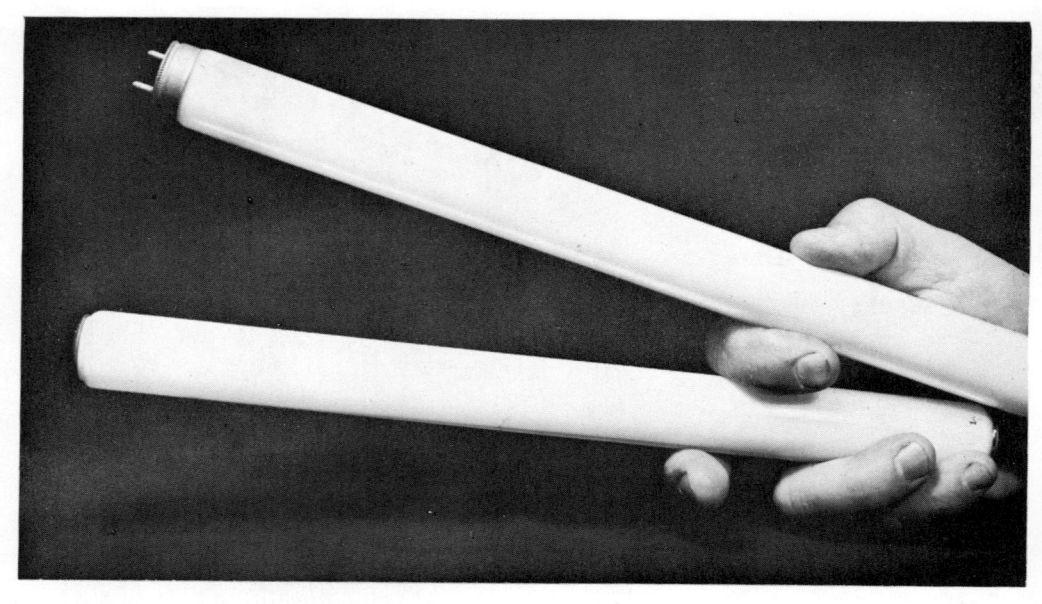

Don't be fooled . . . not all tubular lamps are fluorescents. Here are two of identical size and appearance, but only the top one is a fluorescent, the tip-off being the double pin connectors at each end. The lower lamp is an incandescent, and has only one metal connector at each end, as shown in picture above.

Let There Be Light!

Here is a brief description of the operation and care of the two types of lamps used today—incandescent and fluorescent

THE electric lights commonly used in homes and offices are of two general types: incandescent and fluorescent. The incandescent lamp, invented by Thomas A. Edison in 1879, is a very simple thing. It consists of a wire sealed in a glass lamp, from which the air has been removed or replaced by a mixture of certain inert gases. The wire offers resistance to the flow of electricity. The friction of the electrons in pushing their way through raises the temperature of the wire to the point where it glows or "incandesces." The higher the temperature, the whiter the light.

Tungsten is the metal now universally used for incandescent lamp filaments. It burns at about 5000 degrees Fahrenheit, a fantastic temperature higher than that of any other artificial heat ordinarily encountered by man. At this temperature, asbestos or fire brick would melt like candle wax under a match. Why doesn't the tungsten wire consume itself? Because there is no air . . . that is, oxygen . . . in the bulb to support combustion, or burning.

In lamps smaller than about the 50-watt size, the air in the glass envelope or bulb is merely pumped out, leaving a vacuum or "nothing" inside. In most larger lamps, a mixture of nitrogen and argon is pumped in following the evacuation of the air. The purpose of these gases is to introduce some slight pressure on the filament and to retard evaporation of the tungsten. The filament not only lasts longer than it would in a plain vacuum, but during its useful life it can be burned at a higher temperature. This means better, brighter light.

In manufacture, the gas mixture is introduced at slightly under normal atmospheric pressure. The internal pressure tends to rise when the lamp is on, and in the case of lamps burning very brightly it goes a little *above* atmospheric pressure. This explains why the very brilliant lamps used in movie and still projectors, and in spotlights, often develop blisters and bulges. The intense heat of the filament softens the glass, and the rising gas pressure inside forces it outward. A projection

Will it pop out? Probably not for quite a while. Bulge in side of 300-watt projector lamp is due to combination of high filament temperature and inside gas pressure. Blackening is also natural.

In most straight fluorescent fixtures, the starter is accessible only after the lamp is removed. It is not screwed in, but is held by contact springs. A quarter turn will serve to loosen or lighten it.

bulb that has been used a long time takes on a really grotesque appearance.

Eventually, the filament of an incandescent lamp consumes itself. The metal evaporates to the point of such thinness that it simply burns open. Any lamp burns up almost instantly if the glass envelope is broken. The super-heated tungsten combines with the oxygen of the air and goes pfft!

If heat rather than light is wanted from an incandescent lamp, it is operated at a lower than normal temperature. In this class is the "infrared" lamp, which is widely used for the treatment of muscular pains and aches.

If a great deal of light is wanted, a tungsten lamp is operated at higher than normal temperature. Of course, its life is thereby shortened, and this is the price paid for the increased brilliance. The popular "Photoflood" lamps used in picture-making are actually 64-volt bulbs operated on 115 volts. Their rated life is about six hours, compared with about 750 hours for a regular 115-volt bulb.

When a lamp fails to light, and another lamp tried in the same socket does light, it obviously has expired. Every home should have a supply of spares. It's possible to double-check a lamp by running a continuity test on it, but this is rather pointless. It takes less time to screw in a new lamp.

There are only a few simple precautions to observe in using incandescent lamps, and these relate mainly to their high operating temperature. Don't let paper, parchment, silk or other cloth shades come in direct contact with the glass. The material can readily char, and under some circumstances will actually burst into flames. Don't touch a hot bulb with your bare hands. If you don't want to wait until it cools off, grasp it with a handkerchief or a pot holder. Avoid splashing water on a bare bulb; the glass might implode (get that, *implode*) and scatter fragments all over the room.

DO keep lamps clean and dust-free by wiping them occasionally, when cool, with a very slightly dampened cloth. Bulbs inside decorative globes or fixtures are often neglected in this respect and gradually become dim. *Internal* blackening is another matter, and cannot be avoided. It is the natural result of gradual evaporation of the tungsten filament. Sometimes the blackening reduces the light output to the point where it is more economical to replace the bulb, even though it still lights, than to continue to use it.

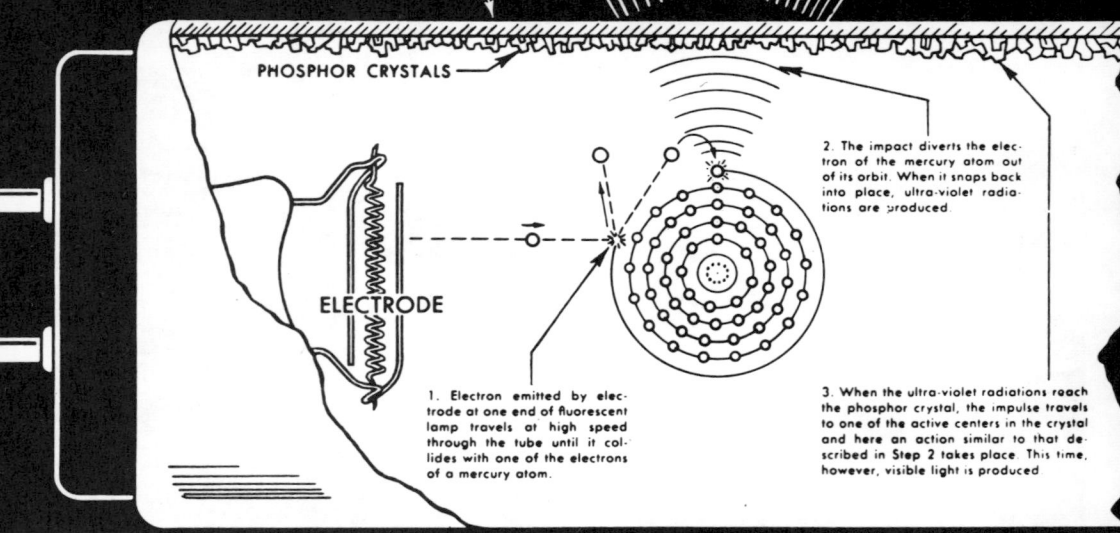

GLASS OF TUBE **VISIBLE LIGHT**

PHOSPHOR CRYSTALS

2. The impact diverts the electron of the mercury atom out of its orbit. When it snaps back into place, ultra-violet radiations are produced.

ELECTRODE

1. Electron emitted by electrode at one end of fluorescent lamp travels at high speed through the tube until it collides with one of the electrons of a mercury atom.

3. When the ultra-violet radiations reach the phosphor crystal, the impulse travels to one of the active centers in the crystal and here an action similar to that described in Step 2 takes place. This time, however, visible light is produced.

Westinghouse Electric Corporation

According to scientists, electrons inside fluorescent lamp release ultraviolet radiation from mercury.

Fluorescents Are Different

In a filament lamp, electric current flows through a solid tungsten wire and heats it to incandescence. In a fluorescent lamp, the two electrodes which are connected to the power line are completely separated inside a long glass tube. The latter contains a small drop of mercury, and its inner surface is coated with a chemical that has the property of glowing or "fluorescing" when struck by ultraviolet light, which itself is not visible to the human eye. Under the proper conditions, electrons flow back and forth between the end electrodes under the impetus of the line voltage. The theory is that they strike atoms of the mercury and release the ultraviolet radiation, which in turn impinges on the chemical coating and causes it to fluoresce.

The color of the light produced by flourescents depends on the chemicals or "phosphors" used as the coating. While white is the most usual color (actually, white is not a color, but a combination of all colors), it is also just as easy to obtain blue, orange, green, blue-white, yellow-pink, deep red and ultra-blue.

The electron-emitting electrode in each end of the tube is called a "cathode." In the

When removing or inserting lamp, make sure pins at both ends drop straight into slots in sockets; then twist quarter turn. Don't force into place.

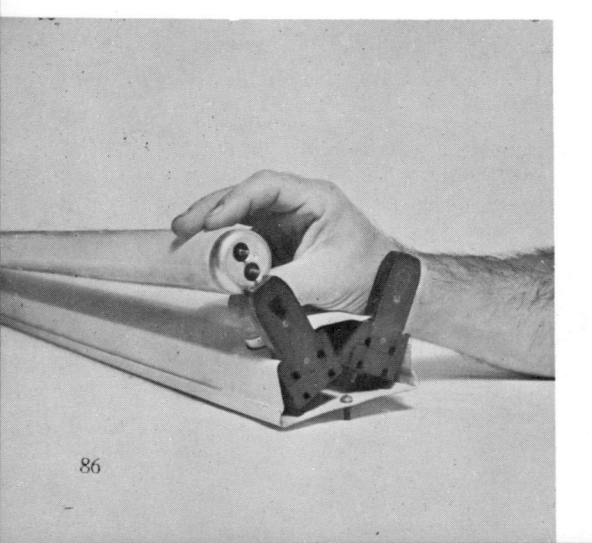

If you suspect that the cathode wire is burned out, a continuity check with Handitester will give the answer. However, filament wires rarely burn out.

86

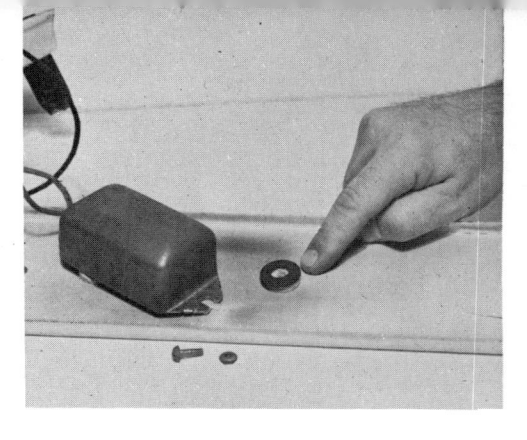

Annoying humming sound heard from fluorescent lamps is from vibration of core of ballasts. Remount the ballasts on large fiber or leather washers.

After installing fiber washers, tighten screws of ballasts only enough to assure grip. If you compress them too much, they won't silence ballasts.

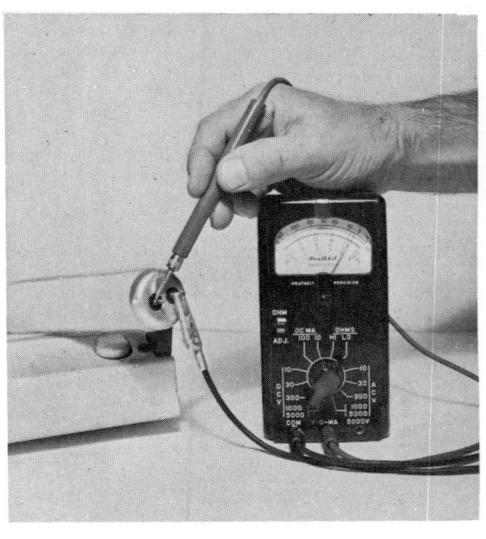

If new starter and new lamp don't produce light, check the ballast with your Handitester for continuity. The normal reading is around 30 ohms.

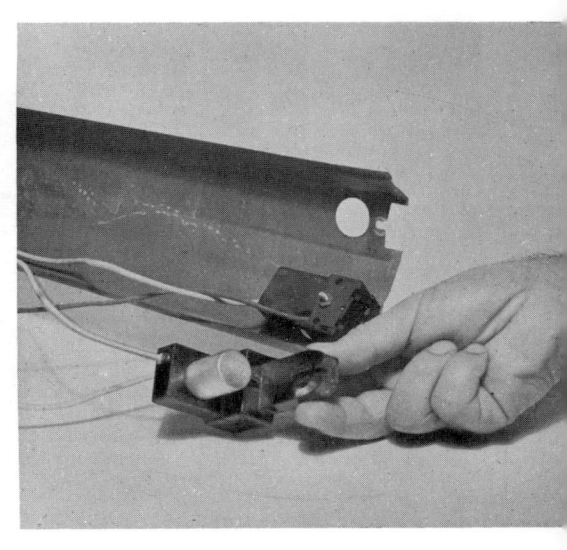

Receptacle for starter and socket for end of lamp are often combined. If they break from being forced, it's a simple matter to replace them.

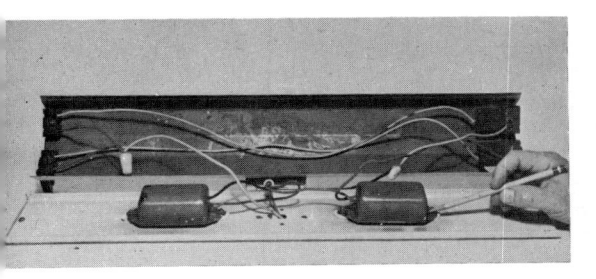

Pencil points to one of two ballasts concealed inside body of fluorescent fixture. When the latter is opened, it is easy to trace wiring.

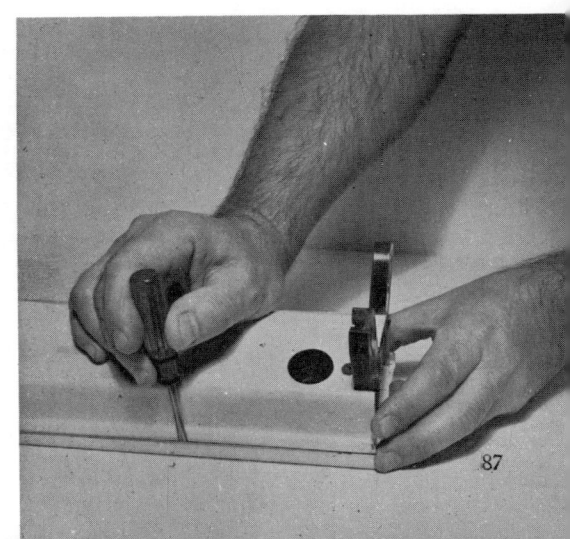

Standard two-lamp fluorescent fixture is usually snap-assembled. To take apart, separate body from base with thin screwdriver, squeeze body slightly.

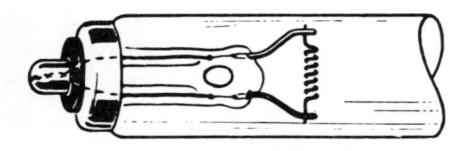

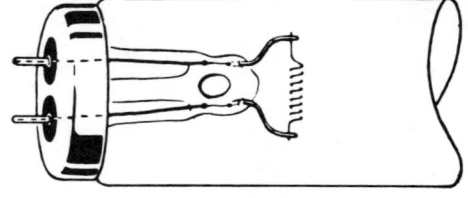

HOT CATHODES

General Electric Company

These are common types of hot cathodes used in fluorescents. In preheat cathode, current flows first through filament, just as in incandescent lamp, and then is cut off. In instant-start cathode, the electrons are pulled off the surface by high operating voltage. While the instant-start type has a filament, its ends are short circuited in the stem and only one external connection is needed for it.

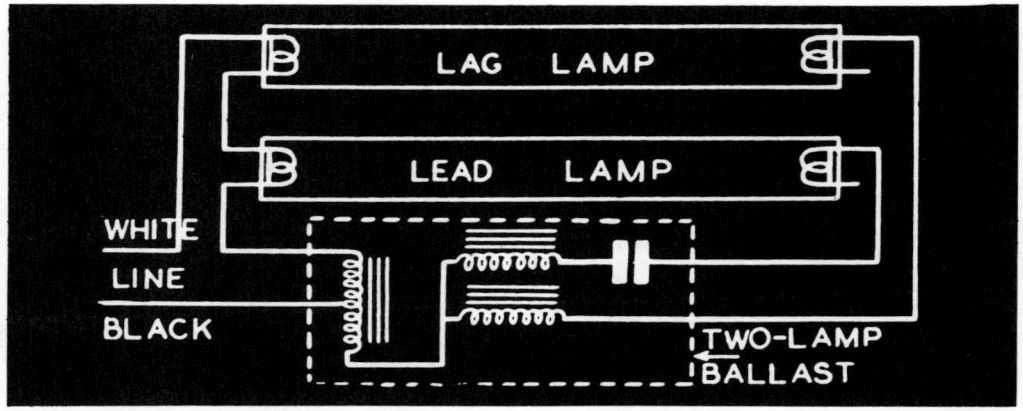

INSTANT START SLIMLINE TYPE

PREHEAT TYPE

Westinghouse Electric Corporation

Above is a diagram of a typical two-lamp instant-start fluorescent. The ballast in this type of lamp contains a step-up transformer for boosting line voltage plus a capacitor for improving power factor.

fluorescents in most common use, this is a coiled tungsten wire filament, coated with a chemical that gives off electrons freely when heated. The tungsten filament does not contribute any illumination directly. Two auxiliary devices are needed to make the lamp work: a "starter" and a "ballast." In a basic lamp, the filaments, the ballast and the starter are connected in simple series. When the lamp switch is turned on, current flows through all the elements. The filaments can be seen to glow slowly. After a second or two, the contacts inside the starter snap open. This cuts off the current to the filaments, and at the same time causes the ballast to develop a momentarily high-voltage "kick." Surging through the lamp, this voltage starts acting on the electrons already loosened from the hot cathodes, and the double cycle previously described gets under way. One side of the AC power line remains connected to one terminal only of one cathode; the other side of the power line goes to the ballast, which in turn connects to one terminal only of the second cathode. The filaments themselves are no longer incandescent. The electrons are pulled off their surfaces by the mere attraction of the voltage between the cathodes.

The ballast is a coil of fine wire on an iron core. It looks exactly like the "choke" coils found in radio and television sets. Once the arc inside the lamp is struck, the ballast acts to limit the current flow between the cathodes within prescribed values for each particular size and type of lamp. Ballasts generally have long life, but they carry current and are therefore susceptible to eventual failure.

Some lamps have "instant" cathodes which do not require pre-heating. They do require much higher starting voltages to jar the electrons loose. No starter is needed, as the first pulse of voltage is enough to start the electrons on their way.

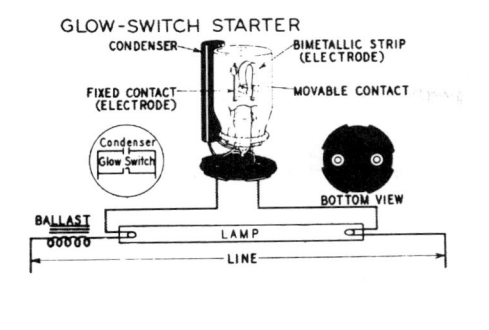

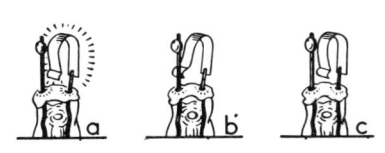

GLOW-SWITCH STARTER

[Diagram labels: CONDENSER, BIMETALLIC STRIP (ELECTRODE), FIXED CONTACT (ELECTRODE), MOVABLE CONTACT, Condenser, Glow Switch, BALLAST, LAMP, LINE, BOTTOM VIEW]

WATCH DOG STARTER

[Diagram labels: RESET BUTTON (PROJECTS THROUGH STARTER CAN), CONDENSER, SWITCH CONTACT, LOCK-OUT SPRING, STANDARD GLOW SWITCH, THERMAL RELEASE ELEMENT, BIMETALLIC STRIP HEATER COIL, CONDENSER, GLOW SWITCH, SPRING, LOCK-OUT SWITCH, BALLAST, LAMP, LINE, BOTTOM VIEW]

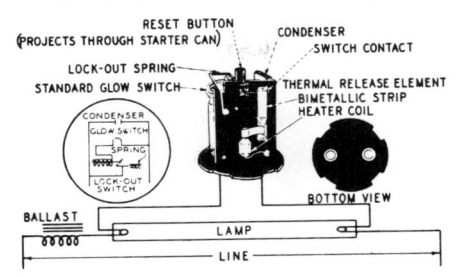

General Electric Watch Dog Manual Reset Starters use glow switch principle. During normal starting switch functions as described under illustration at left. This starter has an added feature which consists of a wire-coil heater element actuating a bimetallic arm which serves as a latch to hold a second switch in a normal closed position. When a lamp is deactivated or will not start after blinking on and off, enough heat is developed by intermittent flow of cathode preheating current so that latch pulls away and releases second switch.

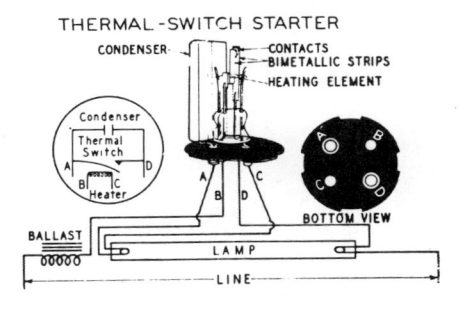

[Figure showing three stages labeled a, b, c]

In the glow-switch starter pictured above, glass bulb is filled with neon or argon, depending on lamp voltage. On starting, voltage at starter is sufficient to produce a glow discharge between U-shaped bimetallic strip and fixed contact or center electrode (a). Heat from glow actuates bimetallic strip, contacts close and cathode preheating begins (b). This shorts out glow discharge, bimetal cools and shortly the contacts open (c).

At right is a diagram of a thermal-switch starter. On starting, the ballast, starter heating element and lamp cathodes are all in a series across the line since contacts of thermal-switch starters are normally closed. Cathode preheating current thus also heats the bimetallic strip in the starter and the contacts open. The inductive kick then starts the lamp itself with the normal operating current thereafter holding thermal switch (inset) open.

THERMAL-SWITCH STARTER

[Diagram labels: CONDENSER, CONTACTS, BIMETALLIC STRIPS, HEATING ELEMENT, Condenser, Thermal Switch, Heater, BALLAST, LAMP, LINE, BOTTOM VIEW]

Unlike incandescent lamps, which will light under almost any conditions of line voltage, temperature and humidity, fluorescents are known to be somewhat sensitive in these respects. Their susceptibility to cold, especially, is not too generally appreciated, and is the reason for many mysterious cases of irregular or unsatisfactory operation. In an unheated garage or a partially heated basement, lamps sometimes don't strike at all in winter weather, but keep blinking on and off.

If a flourescent fixture has been working properly over a period of time, and then either refuses to start or works fitfully, either the starter or the lamp itself might be at the end of its useful life. Always try a new starter first, as it's much cheaper than a new lamp. If the trouble continues, you have no choice but to try a new lamp.

If the ends of a lamp remain lighted steadily, with no sign of the tube striking for its full length, the strong likelihood is that the starter contacts have welded shut, or possibly a short circuit has developed in the little capacitor which is included in some starters to eliminate radio interference.

The filament wires of cathodes rarely burn out because they are heated to full incandescence for only a few seconds during the starting period. However, it is easy to test them with any continuity checker.

A new lamp may show swirling, spiraling, snaking or fluttering effects when first turned on, but usually clears up after it is well warmed up or has been turned on and off a few times. An old lamp sometimes starts swirling violently, and then resumes clear operation without warning. This is probably due to shifting distribution of the phosphors on the inside of the glass. •

Silent Switch Lets Baby Sleep

A mercury-type light switch is easily installed as a replacement for noisy controls—it's perfect for bedroom or bath

THE baby has finally fallen asleep, and with an inward sigh of relief you tiptoe out of the nursery. You go into your own bedroom, which is probably adjacent, and turn on the light so that you won't trip over the furniture. That does it.

"Yahhhh!" The click of the switch, sounding like the report of a .22 in the quiet of the house, has awakened the little darling, and you have to spend another five minutes quieting him/her down again.

There's really no need at all to suffer this sort of thing. For less than a dollar apiece you can buy absolutely silent toggle switches of the mercury type. These are regarded by some parents as the greatest boon since disposable diapers. Removing an old switch and installing a silent one is a simple screwdriver operation. It will take you about ten minutes to do the first switch and probably five for the second. The accompanying series of pictures shows how.

The utility of mercury switches is not restricted to households with children, of course. Plenty of adults of all ages are light sleepers and are disturbed by the short but sharp snap of ordinary switches. An especially important location for a silent switch is the bathroom. It enables a person to make a nocturnal visit to the latter without awakening another occupant of the same bedroom. (See page 93). •

1: Wait! Before you reach for that screwdriver to open up the old switch, remember to pull the fuse that controls the circuit. If this darkens the room, have a flashlight handy, or do the job during daylight when you can see well.

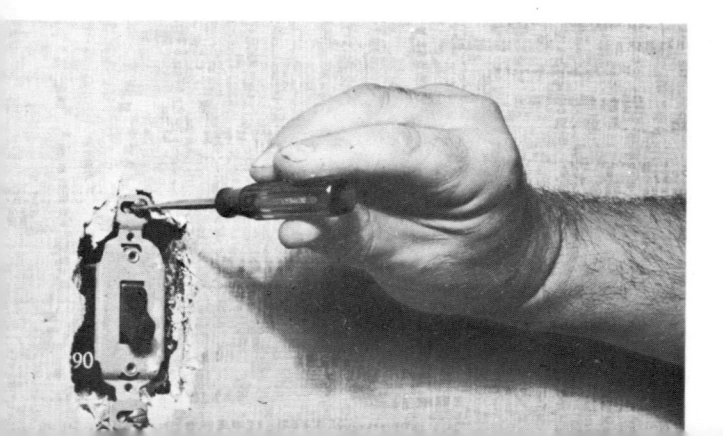

2: With the switch cover plate off, two more screws come into sight. These hold the "plaster ears" of the switch body to the wall box. They are often corroded, and may require a drop of penetrating oil before they come out.

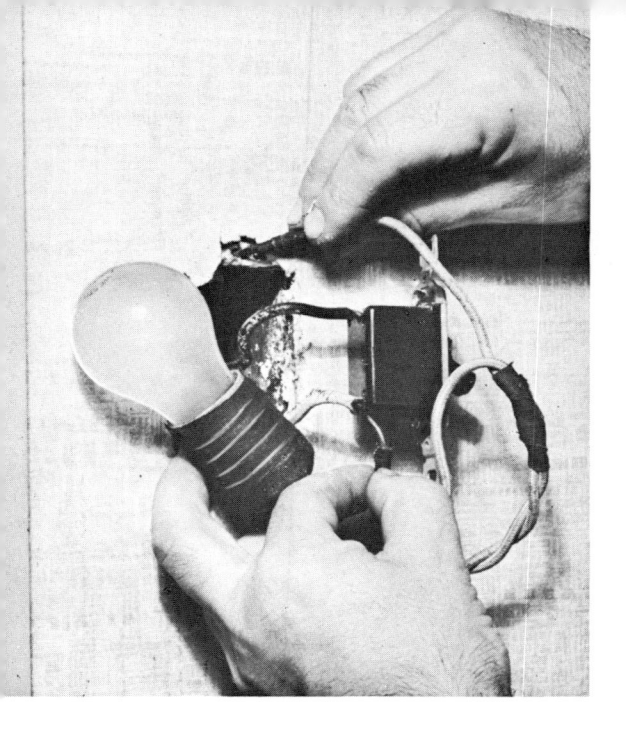

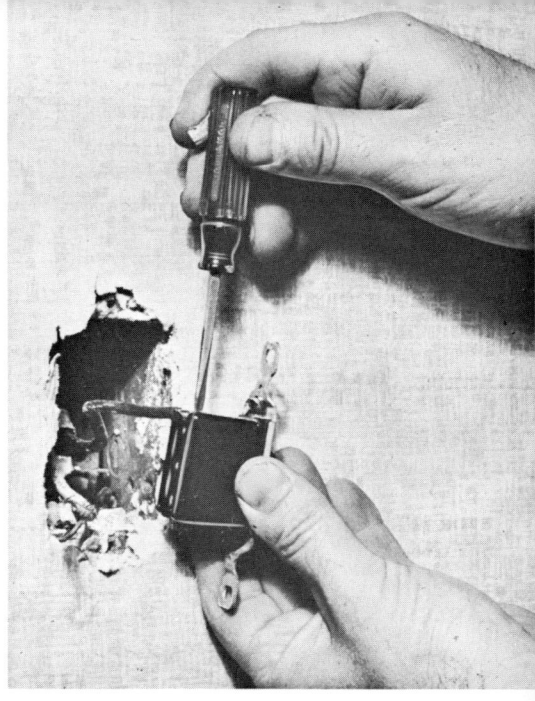

3: To make sure wires are dead after removing fuse, apply leads of a Lightester (see page 32) to switch terminals, and from the metal wall box to each of the terminals in turn. Safety first will pay off.

4: Pull switch out slowly (connecting wires are usually fairly stiff) and remove leads from under terminal screws; save switch for possible future use as a replacement in the basement or kitchen.

5: The wall box invariably has lots of dirt and bits of plaster in it. Clean this out with a brush while you're at it. By the way, an old paint brush will come in handy as a useful odd-job cleaning tool.

6: Clean the bared ends of the wires with the back edge of a pocket knife or use a small piece of emery cloth. A clean and bare wire is easiest to work with and assures you proper contact.

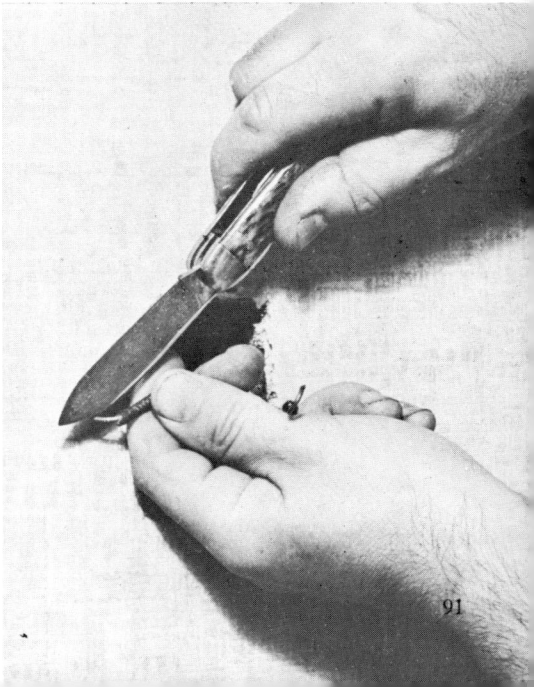

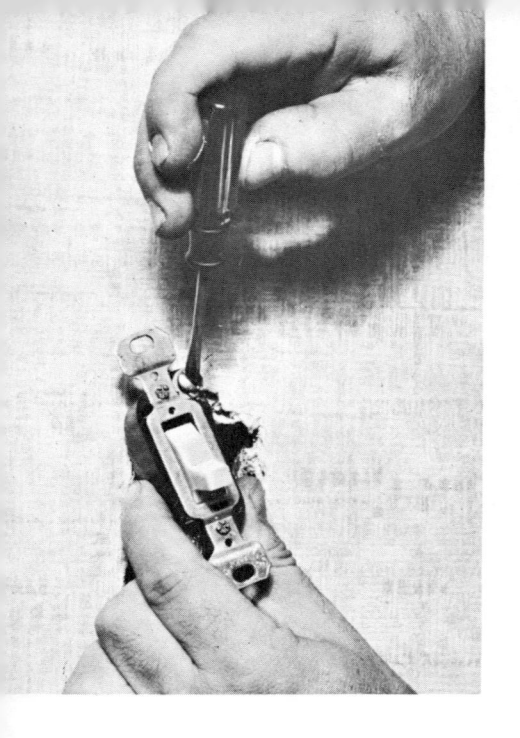

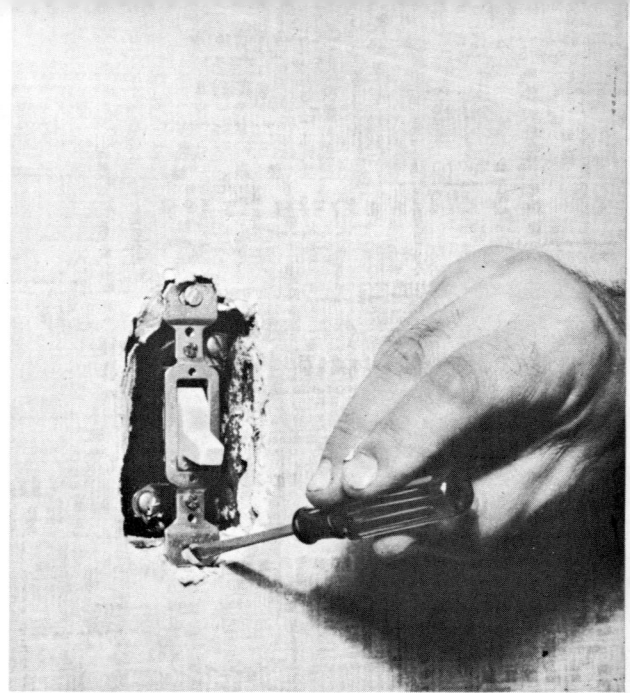

7: The next step is to fasten the cleaned ends of the wires to the terminals of the mercury switch; at this point be sure the end marked TOP is positioned that way before attaching the switch.

8: With wires attached to the mercury switch, push wires carefully back into box and press new switch gently into position. Then pass screws through "ears" of switch, center vertically, and tighten.

9: Using the plate from the previous switch, reassemble with the original screws; a plastic shield overlapping the plate helps keep fingerprints off the wall; it's a good investment.

10: Easy does it. The light goes on and off almost magically as mercury switch is flipped up or down. With no springs to wear out, this type of switch will last indefinitely; they're tops for bedrooms, bath.

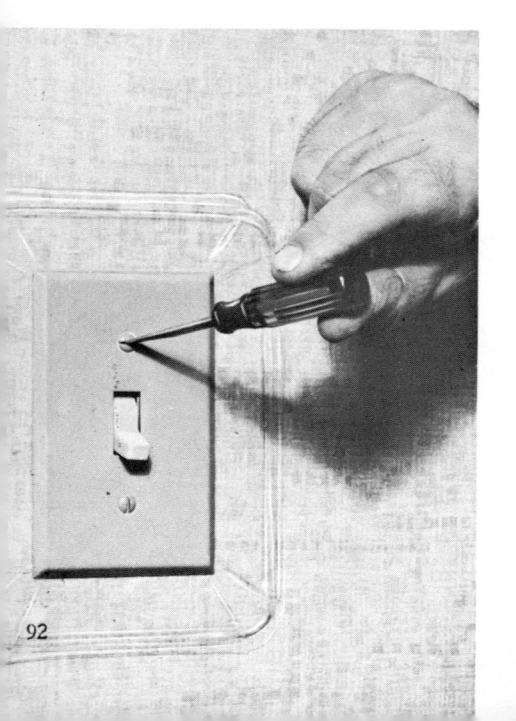

92

Another type of light control that is enjoying new favor among homeowners is the "tap switch." It has a single large center button, which responds to only very light pressure. Tap it once, and the light goes on; merely brush a finger against it, and the light goes off. Wallpaper behind transparent plastic shield makes the tap switch nice addition to any room.

Right: Provided with the tap switch is a cardboard template that can be painted to match the wall or used as a cutting guide for a scrap piece of wallpaper if the room is papered. Position the paper over the old switch plate so that the pattern matches the area around the switch as closely as possible. Then use a sharp knife to carefully cut out hole in the center.

Below: Tap switch, at right, fits standard wall boxes. Slots in ears permit accurate vertical positioning. At the left is the transparent plastic cover plate, with a piece of wall paper inserted on the inside. After the switch itself is wired and mounted in its box, the cover plate is merely pressed into position over the center button and you'll have task all done.

Outlet in garage was on loose flexible cord coming out of switch box. Insulation soon wore away. Owner decided to install a sturdy duplex receptacle on the wall, connected by BX cable.

After main switch was turned off, switch plate was loosened and flexible wires removed. New wire in BX will connect to exactly same points.

BX clamp was placed in knock-out hole in box through which flexible wire passed previously.

Extending an Outlet

EXTENDING a power outlet or replacing an unsatisfactory one is a common electrical job in homes, garages and shops. The accompanying picture sequence shows a typical Sunday-morning operation of this kind on a garage receptacle that was becoming dangerous. Flexible armored cable ("BX") is illustrated, but exactly the same technique is used for thin-wall conduit or non-metallic cable.

Caution: Kill the circuit first by opening the main switch or the circuit fuse.

94

Holes for fastening screws of box were made in cement wall with 3/16" star drill and hammer.

Box for receptacle was mounted with two No. 10 wood screws, securely anchored in lead plugs.

Fiber-and-lead screw anchors were pushed into holes; these give a solid foundation for box.

Short length of BX between switch and new box is connected to duplex receptacle as shown.

At switch box, ends of BX are connected where flexible leads were connected before. Match wires.

Finished installation offers two outlets instead of one, is completely protected, will last a long time.

95

Motors Are Made to Move

Motors which the layman generally deals with are luckily of simple design and accessible construction—here's what you have to know

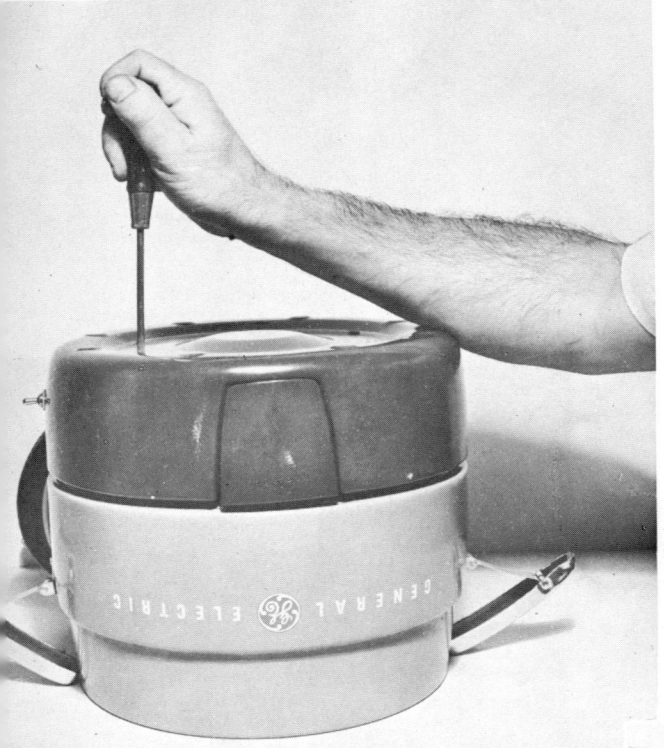

The first step in inspecting a vacuum cleaner motor is to get to it; this is accomplished with the average tank type (such as this GE) by removing six bottom screws.

With the bottom pan off the vacuum cleaner, the switch becomes accessible; to facilitate checking with the Handitester, disconnect two motor wires from the main body of the cleaner. Some connectors at this point are of the screw type; others must be twisted off.

IT is fortunate that motors of rather simple design and accessible construction are used in the labor-saving appliances that get the most service in a home . . . and therefore are most likely to need attention. Vacuum cleaners, portable drills, fans, mixers, juicers, sewing machines, hair driers, etc., generally are powered by "universal" motors that work equally well on AC or DC. They are easy to identify by the presence of two "brush holders," diametrically mounted on the motor frame close to one end. These holders have slotted caps, which, when screwed open with a coin or a screwdriver, spring out to reveal small bars of carbon. The latter bear against a series of copper strips on the rotating shaft, called the "commutator." The carbon brushes being relatively soft and the commutator relatively hard, the

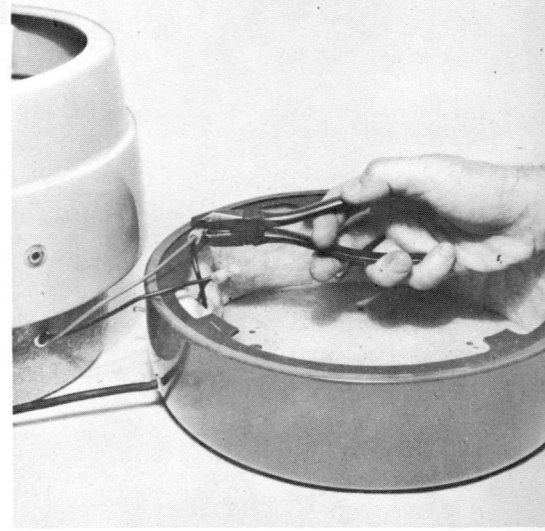

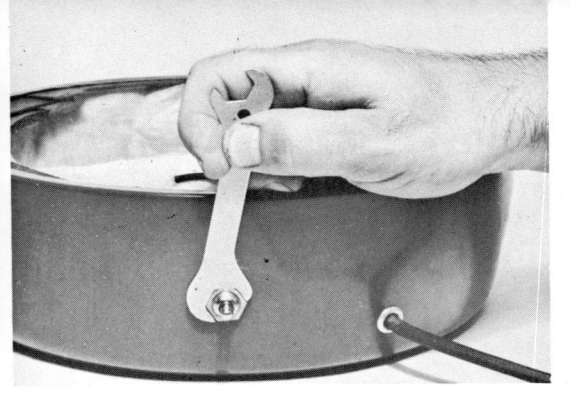

The switch which controls the motor of the vacuum cleaner is held by one hex nut; it is simple to dismount for testing purposes. Next step, below.

Blower motor is concealed inside a perforated cover in the main body of the cleaner. Remove holding screws, lift cover carefully. See next step below.

Switch can now be checked quickly for opens or shorts; switch usually suffers physical rather than electrical damage. Replacement should be strong.

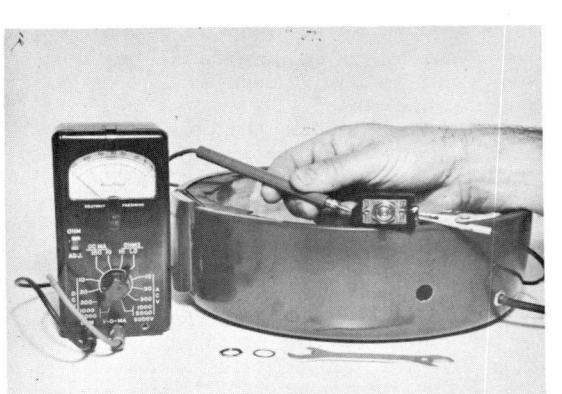

The motor is mounted on a sponge rubber ring; with the cover off and the wires disconnected from switch, the whole unit lifts out in one solid piece.

former are bound to wear out eventually. Sometimes they shatter when the appliance is accidentally dropped, a not unlikely occurrence with portable machines.

Carbon brushes have been a staple in hardware and electrical supply stores for more than half a century. There must now be hundreds of different sizes, in round, square and rectangular cross section. It's helpful to have a segment of an old brush when buying a replacement, but if you haven't, don't worry. Get slightly oversize brushes, and shape them to size by rubbing them gently on a piece of fine sandpaper or emery cloth.

Because AC has replaced DC power in virtually all American homes, the ability of a "universal" motor to work on DC is now purely incidental. The main importance of the "AC-DC" notation on an appliance's name plate is that it tells you positively that the motor is of the basic brush-commutator type and not of one of the more complicated straight AC types.

Universal motors represent an economical way of obtaining medium mechanical power in small packages. They start quickly, and develop very high speeds. Turn on a vacuum cleaner or a portable drill, and it's screaming away at several thousand revolutions per minute before you can take your hand away from the switch. The speed, however, is usually pretty sensitive to the load. It's fairly steady with a fixed load, such as the blades of a fan, the blower of a vacuum cleaner, etc.; but it drops when the machine or tool has to do work at an increased rate. For example, you've probably noticed that a portable drill bites into wood with only a

97

The brush holders on top of the motor frame are insulated by fiber strips; unhook one end, and screw holding brush in place becomes visible; remove with small screwdriver, hold hand over end to catch brush.

slight reduction in speed, but groans noticeably when cutting metal or hard plastics.

Deliberate speed control is easy with AC-DC motors, and requires only the use of a variable or adjustable wire-wound resistor connected in simple series with the power line. This resistor is usually called a "rheostat". The commonest example is the foot treadle for speed control of sewing machines. This is nothing more than a resistor of about 150 ohms, adjustable in five or six steps from this maximum value (lowest motor speed) to zero (highest speed).

The Rheostat

The addition of an external control rheostat to a small fan (10-inch size or under) greatly increases the usefulness of the machine for both summer and winter purposes. Throttled down to about one-third speed, the fan does a fine job of breaking up the stale air found in many rooms equipped with window type air conditioners. Aim the blades toward the ceiling, where the naturally lighter hot air accumulates. During the heating period, aim the fan directly at the biggest radiator, and note how much more comfortable the room becomes. Remember, a fan doesn't "cool"; it can only move air, and moving cool air and moving warm air are equally important in season.

Rheostats in suitable sizes are sold by radio and surplus firms. The maximum resistance should be between 150 and 200 ohms, and the power rating not less than 25 watts and preferably 50 or 75 watts. The control develops an appreciable but not dangerous amount of heat as part of its normal operation.

When an appliance equipped with an AC-DC motor stops working, you have to open the case or frame to gain access to the end of the power cord, the switch, and the motor itself. In many such appliances, particularly fans, sewing machines, driers, small vacuum cleaners, etc., the brush holders are on the outside and the brushes can therefore be checked in a few seconds. In other instances, the motor may be enclosed in the shell of the appliance. Examine the latter carefully. If screw heads are in sight, you can be pretty sure that you have to loosen them to take the machine apart. Just remember where they came from, and keep them safely in a cigar box.

Reasons for Trouble

The cause of the trouble might be any of the following:

1) A mashed attachment plug or broken or shorted flexible cord. Easily tested with the Lightester or Handitester as explained in the section entitled "Don't Let a Cord Tie You into Knots."

2) A broken switch. Quite common with vacuum cleaners because it is invariably kicked on and off by the user's foot. Many of the small toggle switches found on cleaners just are not heavy enough to withstand this punishment very long.

3) Broken, shattered or worn out brushes. Easy to find and easy to replace.

4) Burned out "field" winding, the coil of wire fixed inside the frame of the motor.

Next, the jack-in-box carbon and spring slide out of the holder for inspection. Put back in same position, so that worn end of brush matches diameter of copper commutator bars it presses against.

The commutator is actually a small drum of copper segments; clean with a strip of fine sandpaper; this will reduce sparking. Caution: Do NOT use emery cloth for this purpose. Emery dust that gets into the motor bearings can ruin them after a few hours of running time. Avoid this trouble.

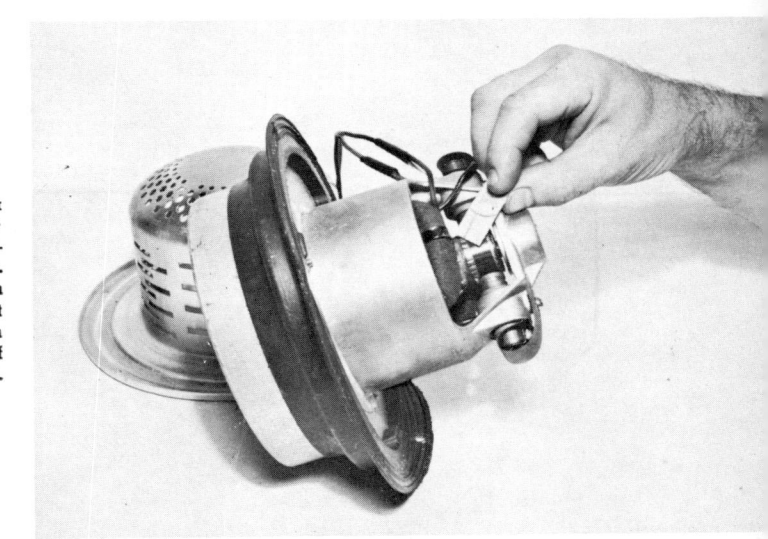

The small tubular device mounted on the side of the motor is a capacitor which functions to kill radio interference; if this is shorted, cleaner will not run, and will blow fuses. Continuity check with meter shows up a short quickly. One wire of capacitor must be disconnected from motor line for this test.

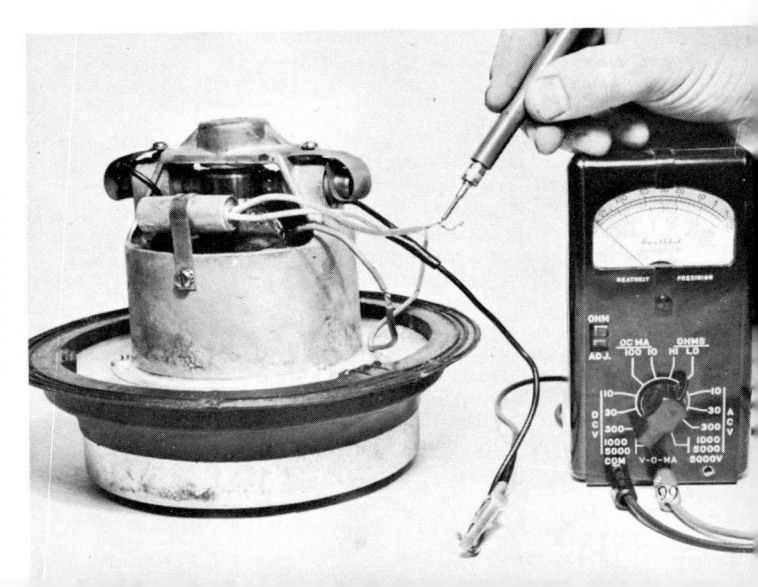

Cleaner cord will suffer less damage if kept rolled up when not in use. Storage reel can be made from plywood discs.

Two discs of plywood or hardboard about 6" in diameter and a center piece about 3" are used to make the reel; the three sections are held by one bolt through them and the side of the cleaner case.

Easily checked for continuity with the Lightester or Handitester. Happens once in a blue moon. An "open" more usually is due to a break in the connection *between* the flexible line cord and the field winding. The line cord is wiggled around a great deal and such a break is common.

5) Burned out "armature" winding. This is the wire on the rotating member of the motor. The winding actually consists of a number of separate coils, each represented by a pair of diametrically opposite copper bars on the "commutator," the member against which the carbon brushes press.

Happens once in a green moon, but easily checked with either tester mentioned above.

6) Short-circuited interference eliminator. One of those concealed jokers that turns up only after you have wasted two hours testing everything else. This eliminator is merely an ordinary paper capacitor of the kind found by the dozen in radio and television receivers. It is sized as ".05 mfd." ("mfd." stands for microfarad, or one-millionth of a farad the unit of measurement of capacitors), and rated for operation up to 250 volts. You can buy one

100

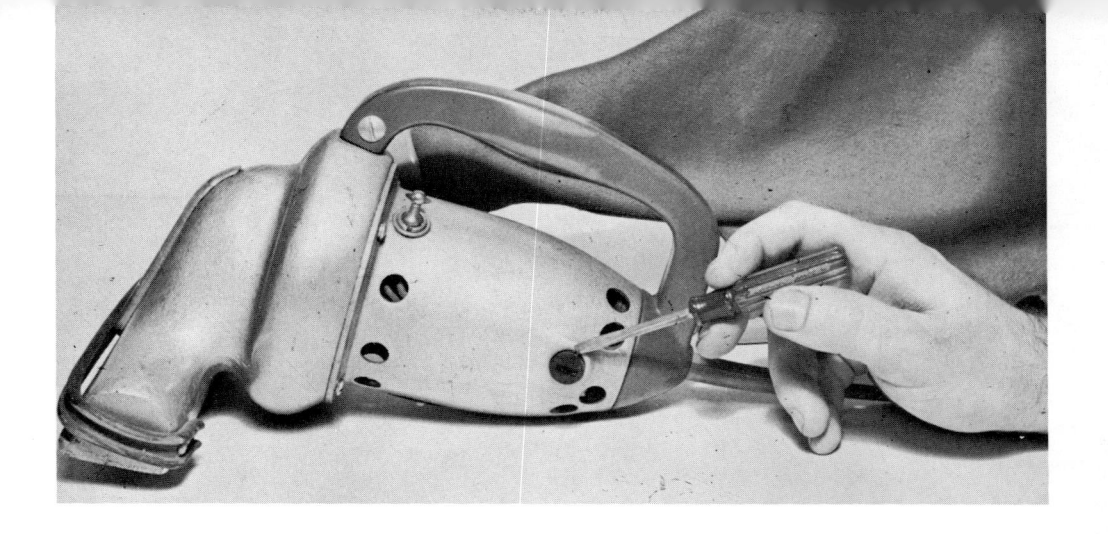

In small hand-type vacuum cleaners, motor brushes are out in the open and always accessible for inspection. The screwdriver points to the slotted end cap of the brush holder; check similarity of yours.

in radio supply stores for as little as a dime. It is connected directly across the power cord, and its purpose is to prevent the radiation of interfering signals created by the sparking of the brushes against the commutator. This interference is heard in radio receivers as a high pitched whine and is seen on TV screens as a series of short white lines or streaks.

If this capacitor merely goes "open", the vacuum cleaner continues to run perfectly well, although neighbors may wonder what's causing the racket in their sets. More often, however, when it goes bad it usually goes thoroughly bad by developing an internal short circuit. Since it is connected across the power line, it blows the fuses and prevents the cleaner from running. To check a suspected capacitor, you must disconnect either of its leads from the line, and then apply the Handitester. A complete or partial short circuit shows up instantly as a very low resistance reading on the LO OHMS scale. If the capacitor is in normally good condition, the meter needle flickers slightly on the HI OHMS scale and then returns to the extreme left-hand position. An open capacitor will cause no reading at all. It is not always possible to distinguish between a good and an open capacitor with a simple continuity test, but with either capacitor the cleaner runs, and that's the main consideration. Depending on the cleanliness of the motor commutator and the smooth fit of the brushes, the capacitor may not really eliminate all interference, but it usually does reduce it considerably. You can readily determine its effectiveness by running the machine with it and then without it, near a radio or television receiver.

The accompanying series of photos shows disassembly, testing and checking operations on two vacuum cleaners of entirely different types and on a typical sewing machine. The larger cleaner, a popular swivel-top model, started to blow fuses... not always, but about three times out of five when turned on. Wiggling the line cord seemed to bring on the trouble, so it was thought that a short circuit had developed inside the cord where it enters the case, a common occurrence. However, everything proved to be intact until the interference capacitor was isolated and tested, and that was it!

If a vacuum cleaner motor runs, but at what seems a lower than usual speed, the likelihood is that the blower unit is fouled up. Dust and dirt pass through quickly into the bag, but string and pieces of sewing materials often wrap themselves firmly around the blades and stay there until you pick them out. An occasional but thorough cleaning of a vacuum cleaner is a good idea.

Shaded-Pole Motors

Brushless motors used for small fans and similar air-moving devices, and for clocks and automatic timers, are usually of the "shaded pole" type and work on AC only. They are favored for these applications because they are extremely simple in construction, cheap to manufacture, and rugged and reliable. The catch is that they have very low starting and running torque and are therefore suitable only for light jobs. When you turn on a fan using a shaded-pole motor, you can count almost to two before the blades pick up speed. If you stick a pencil into them they'll proba-

101

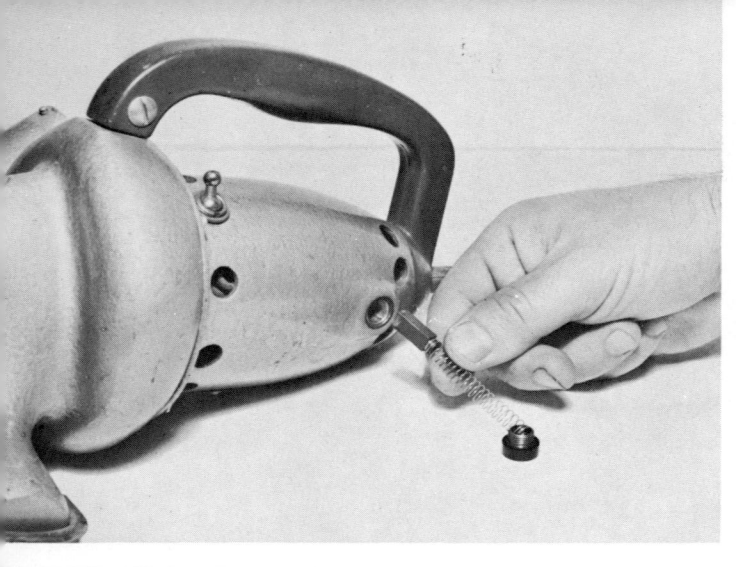

High speed of small cleaner motors makes brushes wear rapidly; it's a good idea to keep a spare pair on hand. Spring maintains pressure of brush against the motor commutator.

Remove the end casing of the cleaner; you may be surprised at the amount and type of material tangled in the blades; occasional cleaning of the blades maintains cleaner efficiency.

bly stop dead, without breaking the pencil. A compensating feature to this low efficiency is that a shaded-pole motor rarely if ever burns out itself or the line fuses if it stalls, as practically all other types do. It might get a bit warmer than usual, but that's all.

About the only thing you can do to a shaded-pole motor is lubricate it once in a while. Over-oiling can't hurt it, because there are no internal switches, commutators or contacts. The rotating member is called a "squirrel cage" because it resembles one.

Both the universal and the shaded-pole type motors are usually found in only small sizes in home appliances, and are easy to take apart for inspection and cleaning. With an AC-DC motor, first remove the brushes, and then the bolts holding the framework together; with a shaded-pole unit, it is only necessary to loosen the body bolts. Watch out for spacing washers on the ends of the shafts.

Motors for Power

For applications calling for better starting torque and constant speed under varying load, straight AC motors of quite different construction are used. In the sizes used in the home or small shop, from about $\frac{1}{6}$ to 1 horsepower, by far the most common type is called the "split phase." One form of split-phase motor using a capacitor (or "condenser") is particularly popular because it develops high starting torque with relatively low line current. Capacitor motors are almost universally used for refrigerators, freezers, air conditioners and home workshop power tools.

Above, the brushes of a sewing machine motor are in the open at the end of the frame. Since the motor is run only intermittently, brush wear is slight; tighten holder and caps occasionally.

Above right, the rubber drive wheel on the end of the shaft has a tendency to loosen; clean shaft of possible oil slick from bearings, and tighten set screw firmly; it may be helpful to flatten end of the shaft slightly with a file in order to give a better bite to the screw holding it.

Motor is usually spring-loaded to make drive wheel press firmly against the large hand wheel; check the tension occasionally for drive action.

There are numerous variations of the split-phase motor, designed to meet particular requirements. In its basic form it consists of two fixed windings of wire on the inside of the frame, one called the "starting" winding and the other the "running" winding. The rotating member is again a "squirrel cage," and has no external connections. However, it is fitted with a spring-loaded, centrifugally-operated switch. When the motor is at rest, the contacts of this switch are closed, and connect the starting winding to the line; the running winding is "on" independently of the switch. When the line switch is closed to start the motor, the shaft starts to turn. When the motor reaches a predetermined speed, usually in a second or so, the centrifugal switch opens, removing the starting winding from the power line. Only the running winding is then in the circuit. When the motor is turned off, the switch closes just before the shaft comes to rest, and the machine is ready for another cycle. A clicking or slapping sound made by the switch as it opens and closes is characteristic of split-phase motors.

Repulsion-Induction Motors

Another common type of motor is the "repulsion-induction," which is noted for its very powerful starting torque, needed for pumps and other "stiff" machines. This type has one fixed running winding on the frame, and also a wire-wound armature complete with commutator and brushes, just like an AC-DC motor but on a larger scale. The armature winding and its accessories are needed only for starting. When the motor reaches its rated

103

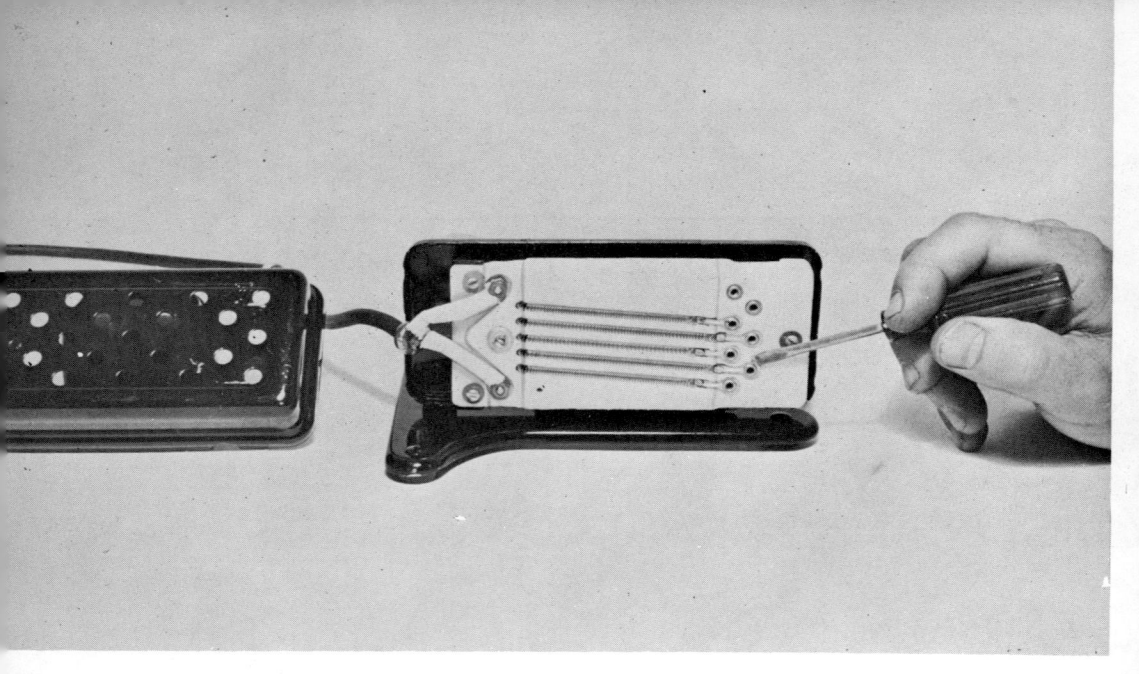

Foot treadle speed control of sewing machine motor is tapped 150-ohm resistor; keep connections tight.

Many small electric fans are driven by "shaded-pole" motors, which work on AC only; this type can be recognized by an absence of brush holders. Construction is simple; pencil points to one of two screws holding motor case together; box on right contains speed control rheostat. This is connected in series with 115-volt line, exactly as when a universal AC-DC motor is used; see Diagram 1 on page 107 for details.

Shaded-pole motor comes apart readily. Above left, end bell; center, main body holds windings through which current passes; right, rotating armature, which has no external connections.

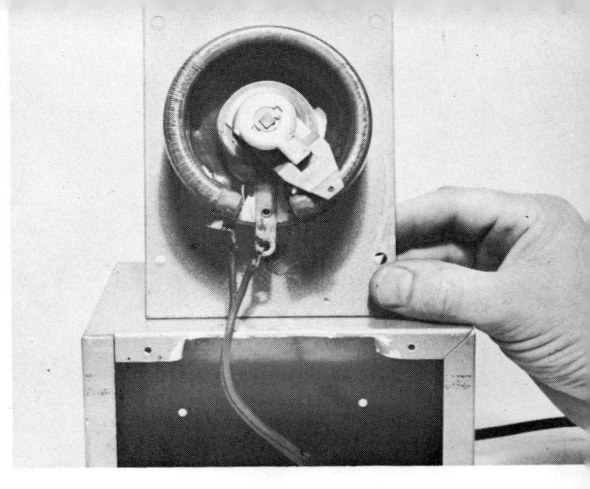

The speed control rheostat is mounted conveniently in a small radio shield box; it must be enclosed to protect user against possible contact with the bare wire on it. It's a handy unit for a fan.

speed, a weighted governor lifts the brushes away from the commutator and at the same time moves in a circular ring or "necklace" which short circuits all the commutator segments to each other.

The throw-out mechanism in split-phase and repulsion-induction motors is very reliable, but it cannot be called simple. The best thing you can do to a motor in running order is nothing. Even be stingy with lubrication, if any is required at all. Many high-grade motors have sealed bearings that are guaranteed to run practically forever. More damage than good is done by over-oiling. The lubricant is likely to get into the switch contacts or onto the commutator surfaces, and since oil and grease are good insulators they can cause real trouble.

When a motor with a starting winding is stalled to a dead stop by an overload, there is some danger that this winding will burn out if the power remains on. It won't if the branch fuse or circuit breaker is of the right size for the line; the protective device should kick out long before the copper wire in the motor has a chance to melt.

Many AC motors in the popular sizes between ¼ and 1 horsepower are comfortably underrated, and are known to develop as much as *twice* their rated values for short periods. Some induction-repulsion motors can produce *three* to *five* times their nominal ratings under heavy starting conditions. You have to mistreat a machine very badly and deliberately to make such rugged motors quit.

Occasional stalling is quite normal with some types of clothes washers when they go into the "spin" cycle with more wet wash in them than they're supposed to carry. An overload breaker is usually provided alongside the regular controls, and it only needs to be reset to start the machine again . . . after a few towels have been removed.

Because there are so many forms and variations of both split-phase and repulsion-induction motors, it is difficult to give anything but the most general suggestions in regard to servicing them. *Before* they give trouble, familiarize yourself with their wiring and construction. Copy off all the data on the name plates and write to the manufacturer for any instructions he has available. Some firms send back elaborate four-page folders, some put all the information on a tag, others just ignore such requests altogether. You have a lot to gain and nothing to lose by at least trying. In the absence of printed instructions, about all you can do is probe around carefully and hopefully.

Continuity Check

A continuity check may give some clue. If a meter like the Handitester shows no movement (that is, infinite resistance, or open circuit) when connected to the line plug, possibly there is only a break in one of the power leads, or in the on-off switch, if it's mounted directly on the motor. Some motors have built-in overheating controls, which open automatically when a predetermined temperature is reached. A defective one that stays open prevents

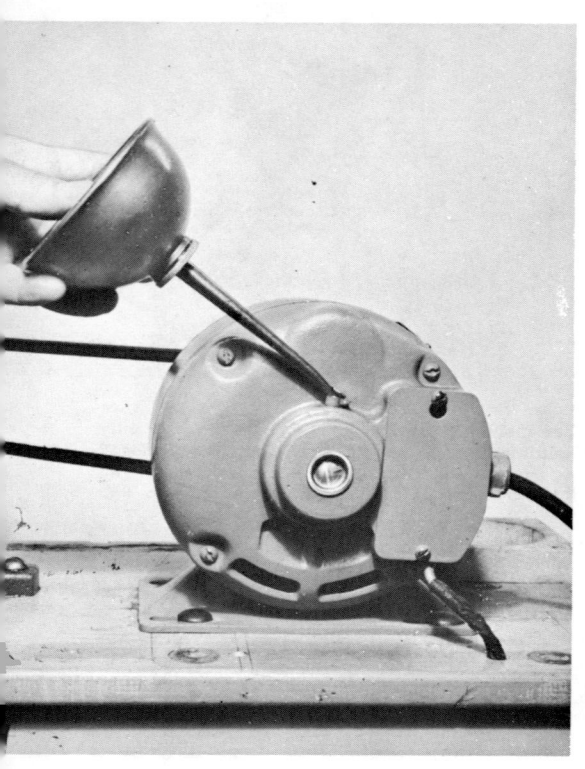

Motors of split-phase type are commonly used for household machines, power tools, etc. If the motor requires lubrication, apply oil sparingly, since excess might get into internal switch contacts.

With four screws through motor frame removed, end bell can be pried off to reveal the switch mechanism in the end bell itself, and will also reveal the centrifugal weights on the motor shaft.

current from reaching the motor. The normal resistance of a motor in the $1/6$- to 1-horsepower range is very low . . . only an ohm or two . . . but some motors will register a reading of about this value even if the starting winding is burned out and cut out of the circuit by a defective centrifugal throw out switch.

Nothing shows on the outside of motors of the aforementioned types except the shaft and the line cord. To check the internal parts, you must, of course, open the frame. This is a simple job, inasmuch as the end bells are held to the central body by only four long bolts, in 99 motors out of 100. Just proceed slowly and carefully and keep a sharp eye for spacing washers and lubricating rings on the shaft ends. What happens when you pry off the end containing the throw-out switch can't be predicted; every manufacturer has his own design of weights and contacts.

In split-phase (including capacitor) motors, the arrangement is not too forbidding, as the throw-out switch is after all only a single contact affair. In repulsion-induction motors the mechanical linkage can be somewhat on the Rube Goldberg side because it has to raise the brushes and also move in a circular ring. If nothing else, you'll have some fun investigating.

Suppose you get a motor apart, isolate the leads of the various windings, and determine pretty positively that one of the latter is burned out. Your nose will also help in the investigation, as burned insulation has a pungent and unmistakable odor. That's a polite expression; the motor will stink, no mistake about it! You can now do one of two things: 1) Have the motor rewound at a shop specializing in the work; 2) Buy a new motor and use the old one as a plaything. After getting an estimate on the repair job, you might readily decide that the second step is simpler and cheaper. New motors are surprisingly inexpensive and are available in a wide variety of sizes and types to suit all purposes. A recent Sears, Roebuck catalog lists no less than 38 of them. •

Diagram 1 shows basic wiring diagram of universal AC-DC motor with speed control rheostat. Diagram 2 shows basic connections of split-phase AC motor; note that there are no connections to the rotor, which is pulled around by magnetic effect. Diagram 3 shows split-phase motor of capacitor type; capacitor is connected in starting-winding section only. Switch opens starting circuit when motor reaches operating speed.

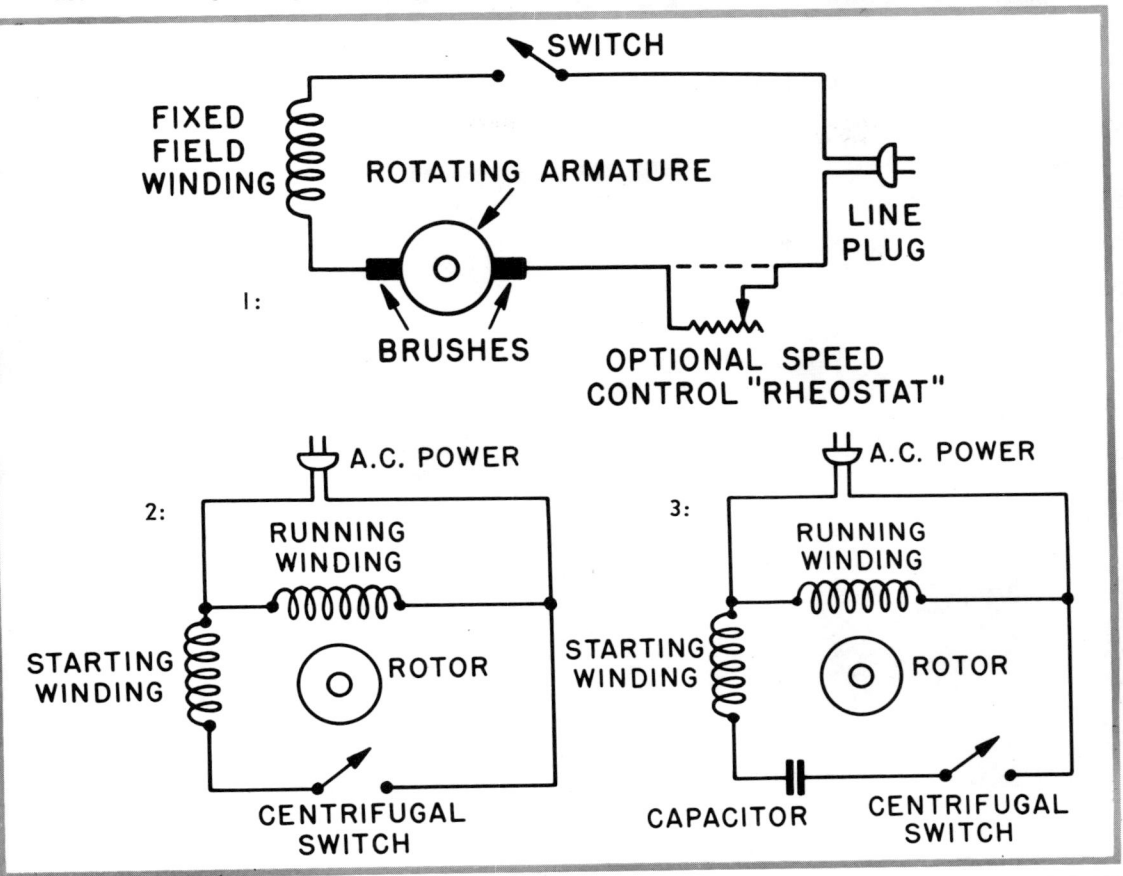

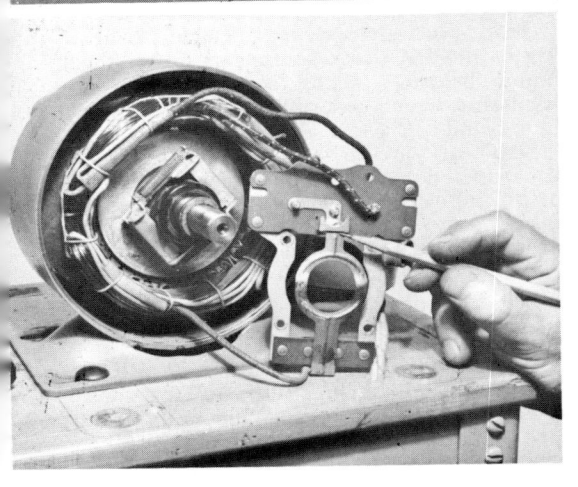

For closer inspection of switch of split-phase motor, switch frame can be dismounted; it is held by screws. Pencil points to contacts of switch, which must be kept clean and free of dirt and oil.

This is squirrel-cage rotor of the split-phase motor; vanes are for cooling. Spring-loaded weights move out when motor attains speed, pressing against and thus opening switch connected to starting-winding.

107

A Plan for a Fan

Neglect is an enemy plotting against the life of your fan; lubrication, a few turns of a screw at the proper time, and an automatic timer will increase its life

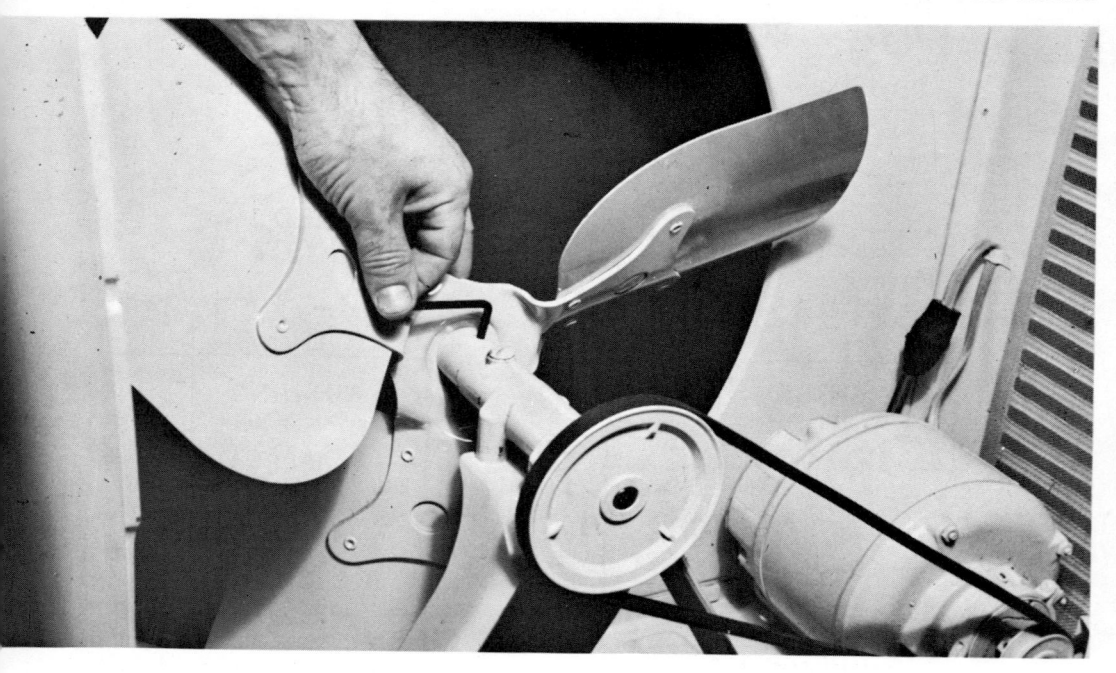

Keep the fan blade well-tightened on its shaft; continuous operation tends to loosen it.

FANS mounted in windows, on floor stands, in attics, etc., for the purpose of keeping air in a house in motion and thus creating a feeling of comfort, must be kept well lubricated and adjusted. Because they turn over at fairly high speeds, sometimes for periods of ten or twelve hours, they must be watched for signs of loosening due to vibration.

Large attic exhaust fans are usually belt driven, and contain two or three set screws that need occasional inspection. The belt itself should be adjusted just like the fan belt of a car: with not more than about an inch of "give" at the center point. Examine the surface of the belt for signs of shredding; this is a sure indication that the pulleys are a little out of line. On practically all belt-driven exhaust fans the motor position is adjustable, and the pulleys can be lined up in a matter of minutes.

Some motors have sealed-for-life bearings. Most have grease or oil fittings. Grease is usually used on the sleeve bearing of the fan blade shaft, and oil on the motor bearings. Small squeeze-tubes of lubricant, which cost only a few cents, are now being sold especially for fan purposes.

Don't drown the motor bearings. Read the instruction sheet that came with the fan or the information on the name plate, and take it easy with the oil can. Three or four drops of light machine oil every month or so are usually enough. Too much oil can cause trouble with the internal starting contacts of some types of electric motors.

Extra Protection for Fingers

The guards or grilles fitted to most fans offer very little discouragement to inquisitive children who are attracted by the whirling blades. They'll poke in fingers, pencils, knives and forks, odd pieces of sticks, and anything else that happens to be within reach. Disaster can be discouraged by the addition of ordinary $\frac{1}{16}$ mesh

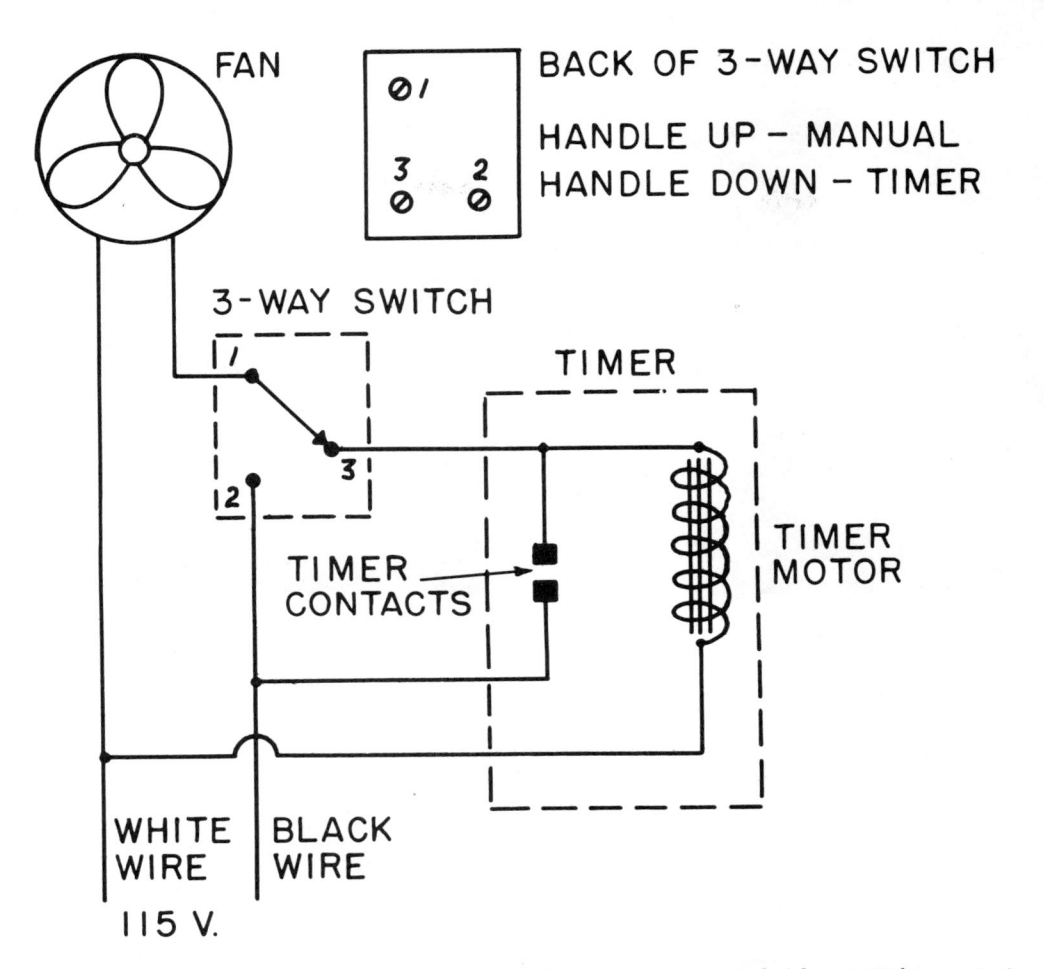

```
                    FAN           BACK OF 3-WAY SWITCH

                                  HANDLE UP – MANUAL
                                  HANDLE DOWN – TIMER
```

Diagram shows connections of timer and extra switch which give flexible control of the remote fan; see text.

metal screening, trimmed to fit all around the existing guard and held in place with little twisted loops of any thin wire. In the case of a window fan, the screening serves the additional purpose of keeping out insects when the machine is not operating. The importance of this feature apparently is overlooked by fan manufacturers.

Better Fan Control

Many excellent fans in the larger sizes ... 16 inches and up ... are equipped with **automatic timers.** These usually are set for any desired numbers of running hours up to 12, after which the motor shuts off by itself. They are designed primarily to operate a fan during the late evening and early morning hours, and to cut it off without requiring the owner to get out of bed to throw a manual switch. However, there are many times when manual control by a hand switch is desirable. This is easily added without affecting the automatic timer action. The diagram (above) shows how.

The timer is usually a small electric motor with a pair of contacts. When at the 12 noon or "off" setting, the contacts are open and no current from the power line reaches either the fan motor or the timer motor. When the knob is turned, the contacts close, and both motors start. When the timer motor returns to the starting point, it separates the contacts and the whole system shuts off.

Manual control is provided by a single-pole, double-throw toggle switch. This is widely sold as a "three-way" switch, and is usually used in pairs to control a stair or hall light from either of two positions. This switch does not have an "off" setting. The contact arm, represented by the arrow line 1 in the diagram, touches either contact point 2 or 3. The new connections are very simple. To identify the timer connections without opening the unit, use the Clicktester or the Handitester. The open

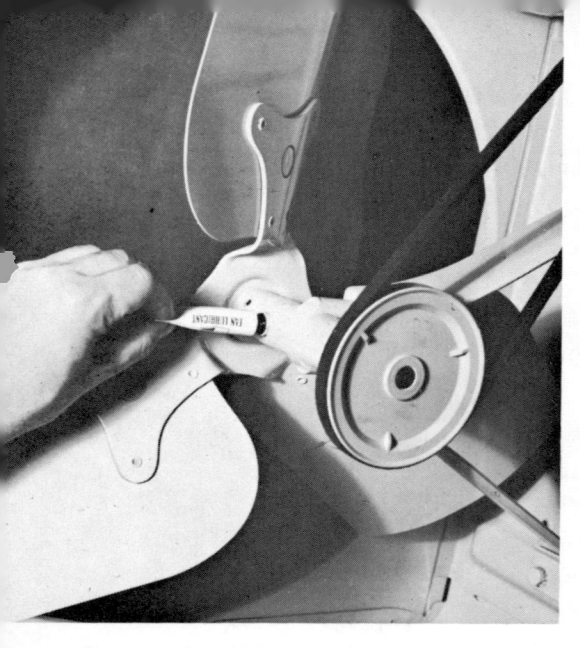

Squeeze-tube of lubricant make it a simple matter to keep the blade bearing properly lubricated.

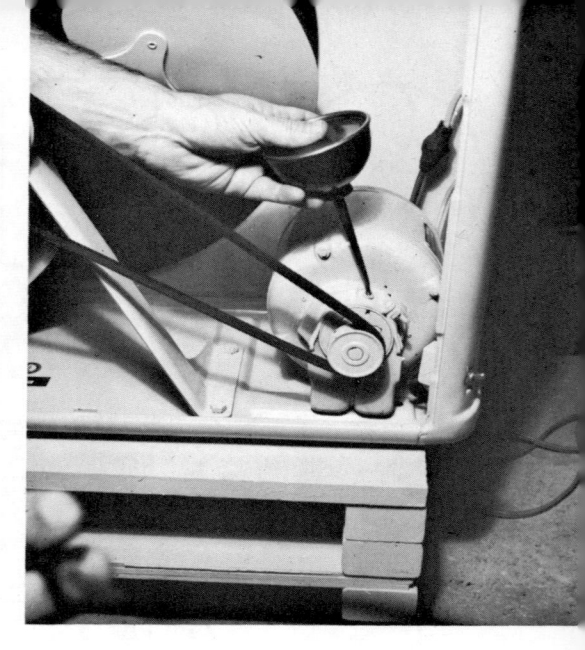

In using an oilcan, keep a light thumb—a few drops at a time are enough. Use light machine oil.

An extra screen covering over a fan will keep insects out and will protect pets and children.

Combination automatic-manual control for attic fan has timer at left, features a three-way switch.

contacts will, of course, register nothing; the motor will be in the neighborhood of several hundred ohms. No. 1 of the switch goes to one side of the fan; No. 2 to the black or "hot" side of the power line and to the free contact of the timer; No. 3 goes to the common junction of the other contact and one end of the timer motor; the free end of the latter goes to the white or "ground" side of the power line and also to the other side of the fan motor.

If no fan operation is desired, leave the switch handle down. This connects the arm 1 to the terminal 3, but it does not complete the power circuit. To obtain automatic timing, turn the timer knob as usual. This closes the timer contacts and puts current into both the fan and the timer. To turn the fan on for short periods by hand, merely snap the switch up. This sends current to the fan without putting any through the timer.

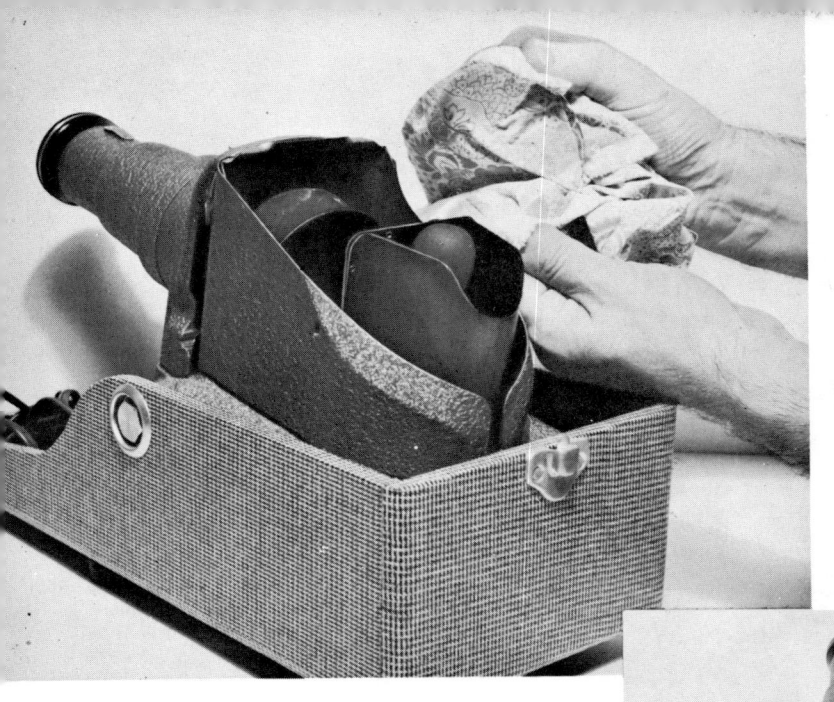

Still projectors contain as many as four or five concentrating lenses which must be polished very often.

Projectors

Whisk dust off with a soft brush, polish lenses and remove bits of film. Little oiling is required

Brush interior of projector with a soft brush to remove dust. The blower fan needs little oiling.

Keep the various film gates and guide of motion picture projector clean of torn film particles.

"KEEP 'Em Clean" is the best advice concerning both still and movie projectors. This applies especially to the reflecting and condensing lenses that concentrate the light on the film. Because of the heat of the latter, they attract a lot of dust. Breathe on the glass lightly, and then polish with a soft, well-washed out rag.

Projection bulbs run so hot that the glass often melts and starts to bulge. The better projectors are equipped with a small fan that starts when the bulb is turned on. Don't over oil this motor, or the drive motor of a movie machine.

In a movie projector, bits of film torn from between sprocket holes have a habit of fouling up the drive mechanism. Clean the latter frequently—after each use, in fact—with a soft brush. The job takes a few seconds and is well worth while. •

First step in disassembling an iron is to remove handle for access to the heat control knob just underneath. Nut-and-bolt assembly might be corroded because of heat of iron. Loosen it with a drop or two of penetrating oil, which will help.

Iron Quit Cold?

The cord might be open or the heating element burned out. Here's how you can spot the offender immediately

BECAUSE it is used often, and then for periods up to several hours, the common clothes pressing iron is bound to need technical attention fairly early in its life.

When an iron quits cold one day, resist the temptation to disassemble it. Always check the cord first. This carries a lot of current, is often damaged by the sharp edges of the iron itself, and can readily go "open" or short circuit. The latter condition almost always blows the branch fuse, but sometimes it is only a partial short circuit and merely makes the cord get hot.

After eliminating the cord as the source of trouble, then tackle the iron itself. Construction varies from make to make, but any iron can be opened after careful study of its nuts and bolts. See the accompanying picture sequence for ideas and suggestions. •

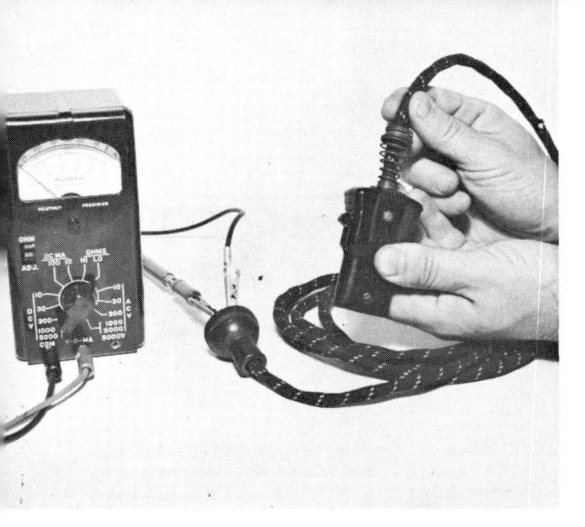

Above: To check cord for internal short circuits (which usually occur near plug), set Handitester for "LO OHMS," connect test leads to line plug, wiggle cord. A short circuit will make needle flicker.

Above right: If cord is not short circuited, test for continuity of wire by inserting pair of tweezers. If plug contains switch, make sure it's on. Needle will bang over to zero ohms if the cord is all right.

Right: After removing handle from iron, as shown in the first illustration, take off the adjustable heat control knob. It is usually held by single small screw. Remove screw and lift off knob as shown.

Below, right: A large hex nut over heat control shaft holds the body of iron to the base. It may be removed easily with arc joint pliers or a wrench. The next step is to check the hex nut itself.

Below: The stud on which heat control knob fits is frequently "splined" to a short vertical shaft. Don't twist it, but lift straight up. A drop of penetrating oil here will help loosen the joint.

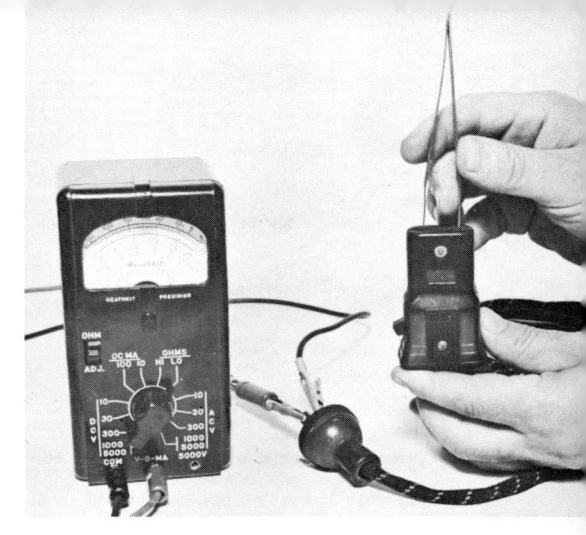

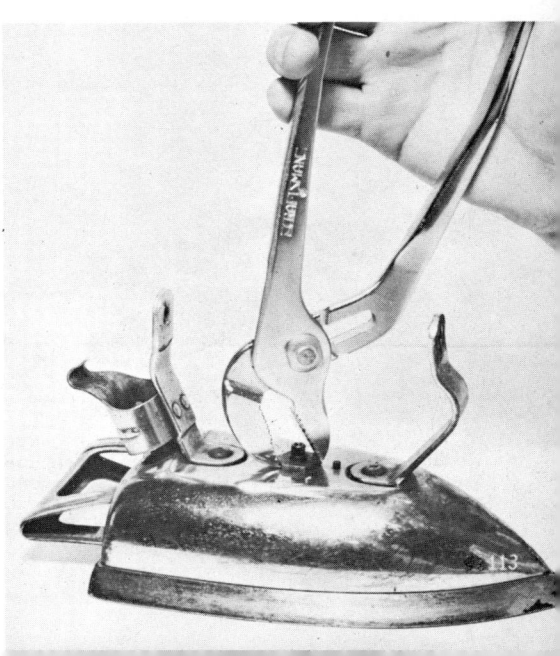

Hex nut turns out to be a deep, hollow threaded stud. Clean threads with a wire brush but don't oil. Now the plated cover of iron may be removed.

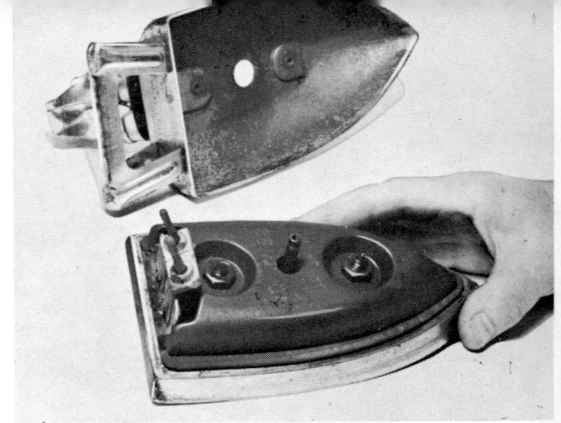

Plated cover lifts off to reveal heavy cast iron sub-base, held by two more nuts. The next step in disassembling iron is to take off the sub-base.

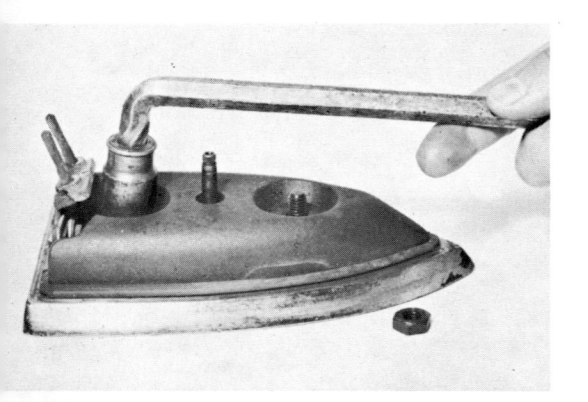

Socket wrench is needed to remove sub-base nuts. Drop of penetrating oil on each helps loosen corrosion. Don't hit connector plugs with wrench bar.

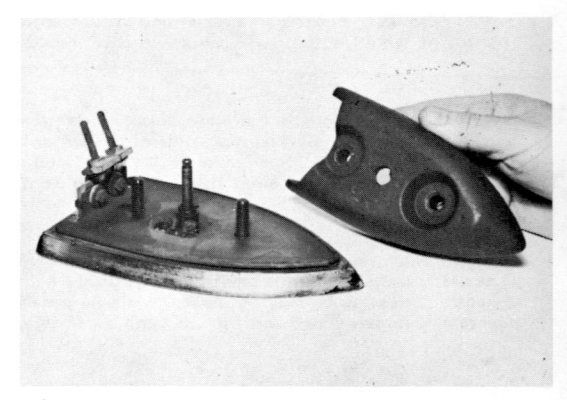

Sub-base lifts off easily and heating plate now comes into view. The threaded studs are anchored in the bottom plate or sole and will not come out.

Heating element comes off complete. Fingers are grasping control shaft of thermostat heat control which is the next item to be removed from the iron.

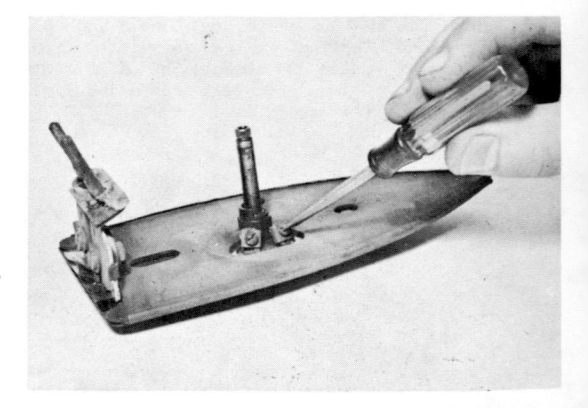

Thermostat is held by two short connecting wires fastened to screws. Loosen latter as shown and thermostat drops out through a hole in the center.

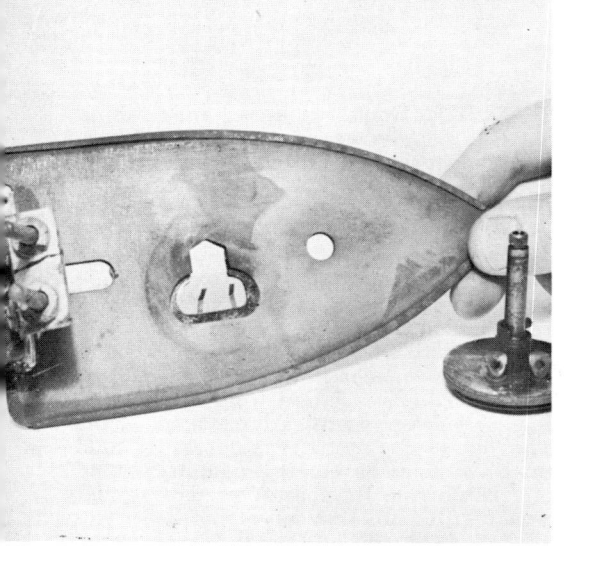

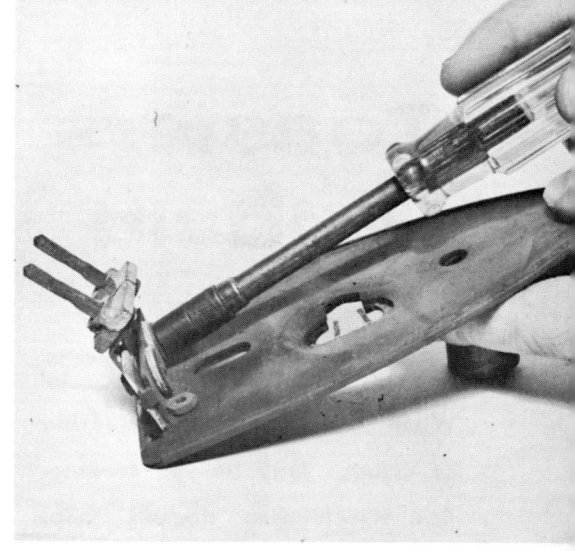

Thermostat (right) is separate unit. Note short tabs of wire sticking up in center hole. These are part of the heating element wires, which are clamped between two halves of boat-shaped form.

Before halves of heating form can be separated, it is necessary to dismount end prongs. This is a simple nut and bolt job. Observe placement of insulating washers and terminals of heating wires.

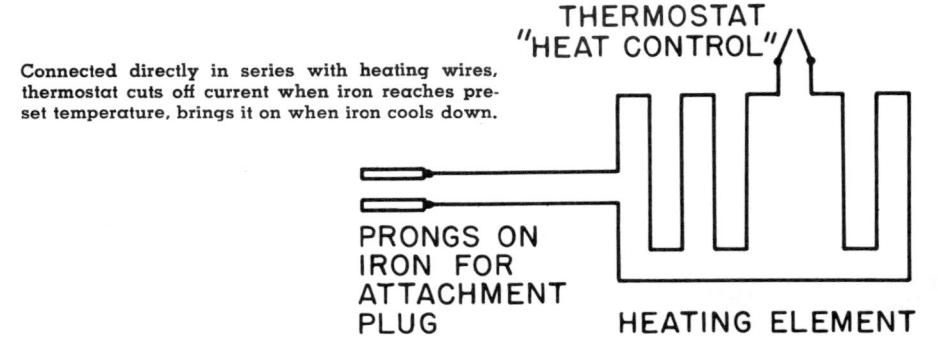

Connected directly in series with heating wires, thermostat cuts off current when iron reaches pre-set temperature, brings it on when iron cools down.

With connector prongs removed, top half of heating element can now be pushed to left, exposing wires inside. Some pieces of mica will come loose. The element consists of flat wire ribbon on mica form.

If wire is burned out, install a replacement element. Arrange mica above and below wires to prevent grounding and test with Handitester to make sure ribbon is not in contact with metal sandwich.

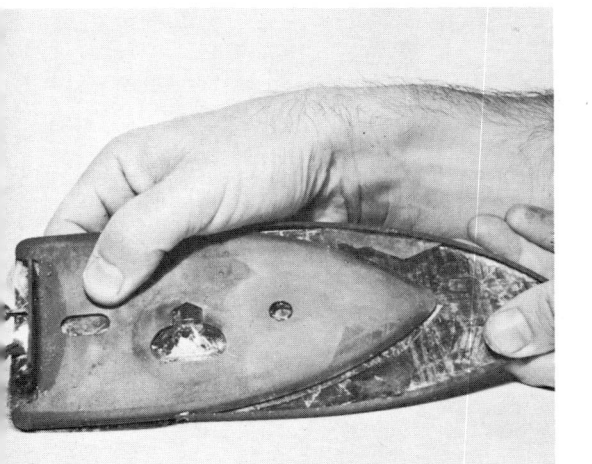

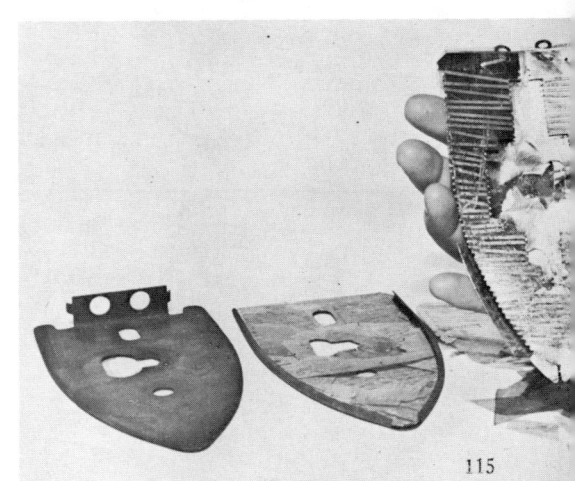

Toasters Should Pop

When they don't, a collection of crumbs may be the trouble. But if cleaning doesn't help, you can repair most toasters with a screwdriver and pliers

UNLIKE irons, broilers, and similar heat-appliances found in the kitchen, a bread toaster is used only for short periods perhaps once a day. Its wire heating element therefore enjoys a long life and rarely needs to be replaced. "Rarely" does not mean "never." With millions of toasters in active service, hardware and electrical shops find it profitable to stock replacement elements.

Most of the troubles that develop with toasters are mechanical rather than electrical. Crumbs accumulating inside can readily jam up the release mechanism, the control switch, the wire guides that hold the bread in place, etc. If the family is fond of raisin bread, the toaster needs frequent cleaning. Raisins that fall out of the bread are baked by the heat to the hardness of pebbles, and may have to be pried out.

Some toasters have clean-out traps in

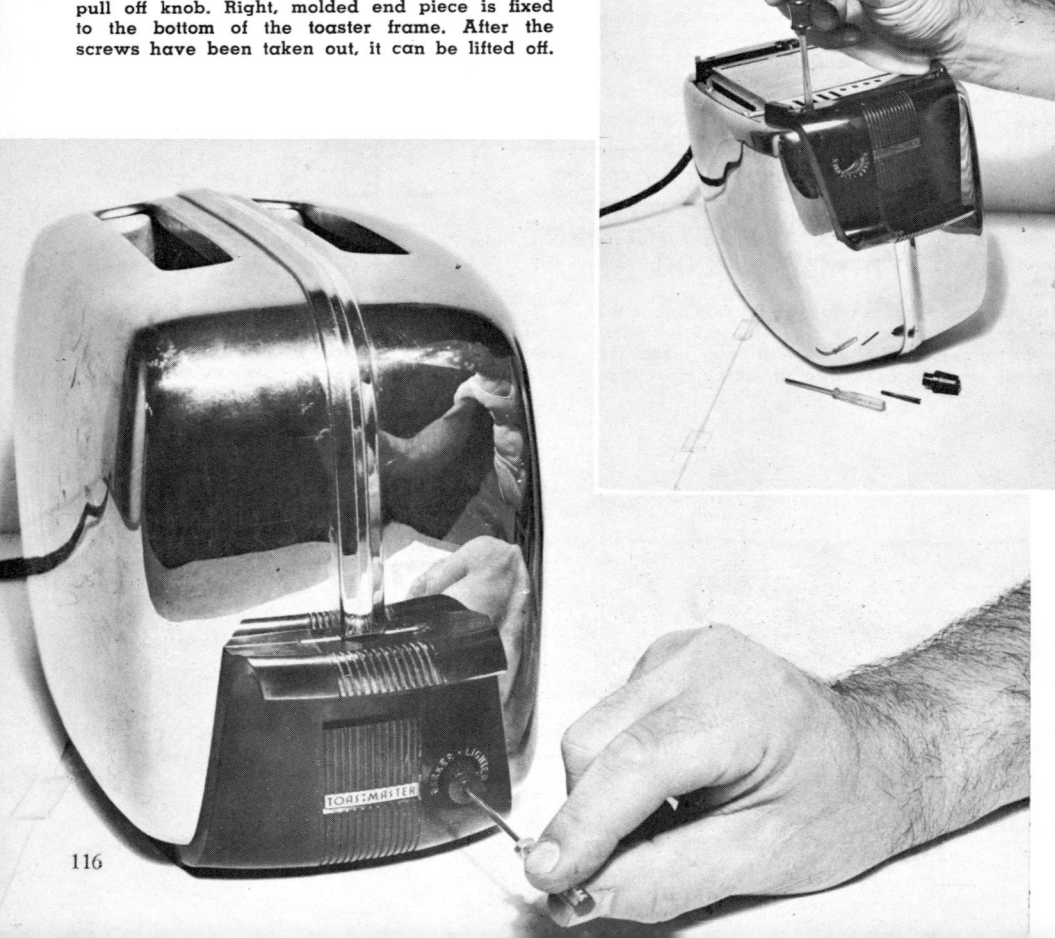

Below, look the whole two-slice toaster over for screw heads. The only one visible topside is a small one on the color-control knob. Remove and pull off knob. Right, molded end piece is fixed to the bottom of the toaster frame. After the screws have been taken out, it can be lifted off.

the bottom. These should be opened once every couple of weeks. Toasters without such traps can merely be turned upside down and shaken vigorously.

Sooner or later, it may be necessary to take a toaster apart, at least partially, to release a jammed mechanism, repair the connecting cord, replace the element, etc. Construction varies with make and price, but generally is rather simple. A screwdriver and a pair of pliers are the only tools needed for the job.

The accompanying photos show disassembly operations for two toasters: a new two-slicer and a single-slicer 25 years old. The latter is cleaned frequently, has needed only one of its two heating elements replaced in all that time, and continues to make perfectly good toast. The general procedures illustrated in the pictures can be applied to practically all toasters. •

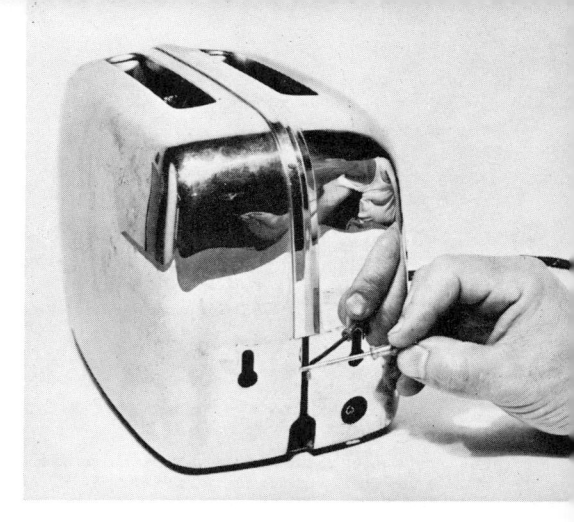

This is the front of the toaster with the molded end piece removed. The small lever that moves the bread-holder down is now in view. If it doesn't work freely, it probably should be scraped lightly.

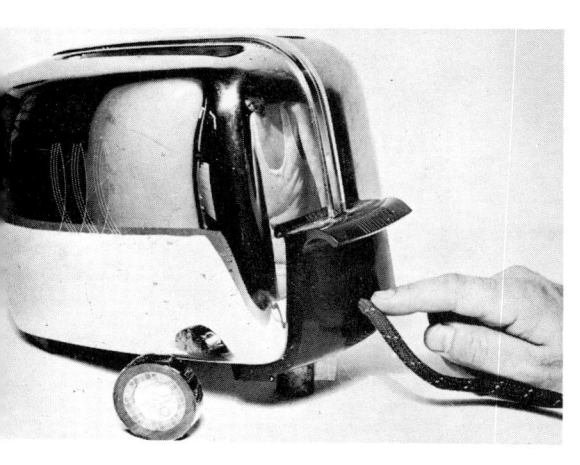

Point where cord enters case needs frequent inspection. Here insulation is apt to wear through.

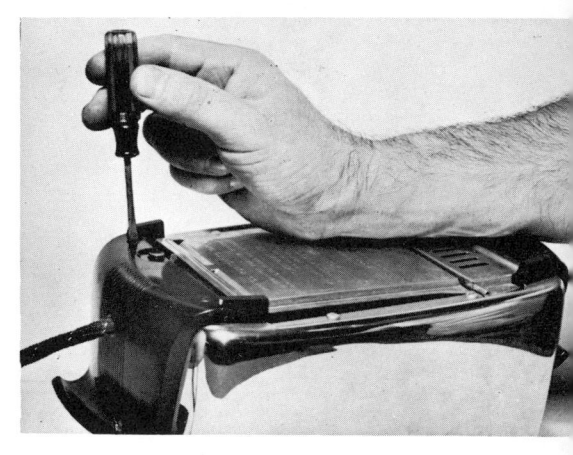

To get at end of cord, remove molded piece. It can be lifted off in same manner as front member.

With toaster upside down, reinforce cord where it passes through molded piece, with layer of tape.

Opened trap door on bottom of toaster is sure to release a shower of crumbs. Clean out with brush.

117

The wire guides of bread holders must move freely. With small screwdriver or knife scrape off all hardened accumulations of crumbs, raisins, etc.

Older single-slice toaster is less streamlined than the new model and of simpler construction. The top is held with screws—comes off in a jiffy.

Vertical sides are held to bottom plate by twisted end lugs. A quarter turn with pliers straightens them out and permits side pieces to be withdrawn.

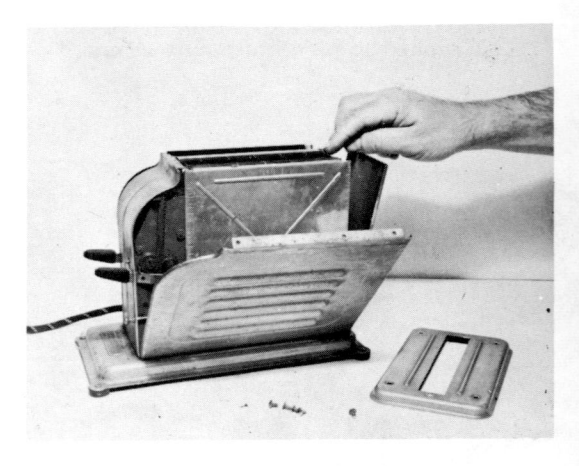

Sides and back of toaster peel off like an orange skin. It isn't necessary to remove front because mechanism connected to push levers is now in view.

Aluminum pan on bottom of toaster catches crumbs. Occasionally it needs a thorough scraping. Check and tighten the connections between cord, heating grid.

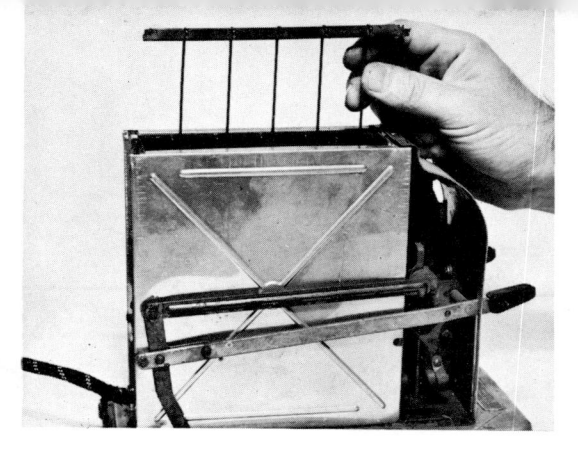

The wire guides fit loosely and come out easily. After removing from toaster, clean off the wires with back of knife blade or a fine emery cloth.

Heating element is held by spring clips in bottom of toaster and has no loose wires. To remove, grasp top edge with pliers and pull straight up.

Breaks in flat ribbon wire of heating element can sometimes be repaired with a patent resistance-wire cement but if element is old, replace it.

Wire on some heating elements cannot be seen too well because of mica covering. Breaks can be located quickly with Handitester set at LO OHMS.

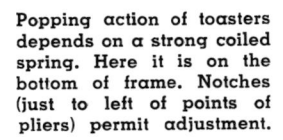

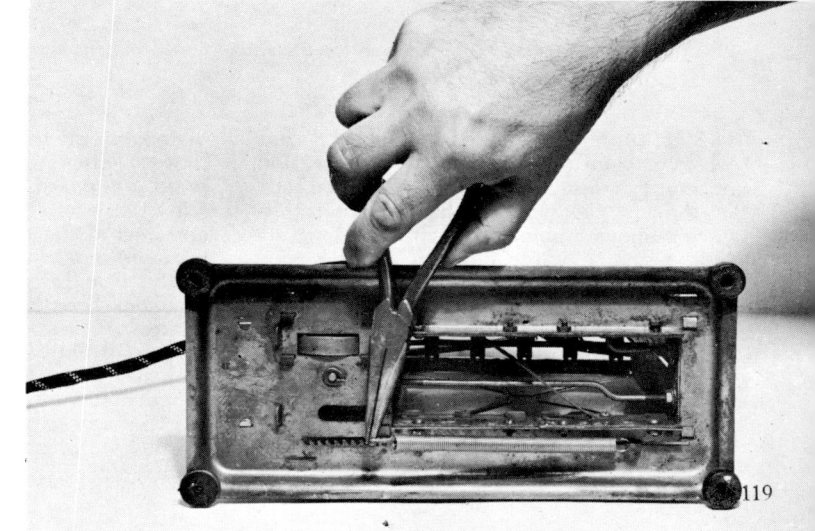

Popping action of toasters depends on a strong coiled spring. Here it is on the bottom of frame. Notches (just to left of points of pliers) permit adjustment.

What's Cooking?

Portable electric stoves or broilers are clean and flameless but potentially dangerous—here's how to avoid the danger—

When the heating element of a common electric stove "burns" out, the wire simply falls apart at one point.

THE table-top electric "hot plate" has long been popular for the preparation of small meals, a pot of tea or coffee, etc. In the last few years it has grown into a very elaborate piece of machinery, capable of roasting a whole chicken or turkey, a husky piece of roast beef, a couple of pounds of steak, a rack full of hot dogs or 'burgers, etc.

The portable electric stove or broiler is clean, flameless, easy to handle and store. In its usual forms it is also, potentially, an extremely dangerous device. It must be treated with care because in nine cases out of ten the glowing coils of resistance wire that produce the desired heat *are completely exposed*. If the surface of a frying pan or any other metallic container touches any part of the wire, the vessel can readily become "hot" electrically as well as thermally. For this reason you should examine any such "cooker" at frequent intervals to make sure that the resistance wire is well below (or above, as the case might be) the insulated form in or on which it rests. The proverbial ounce of prevention here is worth many times the pound of cure.

The simplest electric stove consists

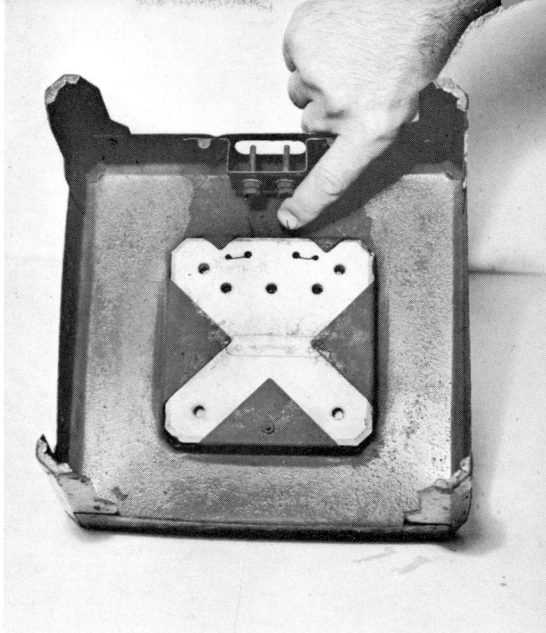

Pull out the broken ends, twist them together tightly with pliers, and push the joint back into the ceramic form. Be sure it lies flat and does not stick up; it must never touch the bottom of pans.

When a metal salt shaker accidentally rolled under this hot plate, it short-circuited the resistance wires at the point where they join the connector prongs. To repair, splice each wire.

Make frequent tests on an electric stove for "grounds." Set the test meter for LO OHMS, connect one test prod to a pan on the stove, and touch the other test prod to each of the prongs of the attachment plug, in turn. If meter needle moves, pan is touching exposed wires. Push latter down into the ceramic form.

In hinged-top broiler, resistance element is in dome, and radiates its heat downward to food on bottom rack. Ceramic grid is held by single screw in center, and is easily removed for cleaning or repair. Ceramic form actually contains two separate resistance coils, one for "low" heat, the other for "high."

Close-up of three-prong connector and two-prong attachment plug of hinged-top broiler shown above. Half of plug casing has been removed to reveal internal arrangement. Center prongs always connect. As plug is flopped either way, the outer prong connects to either the "low" or the "high" heat resistance coil.

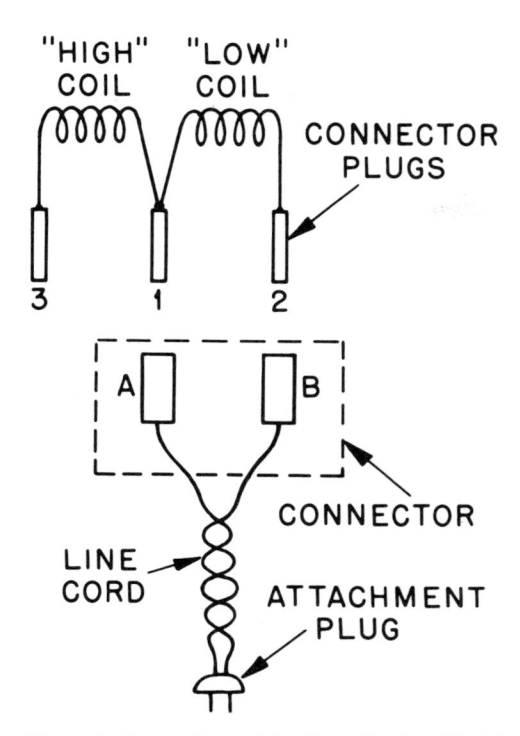

Figure 1: Connections of dual-heat broiler. "High" and "low" heat coils operate independently, but have common center connector prong, 1. Connector has two prongs. When A is on 1 and B on 2, only "low" coil is connected. When connector is turned over, B is on 3, only "high" coil functions.

Inside view of two-burner stove, with top pushed back to show connections to two switches and line cord. Switches are of double-pole, single throw type, with ceramic bodies to withstand heat.

usually of a grid or helix of resistance wire set into a square or circular ceramic form. This in turn is supported by a stamped sheet iron frame with legs. The power rating runs between 500 and 750 watts for a single unit. A switch usually is not provided; to turn the unit on or off, you merely attach or remove the line cord connector.

Since the wire is in open view, it is easy to locate the break in it when it burns out. Pull out the parted ends carefully, twist them together with a pair of pliers, snip the joint short, and push the wire back into the form. The resistance element can be patched in this manner half a dozen times. However, if the stove has had a lot of service, the wire may become excessively brittle, and should be replaced by a new length. Hardware and electrical supply stores everywhere sell replacement wire, which is usually displayed on squares of cardboard.

Thread the new wire into the old grooves, and secure its ends under the nuts on the connector pins. Also clean the connector pins with sandpaper, while you're about it.

Using the Handitester or Clicktester, check for possible "grounding" of the heating wire. Put a pot or pan on the stove and connect one lead of the tester to it. With the connector plug in place, touch the other test prod to each of the prongs on the line cord plug, in turn. There should be absolutely no meter movement on LO OHMS or no sound in the earphone. If there is, the wire is poking up and is touching the bottom of the pot.

Some broilers have the resistance element mounted in a hinged top or dome, which can be closed down against a bottom pan to conserve the heat. They might also have two "heats," selected by a reversible connector as shown in Figure 1. There may be three connector prongs on the broiler itself, the center one common to two different resistance coils. With the connector in one position, one coil is energized; when it is flopped, the other comes on, and the first goes off. A typical broiler takes about 350 watts in "low" and 950 watts in "high."

Two-burner stoves permit two cooking operations to be performed at once. The two grids, working at different heats, are controlled by separate switches. As shown in Figure 2, these are usually of the *double pole* type, instead of the usual single pole variety found on most appliances. In their "off" positions, they *completely* disconnect the exposed resistance wires from the power line, so there is no danger of accidental "grounding" even with the attach-

123

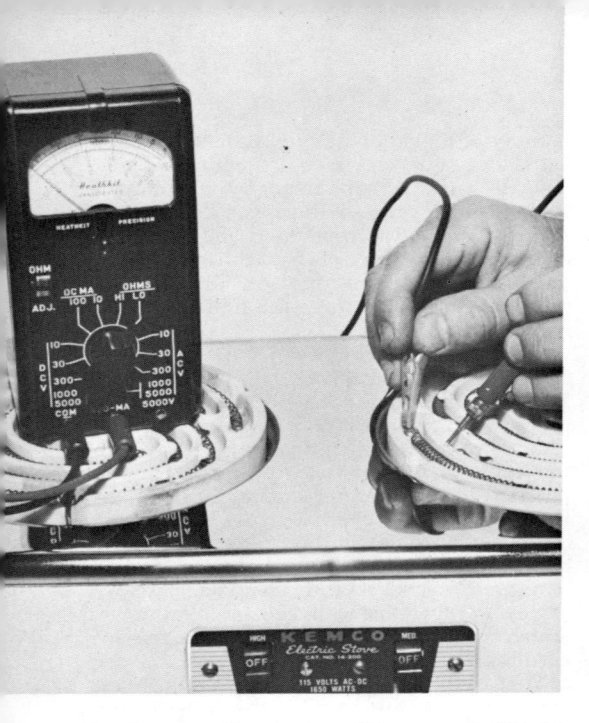

Two-burner table-top stove has separate "high" and "medium" heat units, which can be used separately or together. Continuity check is being made here; no reading indicates an open wire.

In most cases, the break in the heating wire is visible, and can be repaired easily by twisting the open ends with pliers, as shown. Of course, always make sure the appliance is unplugged.

Figure 2: Internal connections of typical two-burner table-top stove. Coils can be used individually or together. Double-pole switches isolate coils completely from the power line when they are not in use.

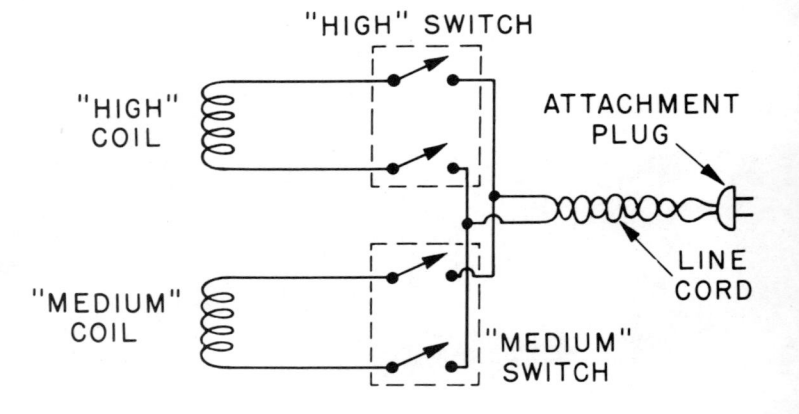

ment plug left in the wall outlet. This is a highly desirable safety measure, as far as it goes.

The "high" element runs to about 1000 watts, the "medium" to 750. Both can be turned on at the same time. The current drain is then just about the safe technical maximum of 15 amperes for a No. 14 line.

Table-top broilers the size of a small trunk are almost the standard gift nowadays for a young married couple. Most of them include a motor-driven spit, heat control in two or more stages, and automatic timing. Basically, they still depend on a grid of resistance wire, which in practically all models is mounted just under the top of the gleaming case. The fact that it's almost out of sight mustn't fool you; it's very easy to poke a tray or dish into it if you're not careful.

Manufacturers are trying to outdo each other in fitting out their broilers with

Stove should be opened and cleaned out occasionally. Construction of unit is usually simple. Here, nut on long center bolt of heating element is being carefully loosened with an end wrench.

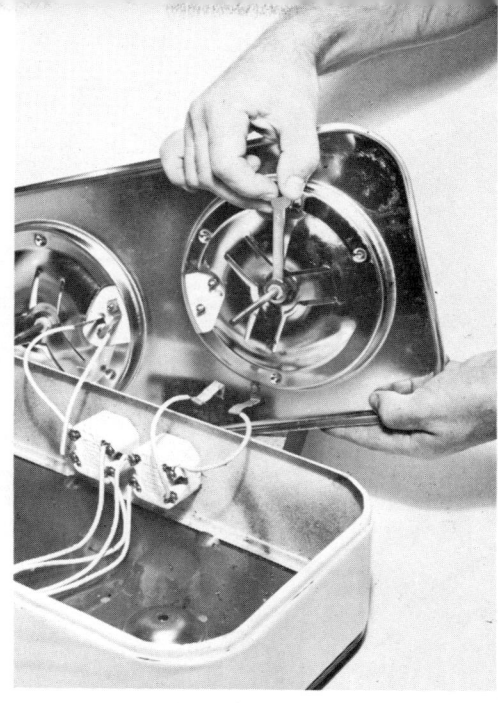

Heating element is fastened to top deck by another nut, on underside. It comes off in a jiffy with the aid of either a small wrench or a pair of pliers. Be careful in handling elements during disassembly.

switches, knobs, buttons, controls of all kinds, shapes and colors. With the aid of the Handitester you can trace out the wiring pretty easily. Many of the connections in these appliances are of the sliding friction type, and can be pulled apart in an instant for convenience in tracing circuits, switches, pilot lights, etc.

When taking connections apart, be sure to identify them in some fashion to facilitate reassembly later. Tie knots in the wires or mark them with matching pieces of colored string, thread, tape, etc.

The resistance elements of these big broilers are quite accessible for inspection, repair or replacement. They usually give little trouble. What requires more attention is the switching and timing mechanisms. These accumulate coatings of grease from meat prepared in the appliance, and eventually become pretty badly fouled. It may be necessary to degunk them with a generous application of carbon tetrachloride or any similar noninflammable cleaning fluid. Caution: When using carbon tet, work near an open window and avoid breathing the fumes of the stuff. It's a wonderful grease solvent, but it's hard on the human system. (See also two pages following.) •

Heating element is now out. Opening in which it rests acts as catch pan for food drippings, and should be washed out thoroughly. Dry well before reassembling parts. New resistance wire, if needed, is easily inserted in ceramic form.

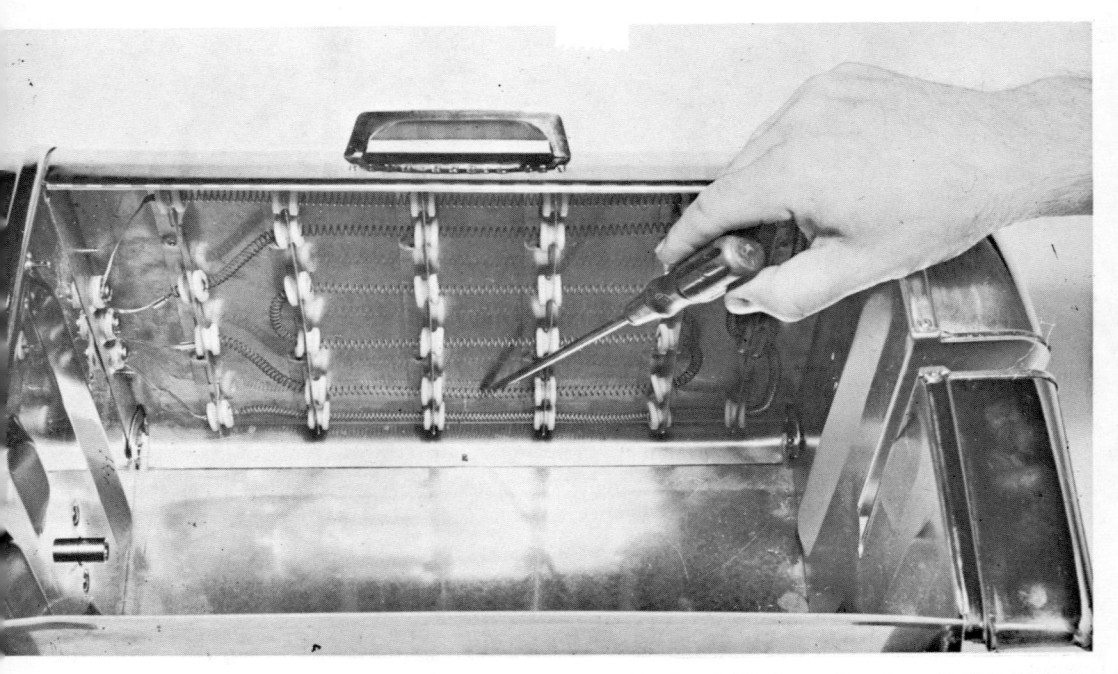

In most table-top "broilers," heating element is on underside of lid. In well-made unit like this one, the wire is supported by series of closely spaced insulators. However, since wire runs near melting point, it is bound to droop. Inspect it frequently, and distribute it evenly in its supports with screwdriver blade.

Grounding test on large table-top broiler is very important safety precaution. Set meter to LO OHMS, and one test prod on metal frame. Touch other prod to each prong in turn. Needle should not move. Urgent suggestion: Remove present two-wire cord and replace by three-wire cord and polarized safety plug, with third wire connected anywhere to frame of broiler. Accidental "grounding" of resistance wire will then only blow the line fuse, and the user of the appliance will be protected against shock.

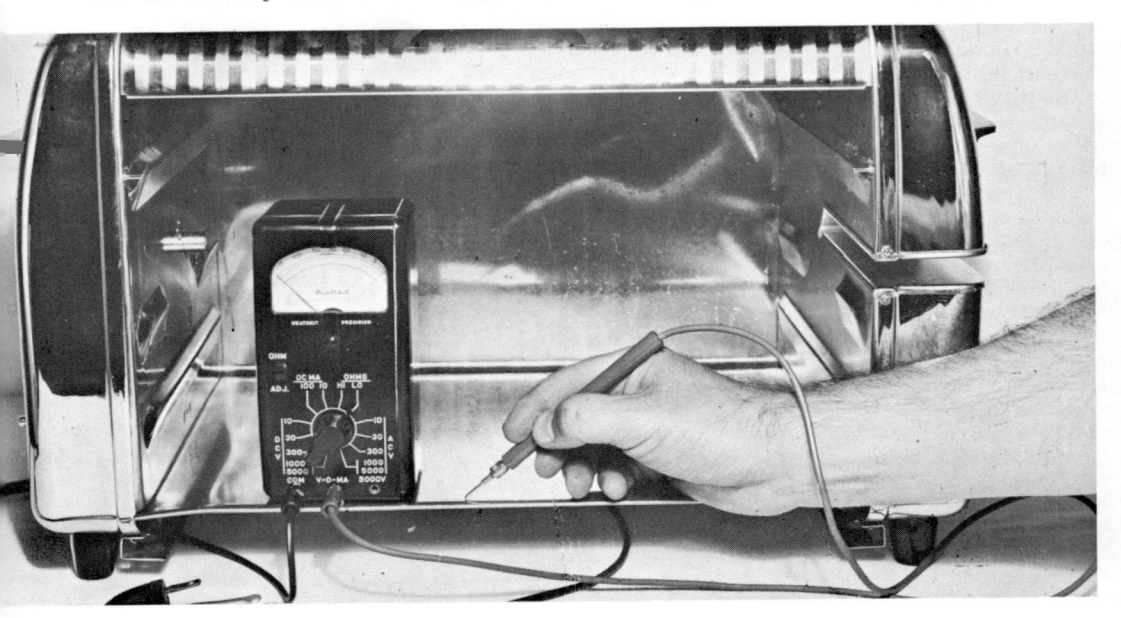

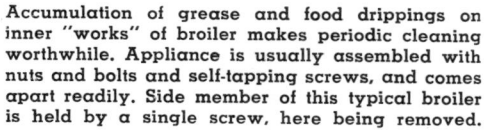

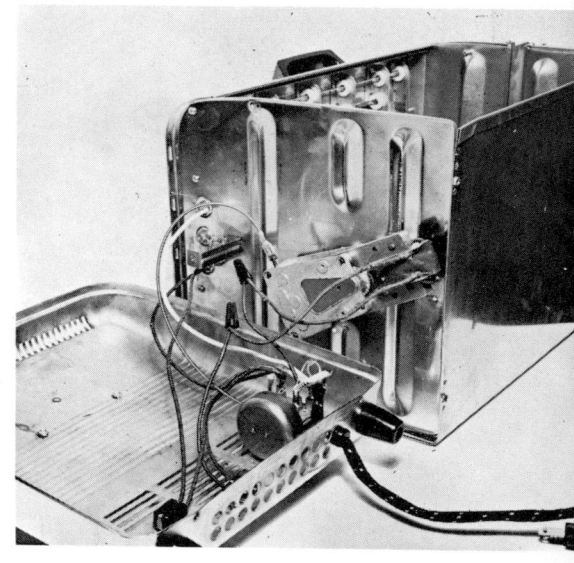

Accumulation of grease and food drippings on inner "works" of broiler makes periodic cleaning worthwhile. Appliance is usually assembled with nuts and bolts and self-tapping screws, and comes apart readily. Side member of this typical broiler is held by a single screw, here being removed.

Timer, motor switch and hi-lo heat switch are mounted on removed side of broiler; spit motor on side of frame. Motor usually is of shaded-pole (brushless) type and has two wires coming out of it. Amount of food "gunk" that seeps into motor and switches of your broiler will astonish you.

To remove motor completely for cleaning or replacement, take out mounting screws from inside. To keep them from going astray, keep all loose fasteners in box or cup. Clean before reassembly.

Spit motor is usually small high-speed unit fitted with reduction gear drive. Food drippings in latter can make it very stiff. Clean with carbon tetrachloride, at same time lubricate it sparingly.

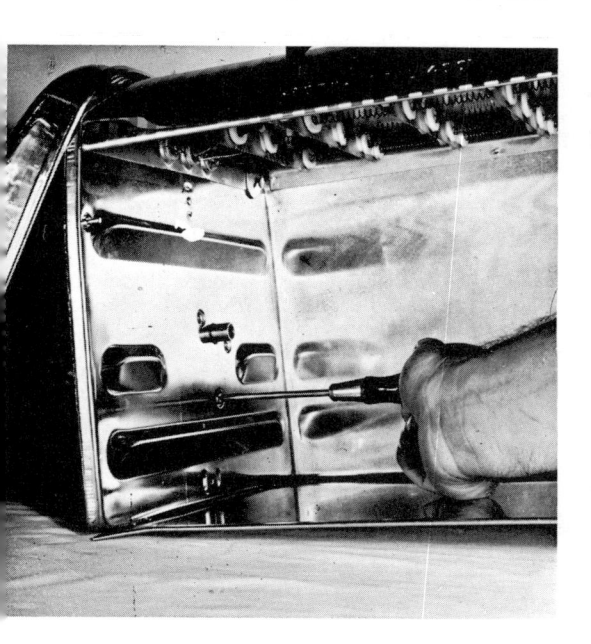

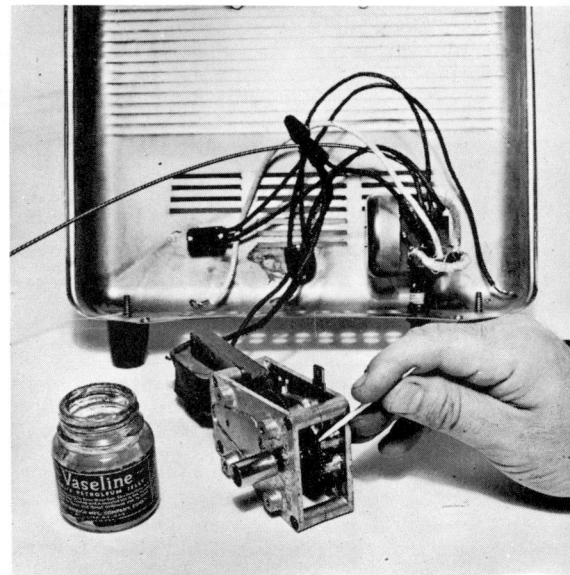

127

Some Like It Hot

Your winter comfort depends on your furnace; learn what makes it work and keep it in repair

An actual cause of oil-burner "failure"—the AC power switch was turned off. In a house with small children, tape the switch in "up" position.

IT WAS after six o'clock in the evening, and Joe noticed that snowflakes were blowing against the small window of his washroom as he scrubbed his hands with a stiff brush.

"Good night to be home," he thought to himself, just as the office phone started to ring.

"Oh, no, not at this hour," he groaned. He let it ring a dozen times, then could resist no further. "A-One Heating Service, Joe Oily speaking."

The woman's excited voice meant only one thing, *trouble*. "Mr. Oily, you must come right over. The house is getting colder every minute and the furnace doesn't come on. I've set the thermostat to 80 and we have plenty of oil in the tank. By the way, this is Mrs. Smith."

Remembering that Mrs. Smith was a steady oil customer and also a subscriber to his annual service plan, Joe did not mention that his own wife had supper waiting for him, but instead he said, "I'll be over in ten minutes."

Joe started his "service" routine without even thinking. First he checked the oil level in the 275-gallon tank and saw that it read about ¾ full. With a lamp (the "Lightester") he checked the furnace line in the meter room and noted that it was alive. He went up the cellar stairs to examine the thermostat in the living room. He moved the adjusting arm back and forth and heard the contacts click softly as they opened and closed.

"Well, there goes my supper," he said to himself as he started back down the cellar stairs to get his tool box out of the car. When he reached the bottom he stopped suddenly, a puzzled expression frozen on his face. Then he laughed quietly, did a quick about face, bounded back up the stairs to the top landing and looked closely at the wall switch with the bright red cover and the white lettering: "Oil Burner Emergency Switch." It was the delayed mental picture of this switch that had stopped him a minute earlier. He looked at the switch in disbelief, but his eyesight was good and there was no question about it: THE HANDLE WAS DOWN, IN THE OFF POSITION.

This is a completely true incident from the records of a heating contractor in a typical residential community. It is by no means an unusual one. In any house with children between the ages of about fifteen weeks and fifteen years, unusual incidents are usual. A bright red oil burner switch, so markedly different from all the other switches in the house, is bound to attract the eyes of inquisitive youngsters, but it's not the only source of trouble. In most oil-burner installations, there is a cut-off valve in the pipe directly off the tank, and another just before the oil pump at the furnace.

Because the heating system of your house is by far the largest, most complicated, most expensive and most important single element in it, you should become thoroughly familiar with it. Your "bible" is the manufacturer's instructions. These were packed with the original equipment and should have been left for you by the builder. If the installer threw them out with the crating materials, as often happens, obtain another set from the manufacturer. Copy off all the identifying model and serial numbers you can find on the equipment and the name and address of the maker, and write directly to the latter. Be sure to mention that you would like to have a complete wiring diagram of your system, among other things. Most furnace manufacturers realize that homeowners don't monkey with heating plants just for the sake of playing around, but only to keep them in good operating order. Some of the literature they send back is very elaborate. The "dope" on the combination warm-air furnace and air-conditioning unit in my own home consisted of 48 letter-size sheets.

Heating Systems by Type

Home heating systems are classified according to the fuel they burn and the method of converting the heat of combustion to room warmth. A generation ago coal was king because it had only to be chipped out of the ground and shipped off to distribution centers. However, all members of a household so thoroughly disliked the heavy, dirty work of shoveling in coal and taking out ashes that "automatic" systems using oil or gas as fuel became popular as soon as they were introduced. Hundreds of thousands of old coal burners have been converted to oil or gas, and virtually without exception new houses built since the end of World War II use these clean, convenient fuels.

In the "steam heat" system, probably the one in commonest use, a quantity of static water in a boiler is heated by an oil or gas flame to the boiling point. Steam is generated, and this pushes its way through connecting pipes to radiators, which become hot as the steam whirls around inside. The outer surfaces of the radiators warm the air in the room. As the steam gives up its heat this way to the radiators and the room, it condenses back to water, which dribbles back to the furnace to be reheated into steam.

In the "hot water heat" system, water is again heated in a boiler, but not to the point where it turns to steam. The hot water itself is circulated through connecting pipes to the room radiators, usually with the assistance of a motor driven pump, and returns to the boiler for reheating.

In the "hot air" system, the oil or gas flame heats up the air in the belly of a furnace. This warmed air rises by itself, or more usually is pushed along by a blower fan, through large sheet metal ducts or pipes which merely open out into the rooms of the house; the openings are called "registers." In older houses the warmed air gradually leaks out through windows and

The screwdriver points to heating resistor that accelerates the action of the contacts of a typical thermostat.

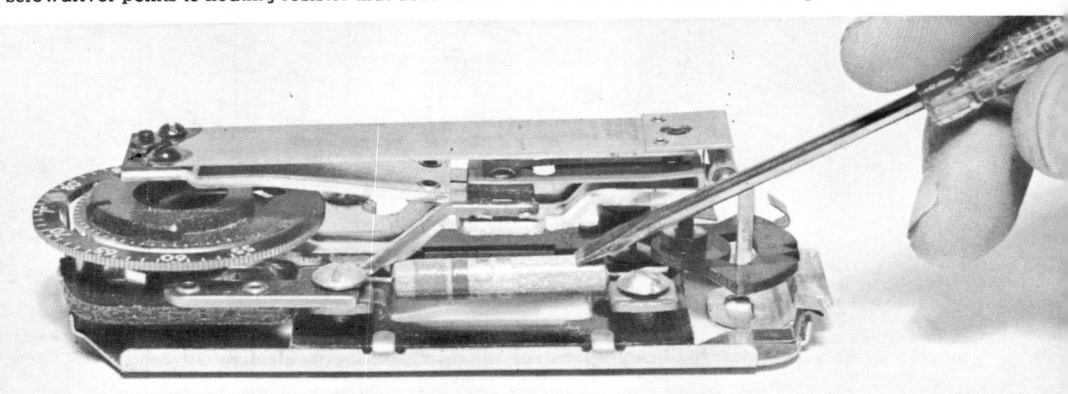

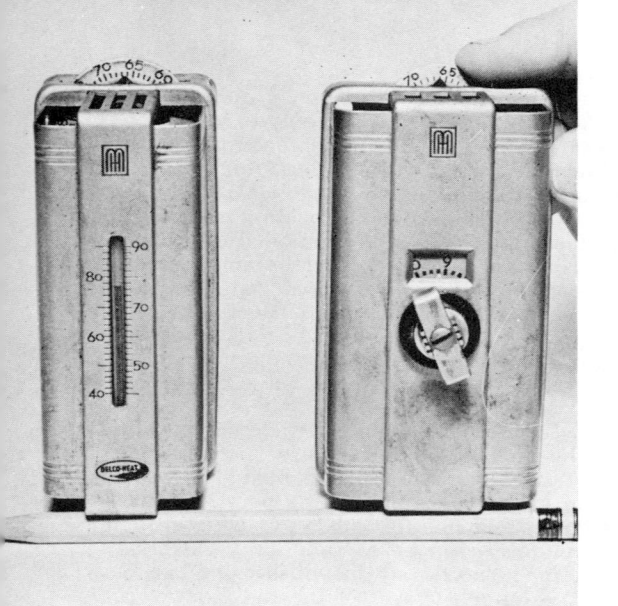

Left, a standard-type thermostat with wheel adjustment at top; right, a matching "night shut-off" with a mechanical wind-up and controlling clock.

doors and only fresh air enters the furnace (from a partially opened window or unsealed door) to be warmed and pushed up. In newer houses, especially those designed for central air cooling as well as heating, return ducts as well as entrance registers are built into the rooms. Most of the air is circulated back to the furnace and re-used after being mixed with a little fresh air to keep it from going stale.

The methods have their advantages and disadvantages, a discussion of which is beyond the scope of this book. What they have in common is a sensitive electrical control system, upon which the entire operation depends.

Although at first glance the wiring diagram of your particular installation may look like that of a television receiver, a little study of it and of the actual wiring will make it understandable.

The mechanism for turning the heat on or off is relatively simple. What makes a complete system a bit complicated is the presence of interlocking safety devices designed to prevent one thing: accidental fire or explosion.

Figure 1 is a simplified version of an oil burner system. The basic parts consist of the room thermostat TH; the transformer T1, which steps down the 115 volt A.C. line to about 24 volts; the relay R, which is an electrically controlled switch; the motor M, which turns the pump that brings oil from the storage tank and forces it through an atomizer nozzle in the furnace; the ignition transformer T2, which steps up the A.C. line to about 10,000 or 12,000 volts; and the spark gap SG, across which the high voltage jumps to form an intense electrical flame.

The thermostat TH is a temperature-sensitive switch, which can be set to close and open within narrow limits. A normal winter setting would be 70 degrees. Suppose the air in the vicinity of the thermostat cools just below this value. The two contacts of the thermostat close, and the device is said to be "calling for heat." The 'stat is directly in series with the 24-volt secondary of T1 and the winding of the relay R. The contacts R1 and R2 of the relay are normally open. When current from the 24-volt transformer flows through the contacts of the thermostat and the relay winding, the action of the relay is to pull the contacts R1 and R2 closed. These are in the 115-volt circuit to the pump motor M and the ignition transformer T. Oil is vaporized into the furnace and this vapor is ignited

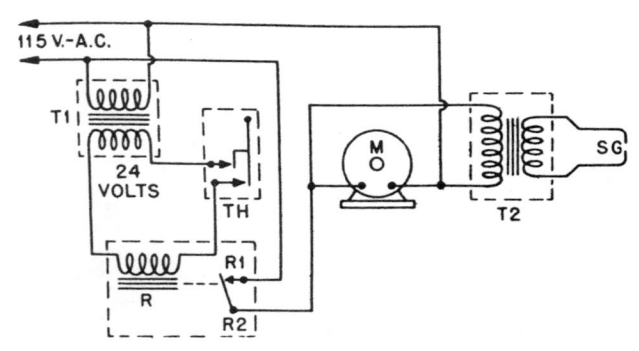

Figure 1: This is a simplified diagram of an oil-burner electrical system as controlled by a thermostat, marked by the symbol TH. Full details of the current cut-off and supply are given in the accompanying text.

by the sparking across the gap SG. The action is very much like that of an automobile engine. Actually, ignition is needed only for a few seconds, after which the oil flame maintains iself.

The flame heats or boils the water in the boiler, or the air in a hot-air furnace, and the room warms up. When the air in the vicinity of the thermostat reaches 70, the 'stat contacts open, breaking the relay circuit and causing the relay contacts to open; this in turn cuts off the motor and the oil supply, and the flame dies out.

A complete diagram of an actual oil burner installation is shown in Figure 2. Let's follow this through and you'll get a pretty good general idea of how systems of this class operate.

A separate branch fuse F usually feeds the furnace line. S1 is the red-plated line switch previously mentioned. Normally it is kept on. Ignore S7 for the moment, except to assume that it is on. The step-down transformer T1 and one side each of the motor M and the ignition transformer T2 connect to the 115-volt line, as before. The thermostat TH now has three terminals, marked R, B and W, for red, black and white, respectively, the colors of the three-wire cable that connects the unit to the furnace. HR2 is a resistor, which provides a small amount of heat inside the thermostat case for a purpose to be described. S2 is a thermal safety switch. Its contacts normally are closed and furnish a path between the left end of the 24-volt winding of T1 and the winding of the relay R. HR1 is a thermal element that causes the contacts of S2 to open if current passes through it for more than a predetermined time. The relay now has three switch units, S2, S3 and S4, which operate together and are normally open. The switches S5 and S6 are part of a mechanism that is rotated by a heat-sensitive arm stuck into the exhaust stack of the furnace. With the latter cold, the central arm of S5 rests against the C or cold contact, and the H or hot contact is open. Switch S6 is a tiny glass tube containing two contacts and a few drops of mercury. It is so angled that the contacts are immersed in the mercury, or closed, when the furnace is cold.

The primary of T1 is connected permanently to the 115-volt line, just as in the case of a bell-ringing transformer. If the room is warm and the setting of the thermostat is satisfied, the B and W contacts are open. Since W goes to the right end of the T1 secondary and nowhere else, the entire 24-volt circuit is dead. This means that S2, S3 and S4 are open, and since S4 controls both the motor and the ignition the whole furnace is at rest. When the room cools down, the B and W contacts of TH close. This establishes the 24-volt circuit as follows: right end of transformer, W contact, metal arm of thermostat, B contact, lower contact of S3, center arm of S5, C contact of S5, heater resistor HR1, relay R, switch S2 and back to left end of transformer T1. Current passing through R causes its magnet to pull S2, S3 and S4 closed. For the moment, the closing of S2 has no effect, because the arm of this switch goes only to contact H of S5, which is still open. The closing of S3 establishes an auxiliary circuit to the heating resistor HR2, which at the moment is unimportant. The closing of S4, however, is most important. It turns on the motor and the ignition through the closed contacts of S6.

The Stack Control

If everything is normal, the oil flames, and hot exhaust gases start going up the stack to the chimney. In flowing over the heat-sensitive arm to which switches S5 and S6 are mounted, they cause this arm to twist. After several seconds, the movement is enough to move the arm of S5 from contact C to contact H; this opens the circuit to HR1 of the safety switch and keeps the relay circuit closed through switch S2. The same movement tilts S6 so that the internal wires are freed from the pool of mercury, and the circuit to T2 then opens, cutting off the ignition. The furnace is now running full blast.

When the room warms up, the B contact of the thermostat opens first. This does not open the 'stat circuit, as you might think. It is still intact, but this time from the W

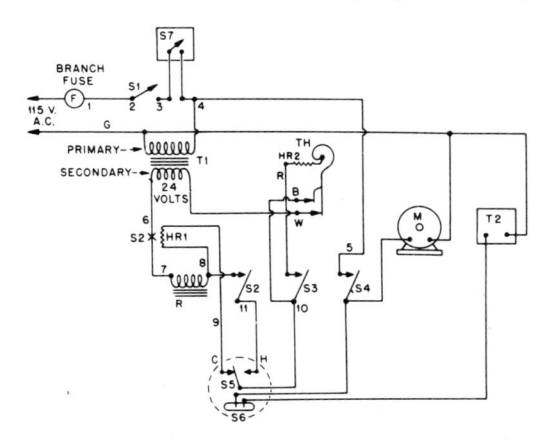

Figure 2: Detailed schematic diagram of an actual oil-burner installation as found in many homes.

131

Modern thermostat with electric clock timer that runs on 24 volts has two temperature adjustments on right side of the case. The upper one is for the daytime, and the lower one is set for night-time lower temperatures.

contact, through the metal arm and the heating resistor HR2, through the closed contacts of S3, S5's contact H, switch S2, relay R, safety switch S2 and back to the transformer. Current flowing through HR2 heats it up, and some of the heat passes to the bi-metallic strip of the thermostat. This artificial heat accelerates the action of the latter and causes the contact W to open sooner than it would without it. With R and W both open, the 24 volt circuit is broken, the relay is deactivated, S2, S3 and S4 open, and the motor stops. As the furnace cools down a little, the heat-sensitive arm of S5-S6 twists back to starting position; S5 moves to the C contact and S6 tilts to close.

Heat acceleration is now more or less standard with room thermostats because it eliminates a lag that seems to be characteristic of unheated 'stats.

Preventing Oil Flood

Suppose now that for some reason the ignition system is faulty: S6 might be bad, T2 open or short circuited, the spark gap fouled. When the thermostat calls for heat the circuit includes S5 and HR1. The motor starts pumping oil, but it doesn't ignite. The chimney stack remains cold. This means that switch S5 doesn't twist, but remains against contact C. Current flows through the heating element HR1 of the safety switch S2. After a predetermined time, usually a maximum of 120 seconds, HR1 causes the contacts of S2 to pop open, as they do in a thermal circuit breaker. With S2 open, R is de-energized, S2, S3 and S4 open, and the opening of S4 particularly shuts down the motor. If S2 did not open, the motor would continue to pump oil into the furnace, and it would quickly overflow onto the cellar floor and cause one grand mess. S2 *stays* open until someone resets it by hand.

When the Flame Fails

If the flame should fail after the burner has gone on properly, the quick drop in stack temperature causes S5 to untwist. The instant the arm leaves contact H, the relay circuit opens and again shuts down the burner. S2 is not affected. A momentary loss of power will also shut down the system. However, as the stack cools down further, S5 closes against contact C, and if the thermostat is still calling for heat the burner will start itself again, or "recycle," after a cooling off period of one to two minutes.

Initial failure of the burner to ignite, causing the safety switch S2 to lock open, might be due to air in the oil line, a bit of dirt lodged in the pump or something else that can readily clear itself in time. If you find this switch open when you are checking a cold furnace, always reset it for another trial before going further. When the motor starts this time it might blow the obstruction clear.

Now suppose a burner *keeps* running. If you leave it alone long enough, in the case of steam and hot water systems, it can build up a lot of steam pressure and eventually blow itself up. Most such furnaces have mechanical safety valves, but long before one of these starts whistling a pressure switch in the water chamber

Here is the inside view of the combination thermostat shown at the left; small pointers on round center dial are set for desired periods. To clean thermostat contacts pass a piece of white paper lightly between them.

should open. Connected into the power line as switch S7, this merely cuts off all power and the system shuts down.

In most oil burner installations the furnace also is the domestic hot water heater. A coil of heavy copper pipe carrying cold water is immersed in the water jacket of the boiler. The cold water is heated by contact with the boiler water, and passes on to a storage tank. In "tankless" systems the copper pipe is big enough to act as its own reservoir. In winter, when the furnace is on a great deal, hot water is plentiful. In summer, an independent thermostat in the water jacket turns the burner on for short periods to bring the water up to 140 or 150 degrees, as desired, but not high enough to bring on heat. This thermostat merely parallels the room thermostat's connections.

Gas-Fired Systems

Gas-fired steam and hot-water systems are somewhat simpler than oil systems because they do not require a pump motor or an ignition system. Instead of the pump motor, there is a magnetically operated gas valve, and for ignition there is a small, permanently lighted pilot flame in the fire box.

Any failure of the gas supply causes a thermal safety valve to cool down and lock the main gas line shut. It cannot come on again by itself until the pilot is relighted and allowed to reheat the safety. This is a primary requirement in any gas system. The bi-metallic shut-off devices found in gas furnaces are extremely rugged and reliable and should be left strictly alone. Cases of failure are virtually unknown.

Forced warm air furnaces, particularly gas-fired jobs, are becoming increasingly popular because they are clean, easy to maintain, and fast in action, in addition to lending themselves to combination with a cold air unit. The wiring is easy to follow once you know the functions of the parts.

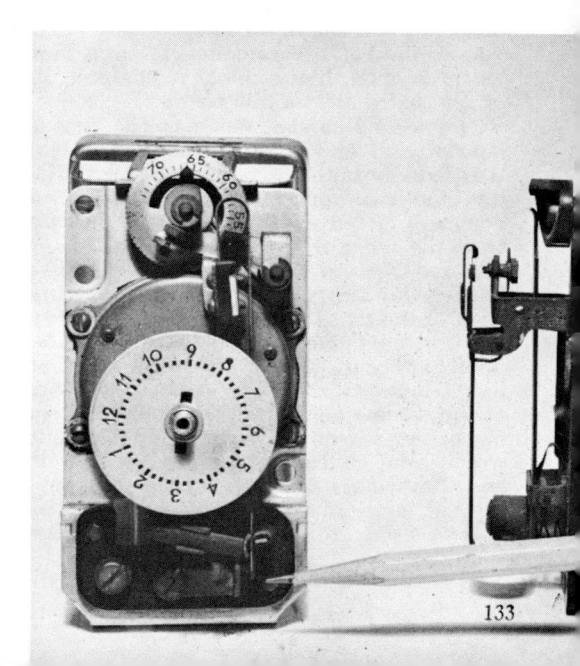

Inside views of standard (right) and night shut-off thermostats show (pencil) locked contacts of shut-off. Controls enable user to time the furnace turn-off.

133

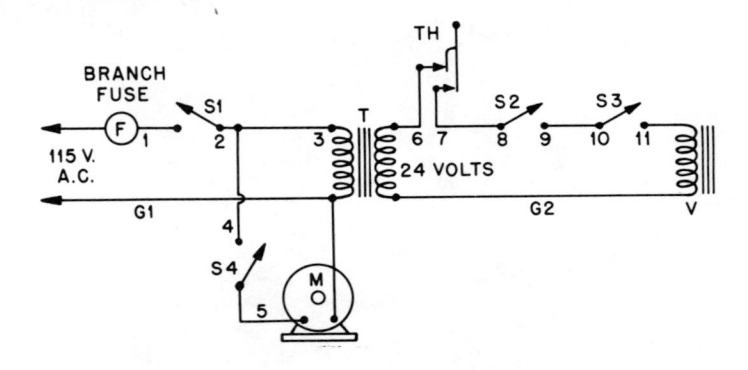

Figure 3: Schematic diagram of typical gas-fired furnace system.

See Figure 3, which shows the actual connections of a typical furnace. Simple, isn't it?

The branch fuse F and the main line switch S1 are familiar. T is again a 24-volt step-down transformer. There are three switches between the 24-volt winding and the electromagnetic valve V, which regulates the gas to the burners. TH is the usual room thermostat, which might or might not have heat acceleration. When the room is cool and the 'stat calls for heat, its contacts close. Before it can actuate the valve V and turn on the gas, two other switches must be closed. The first is S2. This is controlled by a pushrod which is part of a thermostatic element exposed to the pilot light in the gas chamber. If the pilot is properly lighted, the switch is closed. If the gas should fail at any time, the element cools off and quickly locks the switch open. When the gas comes on again, it cannot do any damage, as the valve V remains closed as long as S2 is open. If the pilot is relighted, S2 snaps closed after a minute or so.

The second safety switch is S3. This is normally on, and is called the limit switch. It is usually built in combination with S4, the blower motor switch. With S2 and S3 normally closed and S4 open, let's pick up from the room thermostat. This called for heat, so current from the 24-volt transformer flows through TH, S2, S3, V and back to the transformer. Energized by this current, the valve V clicks wide open, and immediately the gas is ignited by the pilot light. However, the motor M does not start at the same time, a fact that puzzles new owners of warm air systems. If it did, it would send cold air up through the ducts and that would make everyone unhappy. Instead, a thermostatic element in S3-S4 keeps S4 open for a period of three to five minutes, while the air in the furnace chamber gets good and warm. Then S4 closes, and a blast of warm air is pushed through the system. When the room thermostat is satisfied it opens the circuit to V and cuts off the burners. However, the fan switch remains closed for another few minutes while it empties remaining warm air out of the furnace, and then the thermostatic element flips it open.

If the room thermostat is turned up rather high and keeps the furnace on for a long time, the furnace and the air it sends out can get too hot for comfort and safety. Here's where the limit switch S3 goes to work. It merely opens when a predetermined temperature is reached, thus opening the circuit to V and de-energizing the gas valve. The fan continues to clear the hot air into the ducts until its control switch S4 is thermostatically opened.

Night Shut-Offs

Under most circumstances it is advantageous to lower the house temperature during sleeping hours and to bring the thermostat up to a higher value about an hour before the family arises, so that the house is warm when they get out of bed. This is done by means of a double thermostat in one case, with a small electric clock timer as part of the integrated mechanism; or by a "night shut-off" with the night thermostat and the timer in a case separate from that of the main thermostat.

The controls, which can be set for any desired "night" and "day" periods, are arranged so that the two thermostats are connected in simple series. The day unit is always in the circuit, but the night 'stat, during the day hours, is merely short circuited. The timer opens this short circuit, and puts the night 'stat into action at night

Ceiling view of separate transformer to run the clock of combination thermostat; it carries only 24V.

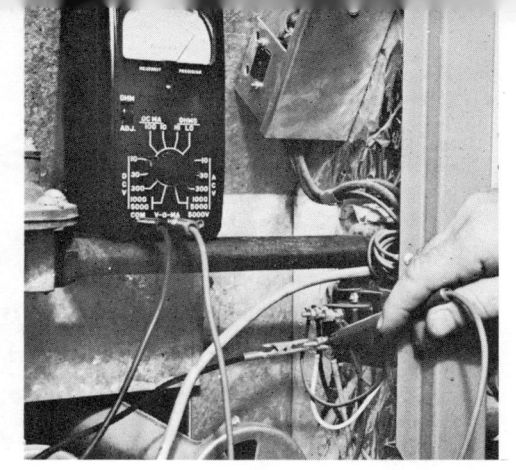

In typical gas-fired hot-air installation, step-down transformer is accessible with furnace front off.

and takes it out again in the morning. During the night, the burner is controlled by the lower setting. For example, suppose the normal day setting is 70 degrees and the night adjustment 65 (those five degrees make a big difference), and the room temperature falls to 68. The day 'stat calls for heat but it doesn't turn on the burner because the night 'stat is still satisfied. When the room drops to 65, the heat will come on.

Accidental misadjustment of the night shut-off is responsible for as many cold houses as is an open main switch. It's one of the last things a frantic homeowner usually looks into, but it should be among the first. Push up both day and night controls to 80; if that doesn't energize the heater, look elsewhere.

Troubleshooting

Before any trouble develops, familiarize yourself with the voltage distribution in the electrical system, with the aid of the Handitester or any similar voltmeter. In most installations, the step-down transformer, relay and stack control are combined in a single box, fitted with a cover that comes off easily. Leave the line power on, and don't touch any bare metal with your fingers; use the test probes of the tester. Study the technical literature from the manufacturer, identify each part and check the wires from point to point by their color.

Remembering Joe Oily's experience with the main switch, start at the fuse box and work on. With the tester set for A.C. volts on the 300 scale, you should read the full line voltage of 115 or thereabouts between the grounded side of the line, marked G in Figure 2, and the following points in the typical oil burner system illustrated: 1, fuse; 2 and 3, main switch; 4, transformer primary and pressure switch; 5, motor switch contact of relay. These readings will be the same whether the burner is on or off.

The R, B and W leads from the room thermostat usually terminate at binding posts with the same letter markings, somewhere in the furnace control box. With the meter on the 30-volt A.C. scale, use W as the common test point, and touch the probe to other points to obtain 24 volts with the burner off: 6, transformer secondary and one contact of safety switch; 7, other safety contact and one end of relay; 8, other end of relay, one end of heating element HR1, and fixed contact of S2; 9, other end of HR1, contact C of S5; 10, S5, S3 and B.

Absence of a reading between W and 7 is a sure sign that the safety switch contacts are open, a common but not often suspected cause of trouble. No reading at 8, after a normal reading at 7, means only one thing: an open relay winding. With the burner running, the only change is that point 11, S2 and H of S5, previously dead, now also read the 24 volts.

To make continuity and grounding tests on individual parts, set the meter for LO OHMS and proceed exactly as indicated elsewhere in this book in the safety, tools, and motor sections.

With a gas-fired air system, the checks are kindergarten stuff. See Figure 3. With the furnace in full operation, get 115 volts between G1 and points 1, 2, 3, 4 and 5; get 24 volts between G2 and 6, 7, 8, 9, 10 and 11. If the thermostat is not calling for heat, only G2-6 is alive with 24 volts, and points 7 through 11 read nothing.

Many cases of jittery furnace operation are due merely to loose connections, rather than to defective parts. Pump and blower motors sometimes run for hours in cold weather. Go over all leads with a socket wrench or pair of pliers. •

Some Like It Cool

Maintenance of your air conditioner is simple but important—if neglected, it will cost you comfort. Here, also, are tips to increase cooling efficiency

AN AIR CONDITIONER is an overgrown refrigerator, designed to cool a big box containing people instead of a small box containing food. Except for size, the mechanisms are pretty much identical, and both have achieved an extraordinarily high degree of reliability. Because an air conditioner is used only a few months out of the year, and then only intermittently rather than steadily, it can be expected to last a long time. It needs only minor maintenance attention.

About the only thing an owner of a conditioner can do for it is inspect the air filter

Stagnant pockets of air can be prevented by directing a stream of air ceilingward with an oscillating fan. This device will help circulate cooler air.

Here the ventilating louver on the underside of the roof overhang is covered with screening to keep out insects. Air flowing through here ventilates attic.

An attic fan keeps a constant flow of air moving; this acts as an invisible blanket of moving insulation in cooling downstairs. Note that it's belt-driven.

This is the most important operation in air-conditioner maintenance—keeping the air filter clean. The filter shown comes from a central-type unit.

frequently during the cooling season, clean it if it is of the renewable type, or replace it if it is of the disposable type. Practically all conditioners contain a filter of some kind to remove dust and dirt from the air before the machine cools and dehumidifies it and then pushes it into the room. As it gradually becomes blocked with the dust it entraps, the filter reduces the cooling ability of the machine. After a month or so of hot weather, during which the conditioner has been pumping away at a good rate, you're likely to find yourself saying, "Funny, the room doesn't seem to be as comfortable as it was." In central air-conditioning installations, which have the job of moving the air in an entire house, a filter can sometimes become blocked almost solid after a few weeks.

It takes only a few minutes to remove, clean and replace a filter. Some filters of the so-called lifetime type are washed under running water. Because the entrapped dirt is usually fluffy, a vacuum cleaner does a quick job on most other varieties. Frequent vacuuming keeps filters of the glass-wool type at top operating effectiveness and eliminates the need for replacement altogether. First take off all the surface dirt. Then slap the filter flat against the floor several times, and vacuum up the dust that shakes out.

With the vacuum cleaner set up, poke its nozzle carefully into the body of the conditioner, wherever you can reach easily without jogging anything. Of course, the control switch should be "off," or, better, the line plug should be pulled out of its receptacle. This internal cleaning is especially important in the early summer, after the machine has been idle for some months. At the same time, inspect the outside end of the machine, and don't be surprised if you find a family of sparrows well bedded down under it. The space between the window sill and the overhanging cabinet of the cooler is evidently ideal for nesting purposes, being sheltered from rain and snow and of just the right size for small birds.

Most of the "trouble" reported by purchasers of room conditioners is not really in the machines themselves, but is due to the inability of the power wiring and/or the fuses to handle the starting load, the running load, or a combination of these loads and other loads on the same line. (See chapter entitled Is Your Wiring Adequate?) If slow-blow fuses or delayed action circuit breakers don't help, the purchaser is just out of luck, unless he has a firm understanding with the dealer covering just such a situation. Some short-sighted dealers will sell a customer any size machine he asks for, with the attitude that it's the customer's responsibility to know the capabilities of the power circuits in his house or apartment. Other dealers, interested in staying in business in their communities, practically make the customer prove his power lines are suitable before they'll take his money. This is a smart policy, because it protects both seller and buyer.

Improving Conditioner Performance

Because of the sealed construction universally used in refrigeration units, there is nothing you can do about changing the operating characteristics of a cooler. However, you can do a great deal to *help* it make the room comfortable and livable.

A conditioner draws air from the room over a series of cold pipes, which reduce its temperature and at the same time cause the moisture in it to condense out. The cooled and dried air is then pushed back into the room. A little fresh air from the outside is mixed with the room air to replenish the supply of oxygen. Without this mixing the recirculated air soon becomes stale, and occupants of the room start feeling woozy.

Even with the best of conditioners, however, the blowers are not always equal to the job of circulating *all* the air in a room. Warm air tends to rise, and cold air, being heavier, tends to sink toward the floor. If people in the room are smoking, inadequate circulation shows up quickly; the room takes on a bluish haze, and non-smokers who are allergic to nicotine display the initial signs of nausea.

The cure for this condition is so simple that it is overlooked by many sufferers. Set up a small electric fan as near the ceiling as possible, aim at the ceiling in the direction of the air conditioner, and run it at low speed. A fan doesn't cool, but it does move air. With a little experimenting as to position, you'll find that it does wonders in breaking up stagnant pockets of warm air near the ceiling and making the whole room feel cleaner.

In a living room or dining room, a good spot for the fan is the top of a breakfront, a book case, a china closet, etc. In a bedroom, a convenient location is the top of a high dresser.

If the fan is of the oscillating type, so much the better. In any case, keep the speed down, to prevent people from getting stiff necks. After all, the prime object of a fan is to achieve the maximum of comfort under any circumstances.

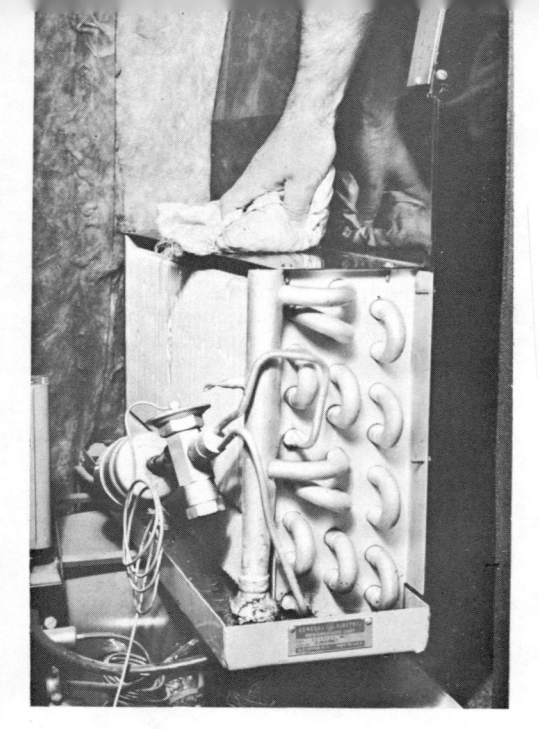

Occasional wiping and cleaning of refrigerating coil of central air conditioner is helpful in maintaining efficiency; this coil is typical of two-ton unit.

Keeping the Emerson Electric air conditioner in top working order is simple; the lifetime air filter slides out in an instant and can be cleaned in a minute.

Sun Protection Important

The effectiveness of an air conditioner in reducing air temperature depends to a large extent on that temperature at the start. No machine made by man can possibly overcome the full heating effect of the summer sun, but you can give a conditioner a fighting chance by keeping *direct* sunshine away from the room you want to "condition." As a minimum, draw the blinds or pull down the shades on exposed windows. Outside awnings that keep the sun from striking the window area are very desirable. A darkened room *feels* cooler than a bright one. A few electric lights generate less heat than a few shafts of sunshine, so the overall result is a gain in the direction of comfort.

It follows naturally that rooms facing north or east are easier to cool than those facing long hours of sunshine to the south or west.

In private houses, the most critical area is the roof, with the attic below it. If the house is in the open and is not completely shaded by large, leafy trees, the attic is a veritable oven after an afternoon of summer sunshine. Temperatures in it can reach incredible values; 115 to 140 degrees!

Trying to "air condition" the rooms under these ovens was a waste of electricity. Oh, yes, the attic floors might have deep blankets of insulation in them. Insulation is no cure-all; it *delays* the penetration of heat from the attic downward but it doesn't *prevent* it. The insulation itself soaks up heat, the way stones do in a slow fire; then, hours after sunset, it is still giving off some of that heat. This explains why room temperature can be in the 80's at ten p.m. when the outside air has already dropped to the 70's.

Since it is next to impossible in most locations to keep all sunshine off a roof, the only alternative is to get rid of the hot air under the roof as quickly as it forms. A powerful attic fan does the trick. The bigger the better! The standard sizes for homes are 24, 30 and 36 inches, these figures representing the diameter of the blower blades. The overall dimensions of the complete unit are greater. The controlling factor in some houses is the size of the trap door or other means of access to the attic. One chap I know installed two 20-inch fans because he couldn't get anything larger through the opening in the ceiling of a closet.

If the attic fan is big enough and the house is of the right shape, it can replace air conditioning altogether! A friend of mine installed a 36-inch blower in the ceiling at the head of the upper landing of a conventional two-story house. When he turns this monster on, newspapers and playing cards on the dining room table start floating upward like the props in a magician's levitation act. His attic temperature on a July day dropped from 121 to 96 degrees fifteen minutes after the fan was put into action. I took the readings, so I know.

In my house the attic is accessible but shallow, and I had to settle for a single 20-inch fan. Although this is small compared with the more desirable 24- and 30-inch sizes, it brings the attic temperature down as much as 20 degrees. In the rooms below, the air temperature a foot below the ceiling used to be about 90; with the fan going, it falls to 82 or 83. Now the air conditioner works to the extent of keeping a party of eleven people comfortable throughout the house on a broiler of a day when the temperature is 93 and the humidity 76%.

When the air in the attic is pumped out through an opening in a side wall, other air must come in to replace it. The source of this air is important. If an individual air conditioner is used in only one room (the master bedroom, in most cases), that room should be kept closed, and air from the rest of the house is allowed to be sucked upward through a grille of some sort in a hallway ceiling or through an open trap door in a room other than the air-conditioned one. If the house has a basement, doors leading to it should be kept open, as cellar air is often noticeably cooler than that in upper rooms.

If there is a unit in a room that cannot be closed off, or if the house is centrally cooled, the attic fan must not be allowed to draw air from the living area, because the conditioner can't possibly cool it at the same rate at which it is expelled through the attic louvers. You have to study the construction of the house and determine if suitable air passages can be cut in the ceilings and floors of closets or through hallways. I know of a 50-year old house in which an ideal "duct" was provided by the shaft of a dumbwaiter that formerly connected the kitchen, in the basement, with the dining room and the bedrooms, upstairs.

If the roof of the house has overhanging eaves that are safely accessible by ladder, by all means cut openings in them about a foot square; two or three on each side, depending on the size of the house. This is a relatively easy job. Bore one-inch holes in the corners, and use a keyhole saw for the rest. Cover the openings with screening, stapled or tacked in place. In the winter cover over with pieces of plywood or hardboard, held with wood screws. These openings have a chimney effect in combination with the roof rafters, and afford very good ventilation in moderate weather even with the attic fan off. Being on the underside of the eaves, they have the further advantage that they do not readily admit rain or snow.

Houses with flat roofs present a special cooling problem. Forced air evacuation obviously is out. Some "breathing" space undoubtedly is provided between the insulation and the roof surface proper, but this usually is not adequate when the weather gets sticky. If the edges or eaves of this roof overhang the walls of the house and are accessible, a series of underside louvers may be a big help. These should be placed at opposite ends of the rafters, so that air can blow through.

"Flat" roofs are never really flat, but are pitched slightly to shed rain. In areas in which water is plentiful, an owner might install a perforated pipe along the high end of the roof, and let water trickle over the entire roof surface to the gutter at the low end. The cooling effect is considerable, and the temperature in the rooms beneath drops to the point where air conditioning becomes successful.

If water is not so cheap that it can be wasted this way, the next best bet is a number of good-sized trees, placed so that they shade the roof, either completely or at least partially. The transplanting of trees is an organized business. You can have a small forest set up around your house in only a day. The trees are trucked in, their roots neatly bundled in burlap. A crew of men dig out holes of just the right size and shape. They drop in the trees, burlap and all, shovel back the earth, and are gone as quickly as you pay the bill.

Central Air Conditioners

There is every indication that the next big "gimmick" in the sale of private houses will be central air conditioning. All other major electrical appliances and gadgets are so commonplace that people take them for granted: refrigerators, freezers, dish and clothes washers, ironers, garbage disposals, broilers, mixers, etc.

Many "better" houses already include full air conditioning. Even some very moderately priced ones have provision for later installation of a unit or for immediate installation as an "extra." Mechanically, the job is less complicated than it appears at first sight. The basic heating system is of the hot air type. (Whether the fuel is oil or gas is immaterial). A system of ducts circulates the warmed air under the push of a turbine-like blower. For central cooling, the same ducts and blower are used, except that now they carry air cooled by a refrigerator unit set directly next to the furnace. In some installations the changeover from heating to cooling, or the other way, is controlled on a completely automatic basis by the relative settings of the hot and cold thermostats in the living area.

If an air conditioner stops working altogether, and you're sure that all fuses, breakers or overload devices are intact and power on, you must call a serviceman. •

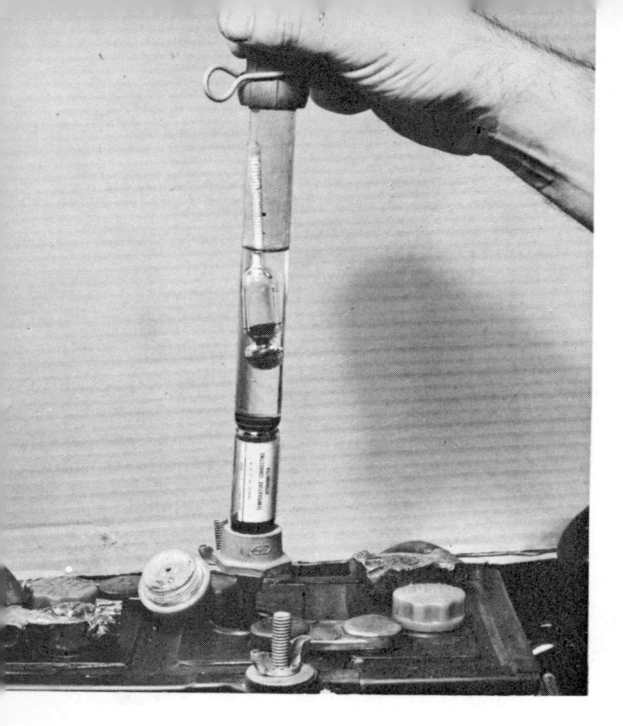

Here a hydrometer is measuring the specific gravity of the battery acid; the higher the float rides, the better the condition of the charge. This battery is pretty well up to full. Return acid to each cell after taking reading, and rinse hydrometer in clear water before storing.

When using an external charger, it is not necessary to disconnect the present wires to the terminals of the battery. Merely connect the charger leads, by their spring clips, directly to the battery posts. Charger plus goes to battery plus, minus to minus.

Batteries and Chargers

You'll not get caught with your charge down if you give your car battery reasonable care

YOU slide under the wheel of the car one frosty winter morning, turn the key in the lock, and start to push down the accelerator to race the engine a little. Only the engine doesn't race; in fact it doesn't even walk.

"Oh, no, stuck with a dead battery!" you groan.

This *won't* happen to you if you consider the car's electrical system merely as an extension of the house's power system, and give it the same type of attention and preventive maintenance.

Why does a car battery hold up perfectly well during the summer and poop out in the winter, just when you need it most?

For two reasons: 1) the oil in the crank case is stiffer in cold weather than in warm, and the starting motor has a harder job ploughing through it; 2) The output or effectiveness of a storage battery falls off markedly as the temperature drops. In other words, when the engine needs the most starting energy, the battery is least capable of providing it!

There *is* a simple solution to this nuisance: check the battery frequently with the arrival of cold weather, and give it an overnight charge with a charger occasionally to keep it to full strength. The more frequently you stop and start the engine, and the less you use the car in the winter, the less chance does the battery have to accumulate a good charge from the charging generator, which works only when the engine runs.

A test on a storage battery with a voltmeter doesn't mean very much. A three-cell battery can read pretty close to its maximum of 6.6 volts, and a six-cell battery to 13.2 volts, and still make very little impression on a current-hungry starting motor. Did you know that a three-cell battery has to deliver between 200 and 300 amperes to kick over a modern high-compression engine?

The only reliable test is made with a hydrometer. This is a syringe-like glass gadget with a squeeze bulb at one end; inside the glass is a shot-weighted float. To use it, you merely unscrew each cap of the battery in turn and suck up about half a syringeful of acid. The weight of the acid compared to that of water (its "specific gravity") is a direct indication of the state of charge. The float is calibrated to show this specific gravity. Theoretical full charge is 1.3, or "1300," although with anything but a brand new battery a reading between 1200 and 1250 or 1275 is very good. When the reading falls below 1200 the battery needs a little shot in the arm.

A battery charger is a source of low-voltage direct current. It consists usually of a step-down transformer that reduces the 115-volt AC line to about 7 or 15 volts (for three- and six-cell batteries, respectively) after passing it through a rectifier that changes the AC to DC. Dual-voltage chargers are now common, to accommodate both types of batteries. To do an overnight boosting job, a charger for three-cell automobile batteries should produce not less than about 5 amperes, although 10 is even better; for six-cell batteries, ratings of about 3 to 6 amperes are adequate. Always disconnect a charger before starting the engine. •

Car vibration can loosen battery leads and sometimes make them jump off; inspect, clean, tighten.

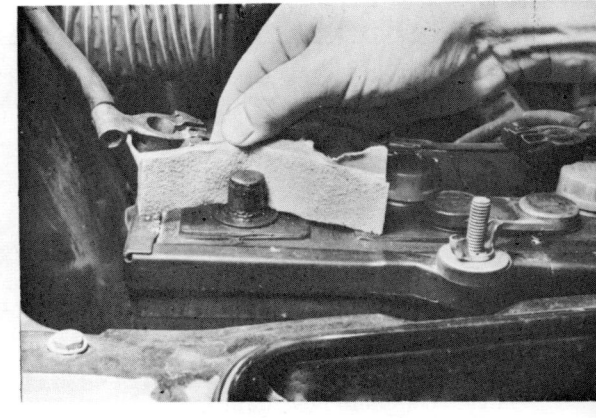

Several times a year, remove the connector lugs from battery and clean terminals with sandpaper.

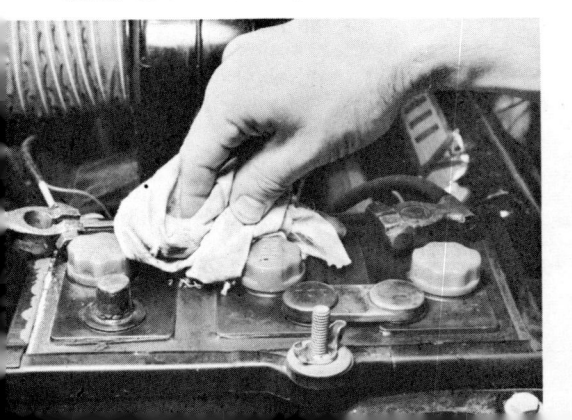

Wipe battery often with cloth dampened with water; check center caps of the battery for fit.

To minimize corrosion around terminals, caused by sulphuric acid vapor from cells, coat with Vaseline.

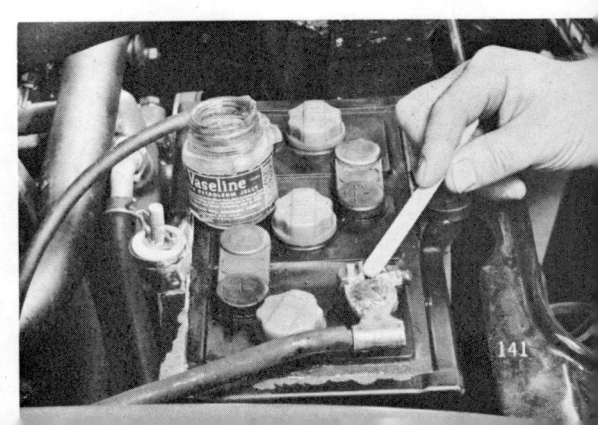

Electricity Outdoors

The current interest in outdoor living brings up the matter of extension of lines from the nearest source, with correct wiring

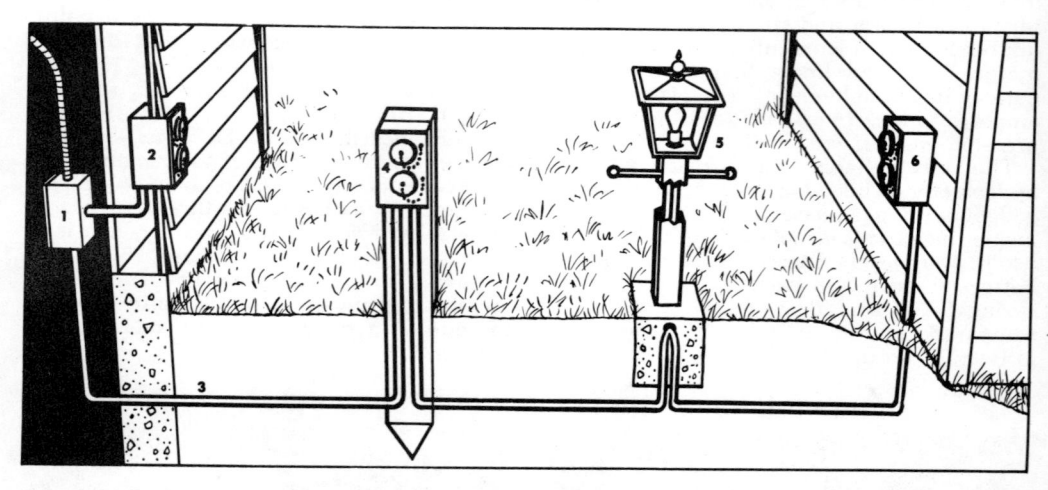

Typical outdoor wiring installation: 1—Junction box, with upper cable picking up power from basement meter. 2—Waterproof duplex outlet on outside of house. 3—Underground cable through hole in foundation. 4—Utility outlet on post set into ground. 5—Pathway lantern. 6—Utility outlet on garage.

MOST small houses are built without any provision for the use *outdoors* of many useful electrical appliances and devices. With the current trend toward outdoor activities, power might be wanted for such things as mowers, hedge cutters, bug traps, barbecues, radio and television sets, phonographs, movie projectors and even commonplace lighting.

From the electrical standpoint, extending a line from the house or possibly a garage is relatively simple. From the physical standpoint it often is difficult because holes must be cut in exterior walls to pass the extra wiring, and trenches might have to be dug to carry the latter to various points in the garden.

A quick and easy solution, if only a temporary one, is to make up a long extension cord of good heavy wire, say three-conductor No. 14 with polarized safety fittings (see "The Third Wire Is a Lifesaver"), and to string this from a heavy-duty outlet in the kitchen, through a window, and out to the patio or yard. Because the normally-damp ground of a well-kept garden is a perfect electrical ground, it goes without saying that any appliance used outdoors should have its frame grounded through the green wire of the three-wire safety cord. Without this, the user of a motor-operated barbecue spit or a power mower stands a good chance of being flipped over on his ear the first time he touches it.

Local building codes can be very tough on the subject of underground wiring, so check on them first before you buy outdoor outlets, lights and other fittings, which tend to be somewhat costly because of their weatherproof construction. In some areas you can get by with plastic-covered nonmetallic sheathed cable, which is very easy to handle. In others the law may call for lead-covered cable, which costs about 50% more, and it might even require the lead-covered cable to run in conduit for extra protection.

In most houses the new line is most conveniently drawn from the basement through a foundation wall. Take it off the meter through its own fuse, and make it at least No. 12 so that it will be able to handle the heavy current load of a rotisserie. A buried line can be too small, but never too big. •

Right:
Clean transformer contacts with a piece of fine sandpaper every two weeks.

Below:
Tape worn spots on the line cord, especially at point of entrance into the case.

Below, right:
Here is an electric clock turned upside down to redistribute the lubricant.

Clocks and Transformers

Keep them running indefinitely by following these simple instructions

THE operation of toy electric trains depends primarily on a transformer that steps down the 115-volt AC line to voltages not exceeding about 15. These are perfectly harmless. The transformer voltage is usually adjustable by means of a lever that moves against a series of contacts. It is important to keep the latter clean. Occasionally rub the contact surfaces lightly with a piece of fine sandpaper, tighten all connections, and inspect the flexible cord that goes from transformer to wall outlet.

Electric clocks rarely stop because they burn out. In most cases the trouble is due to settling or lumping of the lubricant inside. Before throwing a stopped clock away, turn it upside down and leave it in that position for several days. In all likelihood the lubricant will re-distribute itself, and the clock will run for ten years. •